DU311 Earth in crisis

A Warming World

At the Open University we are committed to protecting the environment and to the responsible use of natural resources. We are acting on this commitment by working with paper suppliers and printers to phase out the use of paper produced from ancient and endangered forests. We aim to ensure that all paper products we purchase are derived from environmentally and socially responsible sources.

Text paper used is Precision Matt Blade paper manufactured at the Grycksbo paper mill in Sweden. Cover board is Trucard Duo Matt manufactured at the Tullis Russell board mill in Scotland. Both paper and board are manufactured using pulp certified under the Forestry Stewardship Council (www.fsc.org/en) scheme. Manufacture at both mills is approved according to ISO 14001 for environment systems.

DU311 Earth in crisis

A Warming World

Edited by David Humphreys and Andrew Blowers

This publication forms part of an Open University course DU311 *Earth in crisis: environmental policy in an international context*. Details of this and other Open University courses can be obtained from the Student Registration and Enquiry Service, The Open University, PO Box 197, Milton Keynes MK7 6BJ, United Kingdom: tel. +44 (0)845 300 60 90, email general-enquiries@open.ac.uk

Alternatively, you may visit the Open University website at http://www.open.ac.uk where you can learn more about the wide range of courses and packs offered at all levels by The Open University.

To purchase a selection of Open University course materials visit http://www.ouw.co.uk, or contact Open University Worldwide, Walton Hall, Milton Keynes MK7 6AA, United Kingdom for a brochure. tel. +44 (0)1908 858793; fax +44 (0)1908 858787; email ouw-customer-services@open.ac.uk

The Open University
Walton Hall, Milton Keynes
MK7 6AA

First published 2009

Edited and designed by The Open University.

Typeset in India by Alden Prepress Services, Chennai.

Printed in the United Kingdom by Scotprint, Haddington.

ISBN 978 0 7492 1636 8
1.1

Contents

Introduction   7

David Humphreys and Andrew Blowers

Chapter 1   Climate change: an introduction to a heated debate   13

David Humphreys

Chapter 2   The role of science in climate change policy   57

David Humphreys

Chapter 3   Climate change: economic valuation and policy   97

Graham Dawson

Chapter 4   Collective action or collective failure?: the international politics of climate change   133

William Brown

Chapter 5   Climate emergency: is securitisation the way forward?   165

Claudia Aradau

Chapter 6   Energy and climate change : sustainable options, political choices and ethical considerations   207

Andrew Blowers

Conclusion: summing up and looking ahead   253

Andrew Blowers and David Humphreys

Acknowledgements   260

Index   262

DU311 course team

Claire Appleby, Consultant

Dr Claudia Aradau, Course Team Member

Prof. Susan Baker, External Assessor

Sheree Barboteau, Course Specialist

Melanie Bayley, Media Project Manager

John Berriman, Service Delivery Team (VLE)

Prof. Andrew Blowers, Course Team Member

Dr Susan Board, Critical Reader (Block 1)

Dr William Brown, Deputy Course Team Chair and Block 2 Leader

Dr Jessica Budds, Course Team Member

Dr Nigel Clark, Consultant

Lisa Collender, Assistant Print Buyer

Lene Connolly, Print Buyer

Dr Graham Dawson, Course Team Member

Fiona Durham, Learning and Teaching Librarian

Jane Fairclough, Critical Reader (Block 3)

Dr Juliet Fall, Course Team Member

Dr Susan Fawcett, Critical Reader (Block 2)

Alice Gallagher, Media Developer (Editor)

Bram Gieben, Course Team Member

Richard Golden, Production and Presentation Administrator

Dr Mike Goodman, External Author, King's College, London

Louise Hawker, Course Manager

Paul Hillery, Media Developer (Graphic Designer)

Owen Horn, Media Developer (S&V)

Dr David Humphreys, Block 1 Leader

Dr Petr Jehlička, Course Team Chair

Dr Pat Jess, Course Team Member

Shereen Karmali, Editor (freelance)

Jo Mack, Sound & Vision Producer

Dr Wendy Maples, Course Team Member

Dr Emma Mawdsley, External Author, Cambridge University

Isobel McLean, Indexer (freelance)

Margaret McManus, Media Assistant (Picture Research and Rights)

Katie Meade, Rights Executive

Joanne Osborn, Proofreader (freelance)

Dr Piya Pangsapa, External Author, State University of New York

Jason Platts, Media Developer (Interactive Media)

Eileen Potterton, Course Manager

Marilyn Reed, Media Production Co-ordinator

Dr Philip Sarre, Block 3 Leader

Dr Sandrine Simon, Course Team Member

Lynne Slocombe, Editor (freelance)

Dr Mark Smith, Course Team Member

Prof. Robert Spicer, Consultant

Matt Staples, Consultant

Prof. Grahame Thompson, Course Team Member

Howie Twiner, Media Developer (Graphic Artist)

Susanne Umerski, Media Assistant

Prof. Reece Walters, Course Team Member

Jo Woodward, Course Manager

Chris Wooldridge, Editor (freelance)

Introduction

David Humphreys and Andrew Blowers

We live in a warming world.

By the beginning of the twenty-first century, the gradual but discernible increase in the mean temperature of the Earth had become manifest in myriad ways, such as coastal flooding, loss of species, increasing incidences of drought and melting glaciers. Recent climate change is recognised as fundamentally a problem brought about by human actions, with ultimately the survival of humanity and ecosystems at stake. Climate change is increasingly framed as an issue where the threats are severe, increasingly imminent and potentially catastrophic. If the worst predictions of scientists prove to be accurate, then no one will be able to escape the consequences of climate change. While it is increasingly accepted by a growing number of policy makers that action needs to be taken immediately to address climate change, it is politically difficult to do so when the impacts, in most parts of the world, are still insignificant. This is a classic 'Catch 22'. When it is possible to take decisive action to prevent catastrophe, the lack of major impacts justifies delays; but when the impacts are all too clear and the need for drastic action is recognised it may be too late.

Effective and well-founded climate policies require a careful and informed analysis of the problem, and the possible options available for addressing it. This book aims, in part, to make such a contribution. Drawing from theories and evidence from the natural and social sciences *A Warming World* introduces and discusses some of the various claims and counterclaims that are made about climate change, the economic costs of action, the barriers to international cooperation, the security implications of climate change, and some of the technical, political and ethical issues involved in seeking low carbon energy alternatives to coal and oil.

The intention is not only to explore climate policy making, but also to illuminate some ideas, debates and challenges that arise in environmental policy making more broadly. Environmental policy is a complex and challenging field for researchers, students and, of course, for policy makers themselves. In order to make this complexity more easily manageable we have structured this book – and the course – around a conceptual framework comprising four course questions and six course themes. The four course questions are:

1   *What are the causes and consequences of international environmental problems?*

2   *What have been the political responses to these problems?*

3   *What are the constraints on more effective policy responses?*

4   *What can be done for the future, and what should be done?*

The course questions and themes are introduced more fully in the Course Guide. You should read the introduction to the Course Guide before you start reading Chapter 1 of this book

Making sense of international environmental issues, the framing of environmental problems and the political and policy responses to them, requires analysis using a set of six themes:

1   *Interdependence within and between nature and society*

2   *International political divisions, inequalities and distributions of power*

3   *Contention over values and knowledge*

4   *The relationship between sustainability and development*

5   *Differences across time and space*

6   *Responsibility and citizenship*

The questions and themes each have different purposes. The course questions are intended to structure and guide your learning on the course. The purpose of the themes is to suggest different ways of approaching the questions and interpreting them. The themes indicate different lines of enquiry that you can pursue when thinking through the course questions. They will also help you to identify some of the key concepts which will integrate your learning throughout the course. The conceptual framework introduced in this book applies not only to climate change but to other environmental problems too. So the framework that you will work with in this book will also stand you in good stead for the remainder of the course.

Chapter 1 provides a general introduction to the subject of climate change using the conceptual framework of four questions and six themes. In examining climate change the chapter introduces a number of concepts and ideas that are developed further as the book unfolds. It examines climate change as the result of both natural and social causes and introduces you to the main international policy response to climate change, the Kyoto Protocol. The chapter suggests that coherent environmental policy responses require the active involvement of a broad range of governmental actors. This calls for that most elusive of characteristics, 'joined-up' governmental thinking so that environmental policies are introduced into every theatre of government. A further consideration is that environmental problems are almost invariably transnational: they cross political frontiers beyond the state. So even those problems that, at first sight, may seem to be highly localised in space usually, on closer examination, can be seen to involve transboundary natural and social processes.

Environmental policy making is a process that brings together science and politics. Climate change has moved from being merely a scientific issue to one of immense and compelling social and political importance. A fundamental question that often arises is: how do we know that recent climate change is driven by humans and is not the result of 'natural' factors? Chapter 2 considers this question. While there remains a basic distinction between science as producing knowledge and politics as solving problems, the chapter examines how science and politics combine to shape environmental policy. It argues that a science-based discourse of climate change has become dominant which establishes the causes of climate change as mainly anthropogenic (the emission into the atmosphere of greenhouse gases from human practices, primarily industry and agriculture) and which is primarily anthropocentric (concerned mainly with the human consequences). Yet, there remain elements of a politically influential alternative discourse which denies that climate change is an anthropogenic problem.

Chapter 3 asks if there is an economic case for tackling climate change. In other words, might it not make more sense in economic terms to accept the future costs that climate change will impose upon the world, rather than to expend huge sums of money now to deal with the problem? The Stern Review of 2007 concluded that by the end of this century the environmental and social damage caused by climate change could lead to the value of the world economy falling by a fifth. However, this could be avoided if only about 1 per cent of the economy were directed to dealing with climate change. The chapter outlines how economic thinking can help to address climate change, although it does not lose sight of the limitations of economic theory. It makes clear that spending money to avoid the consequences of climate change is not solely an economic question; it also raises ethical questions of how we value the future and what responsibilities we have for future generations.

An important question in international climate politics is why, at a time when both scientific evidence and public concern on climate change is mounting, have the governments of the world failed to agree an urgent and focused response to the problem. At first sight it would seem that all governments have a common interest in recognising and addressing this problem. However, international cooperation has proved difficult to achieve. Chapter 4 explains this as an example of the collective action problem. Using game theory, the chapter outlines the collective action problem and identifies some of the reasons why states have struggled to reach international agreement on climate policies. National sovereignty, competitiveness and divergent interests combine to inhibit agreement. The chapter also suggests how governments can offer incentives to encourage laggard states to partake in international cooperation.

As in all areas of social life the language we use when describing and analysing environmental issues can matter a great deal. How we think about and define environmental problems helps to shape the policy responses that are agreed, or not agreed. Given the importance of language and discourse in the policy process, Chapter 5 sets out to explore whether a reframing of climate change might help to promote more effective policy responses. In particular, should climate change be placed alongside global issues such as terrorism or nuclear war as a threat to security that requires a focused, high-level response from states? In other words, will it make a difference if policy makers 'securitise' climate change? The chapter carefully examines both sides of this argument. Many policy makers now see climate change as the major threat to international security, although others remain preoccupied by 'old' concerns.

A major part of the problem of climate change is the dependence of much of the global economy on fossil fuels for energy. A shift to low carbon energy alternatives is a pressing priority. Chapter 6 explores some of the political and technological constraints on achieving low carbon energy options. Using the debate over nuclear energy as its example, the chapter provides a discussion of what can and should be done about the future. Nuclear energy is portrayed in terms of ecological modernisation, the contemporary mode of environmental policy making in which market-based and technological solutions are given priority. The chapter argues that engagement with the public in deliberative forms of policy making can counteract a tendency for centralised and closed decision making. Finally, the chapter draws out some wider ethical debates, in particular on the management of radioactive wastes. By focusing on problems of intergenerational equity, it raises challenging issues about how we should deal now with problems that will extend into the far future.

A Warming World is not only a book on what, we would suggest, is the most pressing challenge that our generation faces: the stabilisation of the Earth's atmosphere. It is also a broader introduction to the subject of environmental policy. Throughout the book climate change is used to introduce a wide range of theoretical concepts and ideas that can be used to analyse and understand other environmental issues. The conclusion, 'Summing up and looking ahead', provides a reflection that draws out some key concepts, in particular inequality, which will be further developed in the books to follow. So as this book unfolds you will develop a conceptual toolkit that you will work with and develop throughout the remainder of the course.

Reference

Stern, N. (2007) *The Economics of Climate Change: The Stern Review*, Cambridge, Cambridge University Press.

Chapter 1
Climate change: an introduction to a heated debate

David Humphreys

Contents

1	**Introduction**	**14**
	1.1 Learning outcomes	15
2	**Course question 1: what are the causes and consequences of international environmental problems?**	**18**
	2.1 What is climate change?	18
	2.2 The causes of climate change	19
	2.3 The consequences of climate change	23
3	**Course question 2: what have been the political responses to these problems?**	**29**
	3.1 Framing the issue	29
	3.2 What is power?	32
	3.3 The Kyoto Protocol	34
4	**Course question 3: what are the constraints on more effective policy responses?**	**36**
	4.1 Effectiveness	36
	4.2 Political constraints	37
	4.3 Knowledge constraints	38
	4.4 The role of technology	39
	4.5 Responsibility and the agency–structure debate	42
5	**Course question 4: what can be done for the future, and what should be done?**	**46**
	5.1 Feasibility and desirability	46
	5.2 Equity	48
	5.3 Introducing sustainable development	50
6	**Conclusion: working with an analytical framework**	**53**
	References	**54**

1   Introduction

In 2002 Antarctica's Larsen B ice shelf broke up and collapsed. Over a period of just 35 days the ice shelf – over 183 metres thick and 3250 kilometres miles in area – completely disintegrated, fragmenting into thousands of icebergs that slowly melted into the ocean over the next few months. The process was captured by satellite pictures that were shown in newspapers and on television news bulletins around the world (Figure 1.1). David Vaughan of the British Antarctic Survey described the speed of the collapse as 'staggering' (*Daily University Science News,* 2002). The disintegration of the ice shelf, which had certainly been stable for 5000 years and could have been in place for more than 12,000 years, followed the break-up of Antarctica's Larsen A ice shelf in 1995 and the partial collapse of the Wilkins ice sheet throughout 1998 and 1999. The melting of the Earth's ice is not confined to the Antarctic. Most of the world's glaciers are now in retreat (Figure 1.2). The Arctic ice cap has grown thinner and smaller in recent decades, and in the summer of 2007 the area of Arctic sea ice contracted to the lowest levels ever recorded.

Our Earth is changing. But should we be concerned about this? We live on a dynamic planet that has evolved and changed enormously since its origins some 4.6 billion years ago. Is there anything significant about the changes that are happening in our lifetime? Are melting ice sheets a problem, or merely a natural process about which we need not be concerned? Even if melting ice is not a problem now, might it be symptomatic of a broader, more fundamental problem? If so, what can we do about it?

These are just some of the questions that arise when climate change is discussed and which you will explore in this book. There are no obvious answers to many of them, but one thing is beyond doubt. Scientists have established that the Earth's mean (average) temperature increased by about 0.6 °C during the twentieth century, and that it continues to rise. This recent increase in the Earth's temperature is often referred to as 'global warming', although most scientists use the term 'climate change', a term that also refers to the lengthy periods of warming and cooling that the Earth has undergone in the past.

I shall introduce climate change by taking you in turn through each of the four questions for this course. These questions are introduced in the Course Guide. As you consider these questions you will explore some of the scientific, political, social, economic, technological and ethical debates that arise when policy makers address climate change. You will gain an appreciation of climate change as a complex international policy issue and work with some of the concepts and theories that can help unlock this complexity.

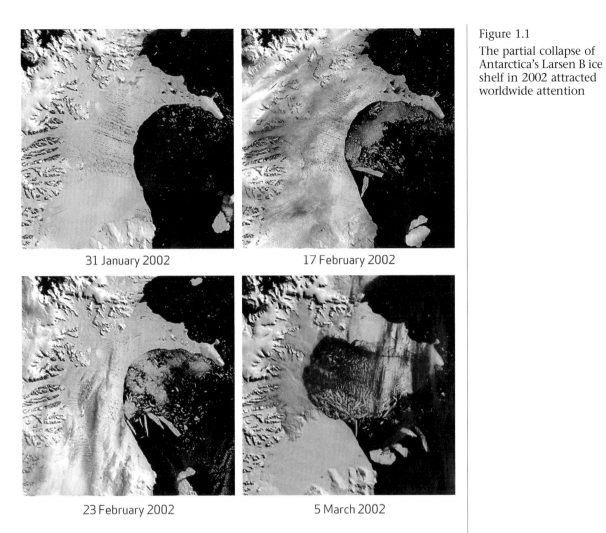

31 January 2002

17 February 2002

23 February 2002

5 March 2002

Figure 1.1
The partial collapse of Antarctica's Larsen B ice shelf in 2002 attracted worldwide attention

1.1 Learning outcomes

This chapter should enable you to:

- identify some of the main causes and consequences of climate change (*course question 1*)

- discuss some of the main political responses to climate change (*course question 2*)

- appreciate some of the constraints to more effective international policy responses to address climate change (*course question 3*)

- recognise some of the responses that might be made to address climate change in the future (*course question 4*).

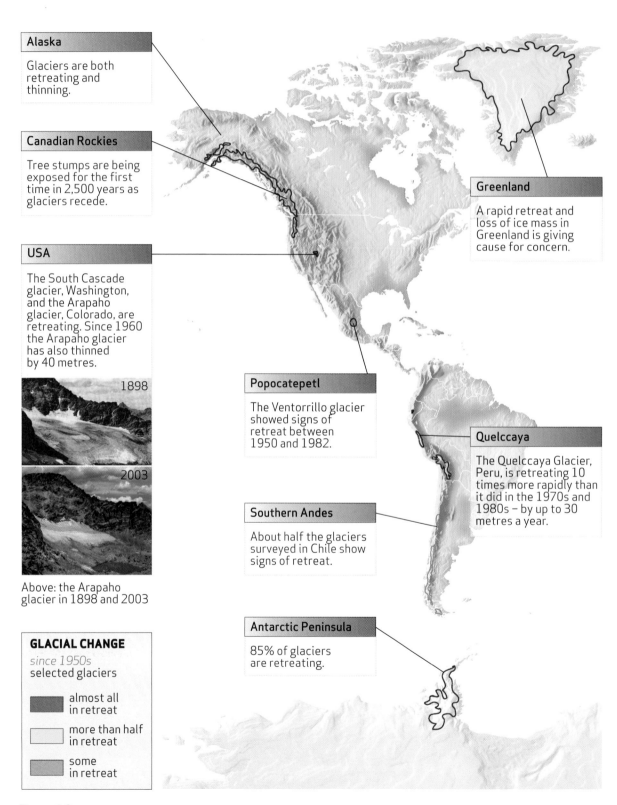

Alaska

Glaciers are both retreating and thinning.

Canadian Rockies

Tree stumps are being exposed for the first time in 2,500 years as glaciers recede.

USA

The South Cascade glacier, Washington, and the Arapaho glacier, Colorado, are retreating. Since 1960 the Arapaho glacier has also thinned by 40 metres.

1898

2003

Above: the Arapaho glacier in 1898 and 2003

GLACIAL CHANGE
since 1950s
selected glaciers

almost all in retreat

more than half in retreat

some in retreat

Greenland

A rapid retreat and loss of ice mass in Greenland is giving cause for concern.

Popocatepetl

The Ventorrillo glacier showed signs of retreat between 1950 and 1982.

Quelccaya

The Quelccaya Glacier, Peru, is retreating 10 times more rapidly than it did in the 1970s and 1980s – by up to 30 metres a year.

Southern Andes

About half the glaciers surveyed in Chile show signs of retreat.

Antarctic Peninsula

85% of glaciers are retreating.

Figure 1.2

Almost all the world's major glaciers are now in retreat (Source: Dow and Downing, 2006, pp. 24–5)

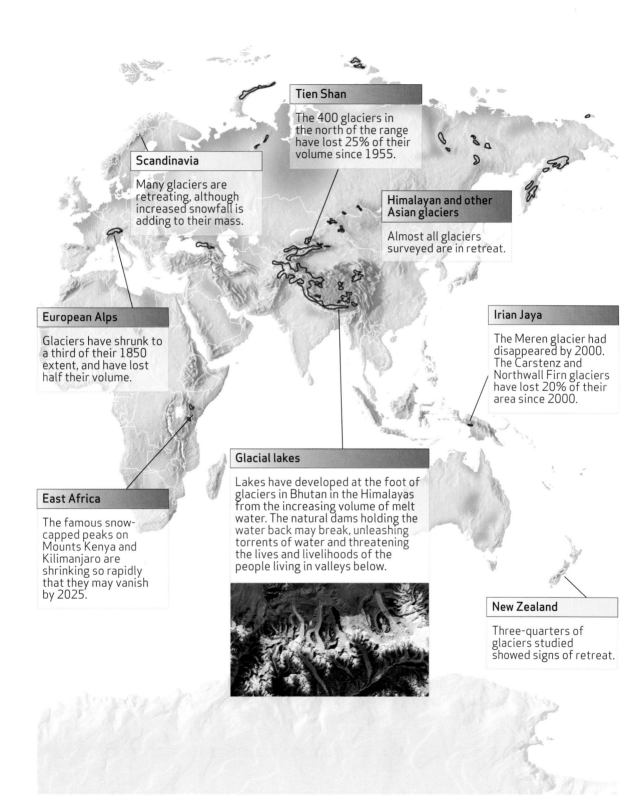

Tien Shan

The 400 glaciers in the north of the range have lost 25% of their volume since 1955.

Scandinavia

Many glaciers are retreating, although increased snowfall is adding to their mass.

Himalayan and other Asian glaciers

Almost all glaciers surveyed are in retreat.

European Alps

Glaciers have shrunk to a third of their 1850 extent, and have lost half their volume.

Irian Jaya

The Meren glacier had disappeared by 2000. The Carstenz and Northwall Firn glaciers have lost 20% of their area since 2000.

East Africa

The famous snow-capped peaks on Mounts Kenya and Kilimanjaro are shrinking so rapidly that they may vanish by 2025.

Glacial lakes

Lakes have developed at the foot of glaciers in Bhutan in the Himalayas from the increasing volume of melt water. The natural dams holding the water back may break, unleashing torrents of water and threatening the lives and livelihoods of the people living in valleys below.

New Zealand

Three-quarters of glaciers studied showed signs of retreat.

2 Course question 1: What are the causes and consequences of international environmental problems?

2.1 What is climate change?

Why did the Larsen B ice shelf break up in 2002?

Melting ice sheets are far from unusual in the history of our planet. Geologists and climate scientists have established that the Earth's climate underwent major changes long before humans evolved. Some of the causes of climatic change include bombardment from asteroids, changes in solar activity, tectonic plate movements and volcanic eruptions. Ice shelves have advanced and retreated several times throughout the Earth's history. There have been periods – the ice ages – lasting hundreds of thousands of years when ice covered much of the Earth, followed by interglacial periods when the ice retreated towards the poles. The last ice age – the Pleistocene – ended only some 11,000 years ago giving way to our present geological period, the Holocene. So, was the melting and collapse of the Larsen B ice shelf an exceptional event when the long-term history of climate change is considered? To what extent was the collapse of Larsen B caused by natural processes, and to what extent was it the result of **anthropogenic** climate change; in other words, change that is the result of human activities?

The term **anthropogenic** refers to something that is caused or influenced by humans.

Our interest on this course is not with the changes to the Earth that have happened over long-term geological time, fascinating though they are, but with changes to the Earth over a much shorter time period, the last two to three hundred years since the dawn of the Industrial Revolution. This is a small moment in geological time, yet one that has seen some major transformations to the global environment. In order to examine the causes and consequences of climate change I will start by introducing you to the scientific theory of the subject. One of the main points I then wish to make is that contemporary climate change – global warming – is, at least in part, anthropogenic in origin. I shall survey the causes of contemporary climate change and some of the actual and predicted consequences. Understanding these causes and consequences requires an awareness of differences across time and space.

Course theme 5
Differences across time and space

You might like to keep an eye open for the course themes as you read the chapter

2.2 The causes of climate change

The theory of climate change holds that the Earth's mean temperature will vary according to the concentrations of certain gases in the atmosphere. The warming effect of these gases is known as the **greenhouse effect** and the gases themselves are known as *greenhouse gases*. If the atmospheric concentration of greenhouse gases increases then, over time, the mean temperature of the Earth will also increase. Similarly, if the atmospheric concentration of greenhouse gases falls then, eventually, so too will the mean temperature of the planet. The world's main greenhouse gases are carbon dioxide (CO_2), methane (CH_4), nitrous oxide (N_2O), chlorofluorocarbons (CFCs) and hydrofluorocarbons (HFCs). If there were no greenhouse gases in the atmosphere then the Earth would be 33 °C colder than it is now, too cold to support life.

To explain why greenhouse gases warm the Earth I need to introduce you to a geophysical process known as radiative forcing. **Radiative forcing** is the difference between incoming solar radiation and reflected – or outgoing – solar radiation in the Earth's climatic system. Greenhouse gases allow short-wave solar radiation to pass through to the surface of the Earth. Some of this radiation is reflected back into space from surfaces with a high albedo. **Albedo** is a measure of reflectivity. Surfaces with the highest albedo – white surfaces such as the Larsen B ice shelf – reflect most of the short-wave solar radiation that strikes them. This reflected radiation does not warm the atmosphere. However, darker surfaces with a low albedo, such as the oceans and land, absorb incoming solar radiation, which is then reradiated as long-wave radiation. This reradiated long-wave radiation is absorbed by greenhouse gases and trapped as heat, thus warming the atmosphere (Figure 1.3).

Anthropogenic climate change is the result of an enhanced greenhouse effect that is caused by human emissions of greenhouse gases into the atmosphere. To help you understand what causes this enhanced effect I would first like to draw a distinction made by scientists and social scientists between direct causes and underlying causes. A **direct cause** is a cause that leads directly to an observed effect. The observed effect that we are concerned with is the rise in the Earth's temperature. The direct cause of this is the change in the radiative forcing of the Earth's climatic system as the result of increased atmospheric concentrations of greenhouse gases. But what is causing these increased atmospheric concentrations?

To answer this question we need to look for the proximate causes. An **underlying cause** is the first in a series of events that results in an observed effect. So event A may lead to event B, which in turn leads to event C, and so on. The underlying causes of anthropogenic climate

The **greenhouse effect** is an atmospheric warming effect caused by the trapping of solar radiation in the atmosphere by greenhouse gases, principally carbon dioxide.

Radiative forcing is the difference between incoming and outgoing radiation from the sun.

Albedo is a measure of the reflectivity of a surface.

A **direct cause** is a cause that leads directly to an observed effect.

An **underlying cause** is the first in a series of causal events that results in an observed effect.

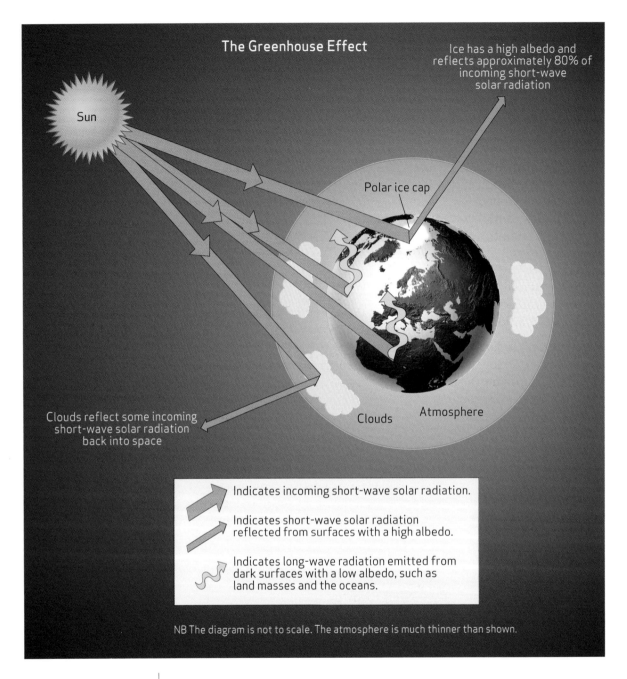

Figure 1.3
The greenhouse effect

change are social rather than natural. The single most important underlying cause of anthropogenic climate change is the burning of fossil fuels, such as oil and coal, which are central to energy generation and industrial production. The burning of fossil fuels emits carbon dioxide. Carbon is often referred to as 'the stuff of life' as it is an element found in all forms of life to have existed on Earth. CO_2 concentrations in the atmosphere have increased owing to the burning of ancient nature and living nature. By ancient nature I mean fossil fuels which contain carbon from plants and creatures that lived during earlier geological epochs. Coal is derived from ancient forests, and oil and natural gas were formed from the remains of marine plants and animals that lived millions of years ago.

Living nature refers, of course, to present life forms, in particular the world's forests. Tropical forest burning is the source of approximately 18 per cent of global CO_2 emissions (IPCC, 2007). Forests are a carbon sink. A **carbon sink** is an ecosystem that absorbs carbon dioxide, thereby removing it from the atmosphere. Forests take up CO_2 from the atmosphere through photosynthesis and then store it in trees, vegetation and soils (Box 1.1). Deforestation, which takes place to harvest timber and to release land for other uses, such as agriculture and urbanisation, both erodes the carbon sink capacity of the Earth and releases back into the atmosphere carbon that is stored in forests.

A **carbon sink** is an ecosystem that absorbs carbon dioxide from the atmosphere.

What are the underlying causes of the emissions of other greenhouse gases? Nitrous oxide is produced from nitrogen fertilisers, fossil fuel burning (again) and from the industrial manufacture of some synthetic materials. The main sources of methane are deforestation, rice farming and cattle farming. Some greenhouse gases, such as CFCs and HCFCs, do not occur naturally and have been manufactured industrially. Although a molecule of CO_2 contributes less to climate change relative to other greenhouse gases, carbon dioxide is the most important greenhouse gas, as far more of it is emitted than any other greenhouse gas (Figure 1.4). CO_2 accounts for 63 per cent of the total warming effect and it takes around 100 years for it to be absorbed back into living plants and the oceans. Methane disappears more rapidly but still needs urgent controls as it is a more potent greenhouse gas.

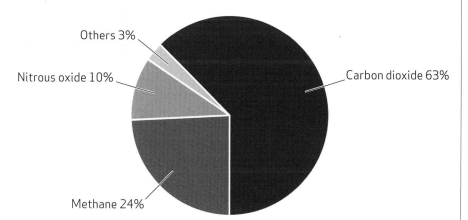

Figure 1.4
Contributions made by greenhouse gases to the enhanced greenhouse effect. Carbon dioxide is the major contributor followed by methane (Source: Brown, 2006)

> **Box 1.1   Carbon sinks and photosynthesis**
>
> Photosynthesis is the chemical process by which vegetation, such as trees and plants, synthesises organic compounds from CO_2 and water using sunlight. Vegetation takes up carbon dioxide from the atmosphere, storing the carbon in its tissue. Vegetation thus acts as a carbon sink. Forests are a major carbon sink, although they do not have an unlimited capacity to absorb CO_2. Another major carbon sink is the world's oceans. Oceans absorb carbon dioxide in part through phytoplankton. These are small photosynthesising organisms that require CO_2 to grow and which form the basis of food for all other marine organisms. Land-based vegetation absorbs about as much CO_2 as oceanic phytoplankton, despite the land area being less than a third of the Earth's surface. Contemporary climate change is taking place because there are more anthropogenic emissions of CO_2 than the Earth's sinks can absorb.

Course theme 1
Interdependence within and between nature and society

Understanding the causes of anthropogenic climate change thus requires an awareness of some complex interactions, in particular the interdependence within and between nature and society. However, some populations and groups have emitted far more greenhouse gases than others. This has influenced how climate change has been handled as an international political problem.

The main actor in the international political system is the state. A state has a defined territory, a population (its citizens) and is represented politically by a government. There are about 200 states in the world. Which states bear the most responsibility for causing anthropogenic climate change? That is the question I would like you to consider in Online Exercise 1.

Online Exercise 1

Now log on to the course website and consider Online Exercise 1: *Analysing emissions data*. When you have completed this exercise, read on.

What I hope you gained from Online Exercise 1 is an appreciation of an important inequality that permeates international climate politics; over time different states have contributed to climate change to differing degrees. This has led to political disagreement about which states should be most responsible for addressing the problem in the future.

2.3 The consequences of climate change

An understanding of inequality is also necessary to understand the consequences of climate change. Some countries and regions will suffer more than others. However, predicting the overall effects of climate change is difficult as the consequences will vary according to how fast the Earth's temperature changes. The Fourth Assessment Report of the world's main climate science organisation, the Intergovernmental Panel on Climate Change (IPCC), predicted a maximum temperature increase this century of 6.4 °C, and a minimum of 1.1 °C (IPCC, 2007). This is a difference of more than 5 °C. Predicting consequences within such a wide temperature range is no easy matter. Why is there such a difference between the IPCC's highest and lowest estimates?

There are four main reasons. One is climate sensitivity. Climate scientists know that increasing atmospheric concentrations of greenhouse gases will lead to an increase in the temperature of the Earth; but they do not know by exactly how much. For example, scientists cannot agree what temperature change will result from a doubling of the atmospheric concentration of CO_2. A second reason is that the Earth's temperature does not respond immediately to changes in atmospheric concentrations of greenhouses gases; there is a *time lag* between greenhouse gases being emitted and temperature changing. Third, future greenhouse gas emissions are not known; they depend in part on the policies that states take to address climate change and whether these policies will be effective.

To explain the fourth reason I'd like to return to the disintegration of the Larsen B ice shelf. There is scientific evidence that Larsen B's collapse was due, at least in part, to anthropogenic climate change, which led to warmer air circulating around Antarctica (Marshall et al., 2006). The disintegration of the ice sheet replaced a surface with a high albedo that reflects incoming short-wave radiation, with a darker surface, namely seawater, with a low albedo. The result is an increase in reradiated long-wave radiation, increased radiative forcing and further warming (Figure 1.5). Scientists call this a feedback effect; the warming of the climate has resulted in a consequence which, in turn, causes further warming. A **feedback effect** is a change within a system that will either enhance or diminish the original effect, in this case the temperature of the Earth. Positive feedback effects will enhance the original effect and lead to further warming, whereas negative feedback effects will mitigate the original effect, leading to a warming effect that is less severe than would otherwise be the case.

A **feedback effect** is a change within a system that will either enhance or diminish an original effect.

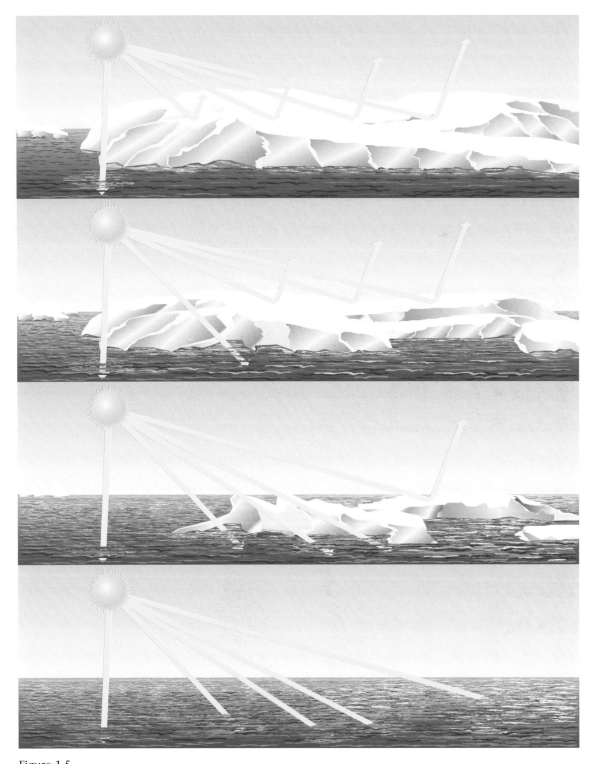

Figure 1.5
Ice has a high albedo so it acts like a giant mirror, reflecting incoming solar radiation back into space. The world's oceans are darker than sea ice; they have a lower albedo. So as sea ice melts due to climate change the oceans absorb more solar radiation, becoming warmer in the process. Scientists call this a positive feedback (Source: Gore, 2006)

Almost all the feedback effects at play in the Earth's climatic system at present are positive. It is predicted that severe climate change will lead forests to dry out, increasing the risk of catastrophic forest fires that will in turn emit more CO_2 (Figure 1.6). Melting permafrost will result in an important positive feedback; there is evidence that warmer temperatures are leading to the release of methane frozen in the permafrost which, in turn, will spur further warming (Figure 1.7).

Figure 1.6
In 2006 the British newspaper *The Independent on Sunday* produced this speculative headline from the year 2040. A timely warning, or needless scaremongering?

Figure 1.7
Dawson City, Canada.
Melting permafrost has
damaged many
buildings in Alaska,
Canada, Scandinavia
and Siberia

These positive feedbacks will result in a quickening of climate change. It is difficult to predict how the positive feedbacks will play out, and over what time horizons. What scientists do predict is that there will come a 'tipping point' after which it will be impossible to halt climate change. Once this tipping point is reached, climate change will continue as the feedback effects already in train play themselves out, irrespective of any measures taken to reduce further emissions. But there's a further problem: climate scientists simply don't know what the tipping point is. Some scientists say that it is possible we have already passed the tipping point; others judge that we will pass it sometime during this century.

Despite these uncertainties scientists are sure about some of the more immediate consequences of anthropogenic climate change. The melting of the continental ice shelves in Antarctica and Greenland will mean more water in the oceans, leading to increased sea levels (although the melting of floating ice shelves, such as the Larsen B ice shelf and Arctic sea ice will not result in increased sea levels, for the same reason that when ice melts in a full cup of water there is no spillage over the sides). A further factor contributing to sea level rises is **thermal expansion**; seawater will occupy an expanded volume as it becomes warmer. Over time sea level rises will lead to human migration from low lying coastal areas and the abandonment of low lying islands.

Thermal expansion is the increase in volume of matter or liquid, in this case seawater, in response to an increase in temperature.

Climate change is starting to disrupt the seasons. In the northern hemisphere there is evidence that the spring and summer seasons are starting earlier and finishing later, with shortened winters. The migratory patterns of species are changing, with some species migrating towards cooler climes. The migrations of species and ecosystems through space takes two forms: latitudinal migration (towards the poles) and altitudinal migration (further uphill). Such migrations cannot, however, be maintained indefinitely. When it is still too hot and there is nowhere else to migrate to – when a species has migrated to the top of the mountain or, if possible, to the Polar regions – then a species will either adapt to the new climate, or become extinct. The golden toad of Costa Rica (Figure 1.8) is sometimes cited as the first global warming extinction. The toad, which bred in spawning pools in cloud forests, appears to have been unable to move fast enough when warmer temperatures led to a rise in the cloud base so that spawning pools dried out (Lynas, 2007, pp. 46–7). The golden toad has not been seen since 1989 and was declared extinct in 2004.

Does the extinction of one species of toad matter? On its own this extinction may not be significant, but I think that to conclude it does not matter would be to miss a broader point. Amphibians such as toads are indicator species. An indicator species is the first to suffer a fall in population when an ecosystem changes or comes under stress. The extinction of the toad could be a first indication that climate change will threaten the Earth's biological diversity, in other words the diversity of the Earth's life forms. Biodiversity depletion will lead to changes in evolution as species and ecosystems try to adapt to the warmer climate. Humans rely on biodiversity to provide food and medicines, so major long-term changes to nature will have profound social consequences. The full magnitude of these changes will not be clear for centuries and will depend on the speed of warming.

Figure 1.8
Croaked it? Is the golden toad of Costa Rica the world's first extinction resulting from anthropogenic climate change?

Despite the many scientific uncertainties in predicting the precise consequences of climate change it is clear that some places will be affected more than others, at least in the short to medium term. The consequences will be unevenly distributed, with some countries and populations suffering more than others. For example, in Africa, a continent where some regions already suffer from drought-induced ecosystem stress, increasing incidences of drought are predicted (Figure 1.9). Biodiversity rich countries, principally those with large expanses of tropical forests, will suffer more from biodiversity depletion than biodiversity poor countries. Low lying coastal countries will suffer land loss from sea level rises. The low lying small island state of Tuvalu in the Pacific Ocean is likely to be one of the first countries to cease to exist as sea levels rise. Populations displaced by the effects of climate change, such as flooding and drought, will migrate to countries that are less threatened, placing additional stress on the ecosystems and economies of those countries. However, it is difficult to predict the timescales over which human migration will take place and the regions that will be most affected by migration.

Sorry to bother you.
Any chance of turning
that thermostat
down a degree?

 Climate change isn't some threat to the future. It's today's reality. Environmental disasters, such as droughts in Niger, are wrecking people's lives with more and more frequency. And it's going to get worse. Want to do something about it? Good, we need people like you. Visit our website to see how the actions of you and your workplace can change the world for the better. Climate changed. Let's get to work. www.climatechanged.org

Figure 1.9
This leaflet circulated by the charity Christian Aid makes the point that one does not need to be present in an environment in order to degrade it. Those who suffer from an environmental problem are not necessarily those who cause it

What is the political significance of our discussion about the causes and consequences of climate change? I think three main points have emerged. First, climate politics is informed both by science and by scientific uncertainty. Although scientific knowledge is constantly evolving and eliminating some uncertainties, this is happening at the same time as nature and society undergo further changes, creating new uncertainties. Second, since the start of the Industrial Revolution some states have contributed to anthropogenic climate change more than others. However, there is disagreement between governments over how these different levels of responsibility should be measured. Third, the consequences of climate change will be unevenly distributed amongst countries, some of which will suffer heavier ecological and economic costs than others. Those countries that have done the most to cause climate change will not necessarily be the same ones that will suffer from it. There are therefore important inequalities and disagreements between states over the causes and consequences of climate change. This has had a direct bearing on the political responses to the problem, to which I now turn.

Chapter 2 of this book will explore the relationship between climate science and international climate politics

3   Course question 2: what have been the political responses to these problems?

3.1 Framing the issue

My focus in this section is not on domestic climate change policy, important though this is, but on international climate policy making. I want to provide you with a flavour of the main political disagreements to climate change and how states have sought to grapple with them.

Anthropogenic climate change is sometimes referred to as a tragedy of the commons (Box 1.2). It is not caused by any single government or country acting alone, and it cannot be solved by any government or country in isolation. Actors in all countries contribute to the problem, hence international cooperation is necessary if the problem is to be successfully addressed. Social scientists describe climate change as a **collective action problem**, that is, a problem which arises when an individual actor's aims cannot be achieved by individual action alone. If anthropogenic climate change is to be solved, a political accommodation must be reached between all states, or at least among those that emit the most greenhouse gases.

A **collective action problem** is a problem which arises when an individual actor's aims cannot be achieved by individual action alone.

Chapter 4 will develop the idea of climate change as a collective action problem

---

Box 1.2   The tragedy of the commons

Some people think of collective action problems as a tragedy of the commons. This phrase comes from an article by Garret Hardin in 1968. Hardin argued that commons, such as grazing land, will face degradation as each individual will seek to exploit the resource as much as he or she can. Hardin argued that although this will benefit the short-term interests of individuals, the overall outcome will be the long-term degradation of the common resource.

Hardin's idea has been criticised by many who argue that it misunderstands how communities are able to collectively manage common resources and prevent a tragedy occurring. It can be argued that the world's atmosphere is a global common; no single state or individual can own the atmosphere, which is the common property of all humanity. Like Hardin's local commons, the degradation of a global common occurs when some actors pursue their self-interests, for example by failing to reduce their greenhouse gas emissions. Hardin's notion of the tragedy of the commons draws attention to a political dimension that runs throughout environmental policy making, namely the conflict between short-term self-interest and the long-term collective good.

In a sense all states have a shared interest in cooperating to solve climate change. Why, then, is this not happening? To get you started on thinking about the different approaches that states may take in international climate negotiations I'd like you to consider the following question.

Activity 1.1

What does climate change mean to you? For example, if you were talking about climate change with family, friends or colleagues, what words would you use to describe the problem? What impression would you wish to convey to the listener on how you perceive the problem? When you have considered this for a few moments read on.

In thinking through this question you may have chosen to describe climate change as a 'crisis'. Or you may have used the word 'problem'. Both expressions convey the sense that something is 'wrong' and it needs to be 'solved'. Or maybe you see climate change as a distant scientific debate that is too clouded with uncertainty to affect your life.

Framing is a social science concept that holds that statements about reality are always shaped at least in part by social influences.

My point is that political leaders may perceive the same issue very differently like you and I, and as a result they may propose very different policies. The notion of **framing** is useful here. This holds that statements about reality are always shaped in part by social influences. So environmental (and non-environmental) issues are framed by different political interests in different ways. The notion of issue framing holds that knowledge, events and politics are interpreted according to the perceptions and interests of the observer. The way an issue is framed will vary according to geography, history, social conditions and the political and economic context within which individuals live and work (Forsyth, 2003; Liberatore, 1995).

Some actors frame climate change in terms of urgency. Proponents of this argument claim that time is running out and immediate measures must be taken to head off catastrophic climate change. Some European Union (EU) countries, such as Germany and the Netherlands, tend towards this view, although the strongest proponents are small island states whose existence will be threatened by sea level rises, and which have formed themselves into the Association of Small Island States (AOSIS). Other actors frame climate change as an issue of uncertainty. For example, the George W. Bush administration of the United States of America (USA) took the position that the scientific evidence did not justify international action to cut greenhouse gas emissions. One of the arguments made by the Bush administration was that the Earth is an evolving biophysical entity and its temperatures have fluctuated considerably over time; there is no clear scientific evidence that recent climatic changes are anthropogenic.

The position of the Bush administration was in marked contrast to the Clinton administration that preceded it; Clinton and his vice president Al Gore framed climate change as an urgent issue on which the USA should take the lead. So the framings of any one state may change as political leaders change and new scientific knowledge is developed. In the USA some political advisers have argued that climate change should be framed as a threat to national security. My point here is different framings may suggest different, even contradictory, policies. States that anticipate that they will suffer most from the problem, especially over the short term, tend to demand strong international policies. However, those states that are best able to supply big emission cuts are the major polluters. The cooperation of these states, primarily the developed countries and the oil producing states of the Persian Gulf, is essential if climate change is to be arrested. However, these states are likely to lose economically from deep emission cuts, at least over the short term.

Chapter 5 will consider how framing climate change as a security issue has affected how the issue is handled politically

The first international agreement on climate change was the United Nations Framework Convention on Climate Change (FCCC) that was opened for signature at the United Nations Conference on Environment and Development (UNCED) in Rio de Janeiro of June 1992. This set out two main policy strategies to address climate change. **Mitigation** strategies involve the reduction of greenhouse gas sources or the enhancement of sinks. Examples of mitigation strategies include switching from fossil fuels to alternative energy sources, improved energy efficiency and planting trees to improve sink capacity. **Adaptation** strategies seek to adjust to the effects of climate change. Examples include evacuating coastal settlements as sea levels rise and constructing sea walls. In 1997 a protocol was agreed to the convention, the Kyoto Protocol. This is not a freestanding international agreement. In other words, only states that have ratified the 1992 convention may adopt the Kyoto Protocol. However, states that have ratified the convention are under no obligation to ratify the protocol as well. The USA has ratified the FCCC but not the Kyoto Protocol. Despite this, the USA remains a powerful state in climate politics that can exert influence on all aspects of climate policy.

A **mitigation** strategy seeks to reduce greenhouse gas emissions or enhance carbon sinks.

An **adaptation** strategy seeks to adjust to the effects of climate change.

3.2 What is power?

I would now like to consider further the concept of *power*. What does it mean to say that the USA is a 'powerful state'? There are different theoretical approaches to power, which may broadly be defined as the capacity of one actor to influence another actor to do something that he or she would not otherwise have done. But upon what is power based?

One common theoretical approach is that power is based on resources. A state has power if it can mobilise resources such as people, technology, military capabilities, finance and so on. According to this view, if state A has more resources than state B, then the former will exert more influence over the latter. The power of the USA comes from the resources it can deploy to change the behaviour of other actors in international politics, including 'carrots' such as aid, technology transfer and loans, and 'sticks' such as the threat of sanctions and the withdrawal of trade. Exercising power can thus involve persuasion, coercion or a mix of the two. Because some actors have more resources than others, power is distributed unequally across the international political system. Different states have different power resources and therefore an unequal ability to influence outcomes. In international politics the exercise of power may involve conflict between different states, although often conflict is mediated by diplomacy and negotiations, including through international organisations such as the United Nations (UN). Power may be institutionalised in other organisations too, such as local and national governments, business corporations, citizens' groups and trade unions.

High-emitting states such as the USA have the power to block an agreement on climate change by refusing to cooperate. Although the Kyoto process has continued without the USA, a post-Kyoto protocol will only be truly effective if it includes the USA. Some of the states that will bear the heaviest costs of climate change have virtually no power in international negotiations and are almost entirely dependent on what other states agree. So there are some important inequalities in international climate politics. Those states that are most vulnerable to climate change are often not the ones that have caused the problem. It can be argued that the vulnerable states are morally justified in arguing that wealthier states should take action to tackle climate change. However, having the moral high ground very rarely gives a vulnerable state influence over more powerful ones.

Course theme 2
International political divisions, inequalities and distributions of power

Understanding international climate policy therefore requires an awareness of international political divisions, inequalities and distributions of power. Wealthier low lying countries, such as the Netherlands, are more likely to be able to afford adaptation strategies compared to poorer countries, such as Bangladesh. Existing economic inequalities can thus help to shape future environmental vulnerabilities. In international negotiations developing countries that cannot afford expensive adaptation strategies have tended to argue for strong mitigation strategies; and they have argued that the developed countries should take the lead on mitigation, as they have polluted the most in the past.

Activity 1.2

Let us consider this last statement. Is it morally right to argue that the present populations of wealthy developed states should assume responsibility for the acts of previous generations? Can you think of any arguments for and against this view?

It could be argued that the present generation of developed countries benefits from past industrialisation as they have inherited a stronger economic infrastructure than people in developing countries. They should now curb their emissions so that developing countries may industrialise. Against this it can be argued that we cannot change what has happened in the past. What matters now is curbing the emissions of all countries. This argument is often made in the USA. In 1997 the USA Senate passed by a vote of 95–0 the Byrd–Hagel resolution (named after the two senators who proposed it) that the USA should not agree to any climate change protocol that 'would result in serious harm to the economy of the United States' and which did not include targets for emission reductions by developing countries (US Congress, 1997). The Byrd–Hagel resolution explains why the USA has not adopted the Kyoto Protocol. Many USA politicians – both Democrats and Republicans – have argued that as China and the USA have a similar annual level of CO_2 emissions, the USA should not agree to cut its emissions unless China does the same. The response of the Chinese government is that the USA has historically polluted more than China, and that China's per capita emission levels are far lower than those of the USA.

This debate has resulted in something of a compromise in international climate politics. The Framework Convention on Climate Change includes the principle of *common but differentiated responsibilities*, which asserts that while all states have a common responsibility to take measures to tackle climate change, different states have different levels of responsibility. The principle thus encompasses the idea that climate change is a cumulative problem that has built up over centuries; it is not solely the result of recent greenhouse gas emissions. However, there is no agreement on how this principle can be applied in practice, and no consensus on how different levels of responsibility should be allocated.

3.3 The Kyoto Protocol

It was not until the 1997 Kyoto Protocol was negotiated that states were able to agree any emission reductions targets. The developed countries agreed to reduce their emissions in line with the principle of common but differentiated responsibilities. Eventually, after protracted late-night negotiating, the so-called Annex I states – developed countries and countries with economies in transition (the former communist countries of eastern Europe and the former Soviet Union) – agreed to an overall reduction in emissions of 5.2 per cent below 1990 levels by 2012. The figure of 5.2 per cent is an average; some states agreed to more, some to less. During the Kyoto negotiations the EU proposed that all Annex I states cut their emissions by 15 per cent. However, other Annex I states were not prepared to follow the EU's lead and the EU eventually agreed to an 8 per cent cut. (Note that EU states do not negotiate separately in international environmental negotiations; all EU states agree a common negotiating strategy.)

Why did the EU fail to adopt its own proposal of cutting emissions by 15 per cent by 2012? In order to understand the reasons we need to examine how the costs to the EU of a 15 per cent cut might affect the EU's competitiveness relative to other Annex I states. To achieve a 15 per cent emissions cut EU countries would need to undertake some severe mitigation policies, such as investing in energy efficient technology and closing down sectors of the economy with high emissions. This would entail costs for the economy that would inevitably be passed on to consumers as price rises. Other Annex I states that did not follow the EU's lead would then be able to sell their energy and goods at lower prices relative to the EU. So if the EU was to implement deep emissions cuts while other Annex I states did not, these other countries would gain an economic advantage over the EU. The EU was prepared to stand additional costs, but only if other Annex I states did likewise. These negotiations illustrate that policies agreed by one state may affect those agreed by others.

Here I would like to return to the earlier discussion on USA power and international climate politics. Although the Clinton administration signed the Kyoto Protocol in 1997 it did so knowing, following the Byrd–Hagel resolution, that Congress would not ratify it. The EU was aware of this too, and it then reconsidered its original proposal; the EU did not want to be committed to making a 15 per cent cut while the USA was, in effect, committed to no cuts at all. This illustrates a concept known as the *first mover problem*. In international cooperation if all states 'move' simultaneously then no state is disadvantaged relative to other states. However, if one state moves first, that state may bear costs that do not fall on other states. The EU was prepared to take a moral lead, but only to a certain degree; the costs of moving first while others did not were such that the EU eventually decided not to follow through on its original proposal. (Note that sometimes moving first can have advantages. For example, a business that is first to develop and market green technology may gain market share at the expense of its competitors.)

This discussion relates to the tragedy of the commons (Box 1.2). If several actors are degrading a resource, it is not in the self-interest of one actor to cease doing so if other actors refuse to change their behaviour. More generally, in all international negotiations there is a tension between the need for states to cooperate in order to agree outcomes that benefit all (collective gains) and the competition between states as each seeks to secure outcomes that suit its perceived national interest (individual gains). An understanding of this tension between the pursuit of collective gains on the one hand and individual gains on the other is essential to understanding all environmental negotiations, both between states and those that involve other actors too.

You have seen that EU countries negotiate together in international environmental politics. In effect they 'pool' their power. Most of the developing countries of Africa, Asia and Latin America do the same; they have formed a UN negotiating caucus, the Group of 77 Developing Countries (G77). The G77 argues that as the developed states are most responsible for anthropogenic climate change, they thus have an obligation to help the developing countries to reduce their future emissions through the transfer of financial assistance and environmentally clean technologies. The G77 has framed climate change as a technical issue, arguing that without such assistance the emissions of the developing countries will inevitably rise. In climate negotiations the EU countries and Norway have showed some willingness to provide some new resources to developing countries, whereas the USA, Australia, Canada and Japan have so far been less willing.

The demand of the G77 for additional finance and technology can be likened to price negotiations. In effect, the G77 states were trying to extract as much as they could from the developed states in exchange for their cooperation. The unspoken message during the Kyoto negotiations was, 'If you want us to sign the protocol you must pay us to do so'. The developed states agreed to transfer only very limited financial and technological resources to developing countries. However, they did open up the possibility for countries to gain financially through the adoption of three flexibility mechanisms (the so-called 'flex mechs'). These mechanisms allow the Annex I states to meet their greenhouse emission targets by purchasing emission reductions or credits from other countries, including developing countries (Box 1.3).

> **Box 1.3   The Kyoto Protocol flexibility mechanisms**
>
> ■ **Emissions trading** allows Annex I states that will exceed their Kyoto targets to buy emissions credits from other Annex I states whose emissions will fall below their Kyoto target. Critics claim that selling emission credits for money is more about profit than climate stabilisation. Emissions trading is further considered in Chapter 3.
>
> ■ **The Clean Development Mechanism** (CDM) allows an Annex I state to pay for emission mitigation or sink activities in a developing country and then deduct the emissions saved or offset as its own. Examples of CDM projects approved include wind farms, the recovery of waste heat from industry and its conversion into energy and reforestation projects to increase carbon sink capacity. Private sector businesses are encouraged to invest in CDM projects.
>
> ■ **Joint implementation** is similar to the CDM although it applies only to Annex I states. An Annex I state may invest in emission mitigation or sink activities in another Annex I state; the former can then count the emissions saved as its own. As with the CDM, the private sector is encouraged to invest in projects.

4   Course question 3: what are the constraints on more effective policy responses?

Although there has been a lot of international political activity on climate change, atmospheric concentrations of greenhouse gases continue to increase. Why is this, and what are the constraints to more effective policy responses?

Before I turn to this question I first would like to consider what we mean by 'effective'.

4.1 Effectiveness

Effectiveness is defined in relation to a desired outcome. A policy may be considered to be effective if it changes the behaviour of actors in a desired direction, such as cutting emissions of greenhouse gases. Effectiveness may be imagined as a continuum with two poles. At one pole is the weak notion of effectiveness, namely minor behavioural changes that are insufficient to address the problem at hand. At the other pole is the strong notion of effectiveness, namely fundamental shifts in behaviour that produce the desired outcome that the policy was intended to realise. In the case of environmental policies the desired outcome is often defined as an improvement in, or at least the maintenance of, environmental quality.

It needs to be stressed, however, that environmental quality rarely responds straight away to environmental policies; there are often time lags between a policy being implemented and a discernible improvement in environmental quality. This leads on to an important question: might it be the case that recent policies to counter global warming are effective, but have just not yet had sufficient time to affect the global mean temperature? We certainly need to be aware of time lags when considering policy effectiveness. Changes in the atmospheric concentration of greenhouse gases may take so long to work through the climate system that it may take decades, possibly centuries, before measures to tackle climate change result in a stable atmosphere. Policies that could lead to rapid worldwide reductions in greenhouse gas emissions would certainly count as effective, even though it may be several generations before the full effects of such reductions would be apparent. However, it is clear that contemporary policies to address climate change, while they may have resulted in some modest behavioural change, are not effective in the strong sense of the term, as greenhouse gas emissions are continuing to rise. In order to assess why this is so we need to search for the constraints.

4.2 Political constraints

The discussion in the previous section suggests that one area where constraints may exist is the international political system. As you have seen, although states cooperate in making international policy, they also compete. International inequalities lead some states to perceive they are the victims of injustice, and such perceptions complicate the quest for effective policies. Could international politics be organised differently perhaps? Are there alternative ways in which the international political system can be governed that might lead to more effective environmental policies? There are no easy answers here, but I raise these questions for you to bear in mind as you explore environmental problems in the weeks ahead.

If the organisation of international politics is one area where we may find constraints then a second area is domestic politics. Here is an example. In the United Kingdom (UK) the Labour government announced in 2007 measures to reduce greenhouse gas emissions through, for example, wind farm construction and grants to householders who install solar panels. That same year the government also announced plans for airport expansion and the building of new roads. As aircraft and car exhaust includes CO_2 these policies will increase greenhouse gas emissions.

Why do governments often adopt separate policies which, from an environmental standpoint, are clearly contradictory? There are a number of possible explanations. Here I would like to suggest just one. Within a government, different ministries and departments may have different policy priorities. According to Graham Allison's **bureaucratic politics model**, government policy can be seen as the result of interactions between different bureaucracies, each of which have different interests and priorities. Furthermore, in any one state some bureaucracies will have more power within the policy-making process than others (Allison, 1971). Bureaucratic politics may therefore result in policy incoherence and the dominance of policy making by some government departments at the expense of others.

The **bureaucratic politics model** holds that policy decisions are the outcome of interactions between different groups and ministries.

Allison's bureaucratic politics model draws our attention to the complexity and 'messiness' of policy making. Individual states may not always have coherent policy objectives. National environmental policies are the product of continual negotiation between different ministries, each of which may frame environmental issues in different ways. When different ministries have different priorities then central government has to make choices between competing policy objectives. Furthermore, different actors may lobby government to adopt very different policies. These actors include non-governmental organisations (NGOs) such as Greenpeace and the World Wide Fund for Nature (WWF), trade unions, human rights groups and the business sector. Some have greater access to decision makers than others and consequently are able to exert more influence over policy making. The opposition of the USA Senate to the Kyoto Protocol is often attributed to the power of the American oil lobby and the political influence it wields in the USA.

4.3 Knowledge constraints

Another set of constraints to effective environmental policies is incomplete or uncertain knowledge. Policy makers do not like uncertainty. They want firm, clear predictions on which to base their decisions, but this is rarely possible. For example, economists may disagree on where scarce economic resources should be directed. Should government resources be directed towards mitigation or adaptation policies? Will trading in emission permits lead to a reduction in carbon emissions? Can a carbon tax help to reduce CO_2 emissions? Different economists may arrive at different conclusions to these questions.

Chapter 3 examines the role that economic policy instruments can play in limiting carbon dioxide emissions

As you have seen, another important area of uncertainty in climate policy making is science. As a result of scientific uncertainties policy makers cannot know what the precise effects of their policies will be; the future is both unknown and unknowable. Knowledge may be disputed, with different experts offering different interpretations of the available evidence. At their most severe, knowledge constraints can prevent the identification of a problem. Even when a problem is known to exist, knowledge gaps may mask the real extent of the problem, as the case of global dimming illustrates.

As well as emitting CO_2 and other gases, fossil fuel burning may emit sulphur particles. These particles contribute to acid rain. They also act as aerosols. An aerosol provides a site around which water vapour can attach, leading to raindrop formation. Aerosol emissions increase cloud formation and turn those clouds that do form into giant mirrors that reflect solar energy back into space. The result is a cooling effect on the Earth's temperature. Scientists refer to this as the 'enhanced aerosol effect' or *global dimming*.

Whereas global warming is about increases in heat, global dimming is about decreases in the levels of sunlight reaching the Earth's surface. Global dimming was first identified in the 1950s, although it is only since the 1970s that the full extent of the problem in masking global warming has been understood (Rotstayn et al., 2006; Travis et al., 2002, 2004). At least some of the observed global warming effect since the 1970s is due to the success of governments and businesses in Europe and North America in countering acid rain by reducing aerosol emissions from industry. Success in dealing with one atmospheric problem has thus exposed the full extent of another.

The phenomenon of global dimming suggests that we may be changing the world quicker than we can understand it. If climate policy is to be effective then scientific knowledge will need to evolve fast enough to keep up with the full extent of the consequences of human action.

4.4 The role of technology

It is often asserted that one constraint to more effective environmental policies lies with technology. According to one view, environmental problems continue to exist because the present pace of technological innovation is too slow. What is needed to solve climate change is the rapid invention and development of a new generation of 'clean and green' energy technologies that do not emit greenhouse gases and other pollutants. This view has been termed by Tim O'Riordan as

Technocentrism is the view that environmental problems can be solved through invention and technology.

technocentrism. **Technocentrism** may be defined as the view that human invention and technology will, given time, find the answer to all environmental problems. According to O'Riordan, those who adhere to a technocentric view argue that technological innovation can solve environmental degradation while continuing to deliver economic growth (O'Riordan, 1981). Proponents of technocentrism point to the recent innovation of carbon dioxide capture and storage (CCS) technology to support their arguments. CCS involves the separation of CO_2 during energy and industrial manufacturing process and its compression and transport to a location in isolation from the atmosphere. There are two types of CCS. First, CO_2 can be pumped directly into oceans. Second, CO_2 can be pumped into rock formations, such as old oil wells and empty aquifers, and sealed from the atmosphere beneath a caprock (IPCC, 2005).

Activity 1.3

The oceans form a part of the biosphere, namely those parts of the Earth where life is found. Now examine Figures 1.10 and 1.11. Which of the two types of CCS – ocean and underground – holds out the promise of permanent removal of carbon dioxide from the biosphere?

Figure 1.11 shows that for ocean storage at less than 3 km in depth the CO_2 would disperse in the oceans. Below 3 km the CO_2 would initially form a liquid lake. However, it too would eventually disperse. The IPCC acknowledges that CO_2 pumped into the oceans would gradually be released into the atmosphere over hundreds of years. In principle underground storage in rock formations will completely remove CO_2 from the biosphere. The IPCC acknowledges that there are risks of leakage from underground storage. However, the risk is very low providing that sites are chosen where there is geological stability and an absence of fault lines (Figure 1.11).

Ecocentrism is the view that humans should respect nature and its limits, rather than try to control nature.

The technocentric approach is not accepted by everyone. It is challenged by what O'Riordan calls ecocentrism. Proponents of **ecocentrism** frame environmental problems as the result of profligate resource use by actors who fail to recognise that there are ecological and social limits to economic growth. Far from being the cure technology is, in this view, a cause of environmental problems. Technology has enabled the extraction of fossil fuels from deep under the Earth's surface and their burning in power stations. Rather than rely on grand technological innovations to solve climate change, such as CCS, ecocentrics argue instead for reductions in the use of fossil fuels and a respect for nature and its limits. Ecocentrics and technocentrics thus have very different ways of relating to and valuing the environment.

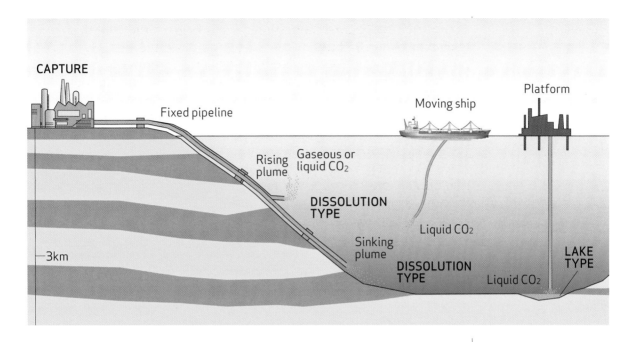

CAPTURE

Fixed pipeline

Moving ship

Platform

Rising plume

Gaseous or liquid CO_2

DISSOLUTION TYPE

Liquid CO_2

3km

Sinking plume

DISSOLUTION TYPE

Liquid CO_2

LAKE TYPE

Liquid CO_2

A common distinction made in environmental studies is between instrumental and intrinsic values. Those actors who view the environment principally as a resource for economic activity emphasise the *instrumental* value of the environment: we should conserve the environment as a means to an end, because we can use it in the manufacture of foods, medicines, industrial products and so on. Other actors stress the *intrinsic* value of the environment: we should conserve the environment as an end in itself, because it has value in its own right. So environmental policy making involves contention over values as well as contention over knowledge. Values and knowledge should not be seen as separate dimensions of environmental policy making; rather, the two interact. For example, knowledge will be framed, interpreted and understood very differently by actors who value nature in instrumental terms compared to those who value nature intrinsically.

So is the current pace of technological development a constraint on more effective climate policies? There is no clear answer here. The constraints to more effective environmental policy are not necessarily objective and given. Views on what constitutes a constraint are relative and will vary from actor to actor. This is particularly the case with constraints that are social in origin, for example when people continue to perform routine actions – such as turning on a light or driving a car – that they know will generate greenhouse gas emissions. To what extent, therefore, do the constraints to more effective environmental policies rest with individuals, people like you and I? What responsibilities, if any, do we have as citizens? I now turn to this question.

Figure 1.10
Ocean storage of captured carbon dioxide

Course theme 3
Contention over values and knowledge

Course theme 6
Responsibility and citizenship

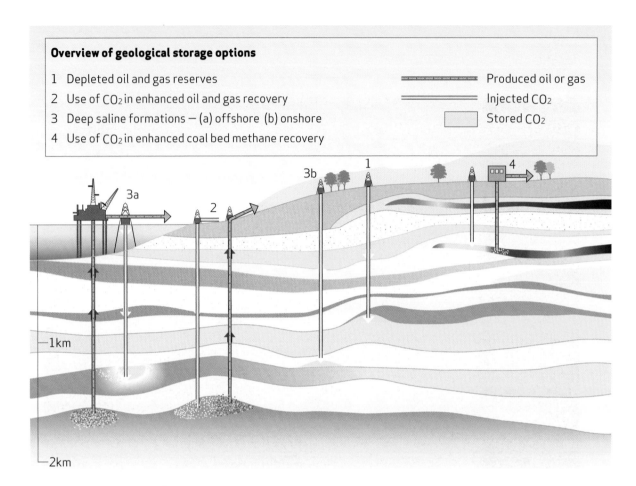

Overview of geological storage options

1 Depleted oil and gas reserves
2 Use of CO_2 in enhanced oil and gas recovery
3 Deep saline formations — (a) offshore (b) onshore
4 Use of CO_2 in enhanced coal bed methane recovery

⎯⎯⎯⎯ Produced oil or gas
⎯⎯⎯⎯ Injected CO_2
☐ Stored CO_2

—1km

—2km

Figure 1.11
Geological storage of
captured carbon
dioxide

4.5 Responsibility and the agency–structure debate

Activity 1.4

Look at the newspaper advertisement from the Energy Saving Trust, a non-profit organisation that promotes reduced CO_2 emissions in the UK (Figure 1.12). Who does the advert suggest is responsible for greenhouse gas emissions? When you have considered this question for a few moments read on.

When I first saw this advertisement it hinted to me that I should assume responsibility for the consequences of my actions. Of course, I do not always know what these consequences will be, partly due to scientific uncertainties. However, I do know that my lifestyle results in greenhouse gas emissions, and these emissions contribute to climate change; the advertisement made me feel uncomfortable by reminding me of that.

Leaving the TV on standby for instance, or using the car for short journeys, wastes energy and results in needless carbon dioxide emissions. If we all commit to save 20% of the energy we use every day, together we can help prevent climate change. For more energy saving actions and to make your commitment, visit **www.energysavingtrust.org.uk/commit**

Figure 1.12

An advertisement from the Energy Saving Trust. Who is responsible for carbon dioxide emissions from the energy sector?

The **agency–structure** debate concerns the extent to which individual agents or social structures shape behaviour and social change.

But to what extent does the responsibility for climate change rest with individual people? The greenhouse gas emissions from energy consumption are caused both by the energy industry and the energy consumption decisions of individual consumers. (The advertisement depicts this; note that the slogan begins over the coal-fired power station in the background and ends over the houses in the foreground.) As long as the energy I use at home comes from an energy industry that relies in part on fossil fuels then unless I completely cut out domestic energy consumption I am inevitably contributing to climate change. My choice seems to be not between consuming energy created from fossil fuels, and consuming energy from 'green' sources, but between emitting more or less greenhouse gases. So I can blame the energy industry, but does this absolve me of all responsibility? And how can I make a difference?

I shall now place this discussion on a theoretical basis by distinguishing between the roles of agents and structures in generating environmental problems. The **agency–structure** debate is a long running one in the social sciences. It focuses on how social structures (established patterns of social arrangements and relationships that provide order and predictability to social life) may determine the behaviours of agents (individuals, organisations, groups and other actors), and how agents may create new social structures.

A structural view of climate change would see it as the consequence of deeply established systems of industrial, energy and agricultural production and consumption that routinely generate greenhouse gas emissions. However, if in one respect climate change is a structural problem, in another it is caused by the accumulated emissions of numerous individual agents. Not all agents, however, are equal. Power is unevenly distributed across social structures, and some agents wield considerably more power than others. The most politically and economically powerful agents tend to be those that benefit from carbon-intensive energy production and industrial manufacturing. But relatively powerless actors, such as you and I, also contribute to climate change through the decisions we make – and do not make.

So can we as individuals make a difference by changing our behaviour, or should we look to those that hold political and economic power to take the lead? There are different views here. To strong structuralists, independent agents have little if any influence. The actions of agents are determined almost entirely by dominant social structures. Strong structuralism promises a bleak and forbidding future. It suggests that we are trapped in social structures that will continue to degrade the environment, and there is little, if anything, that any single individual or group can do about this. Strong structuralism assigns little if any independent role to individual agents, and suggests that social structures are resistant to change.

Nevertheless, the strong structuralist approach flies in the face of history, which tells us that while social structures may sometimes seem immovable they are always changing and that independent agents can sometimes catalyse important social changes. The sociologist Anthony Giddens proposes an alternative theoretical approach in his **theory of structuration**. Giddens acknowledges that power is unevenly dispersed across social structures, and is concentrated more in some agents than in others. However, Giddens also argues that relatively powerless agents are always more than mere structural proxies. Agents always have a choice. They are never totally powerless and can have a transformative impact on broader social structures. Giddens offers a weak variant of structuralism, although he does acknowledge the existence of structural properties that mediate behaviour (Giddens, 1984). There is thus a dualism between agency and structure: structures shape the behaviour of agents, yet agents contribute to the evolution of social structures, which are dynamic rather than static entities.

The **theory of structuration** holds that there is a dualism between agents and structures, with each shaping the other.

Giddens' approach is thus more optimistic than strong structuralism. In this view, individual agents have the choice to cut down on their greenhouse gas emissions. This may be difficult in the short term, but over time people can change their lifestyle by, for example, installing solar panels, cutting down on car usage and taking fewer flights. Giddens' theory of structuration also suggests that by acting independently people may help to transform broader social structures, especially if they act together with others, perhaps by joining or forming a social movement or through lobbying government.

Some constraints on effective policies may be overcome fairly easily. Nonetheless, if environmental policies are to lead to an improvement in environmental quality then we cannot rule out the possibility that overcoming some of the more fundamental constraints may require us to call into question some foundational principles and values of contemporary social life. A key question that then arises is 'If we are to safeguard the global environment how radical must future change be?' Is deep social and political change unavoidable? Or are there less disruptive solutions? This leads me on to the final course question.

5 Course question 4: what can be done for the future, and what should be done?

5.1 Feasibility and desirability

An awareness of the constraints that you examined in the previous section will inform my discussion of the fourth course question. This should be seen as two seperate, but interrelated, questions. The question 'What *can* be done?' requires a focus on the *feasibility* of policy proposals, whereas the question 'What *should* be done?' requires an assessment of the *desirability* of policy proposals. A policy proposal that is desirable may not necessarily be feasible, and vice versa. In the rest of this section I want to give you a flavour of some of the questions and arguments that arise in international climate policy when policy makers consider these interlinked dimensions of feasibility and desirability.

Feasibility depends on natural and social factors. In the case of climate change the most important natural factors are the various feedbacks in the climate system. If climate change is to be arrested then action needs to be taken before the tipping point is reached. Effective action becomes less feasible as the problem worsens. This suggests that urgent responses are needed. But as you have seen, there may be a variety of constraints to implementing strong policies urgently. For example, most governments are preoccupied with short-term problems, whereas arresting environmental problems demands long-term solutions.

Chapter 6 will explore the role of ethics in future energy policy

Desirability is a matter of ethics. Ethics is the study of the moral rules and values that guide, or should guide, human behaviour. The study of ethics, or moral philosophy as it is sometimes called, involves judgement, reasoning and some vision of what the world should be like (Warnock, 2001). However, there is no single ethical view, so we cannot look to ethics to provide a clear and unambiguous moral compass for environmental policy. Even a widely shared ethical principle can be open to different interpretations. For example, an ethical case can be made for 'climatic stability'. The idea of a stable climate seems uncontroversial – I think most people would agree that it is desirable – but what precisely does 'climatic stability' mean? Does it mean a return to pre-Industrial Revolution atmospheric concentrations of greenhouse gases? Or stabilisation at today's temperature? Might 'a bit more' warming be desirable before climatic stability is achieved or, if not desirable, then at least acceptable?

This last question has arisen in the climate policy deliberations in the EU. In 2005 the EU announced that it was committed to the stabilisation of the global mean temperature at no more than 2° C above pre-industrial levels (Commission of the European Communities, 2006). At present the global mean temperature is 0.6° C above pre-industrial revolution levels. The EU has judged that the risk of a 2° C increase is acceptable, but scientific opinion is divided on this. Many scientists have concluded that a 2° C rise will not cross the tipping point and lead to catastrophic climate change. Others disagree. To the UK Institute of Public Policy Research an increase above 2° C would risk effects that, 'may widely be considered as being dangerous, and in some cases irreversible' (Baer with Mastrandrea, 2006, p. 4).

What should policy makers do when faced with contradictory scientific evidence? A commonly invoked principle that seeks to answer this question is the **precautionary principle**. Because of scientific uncertainties policy makers cannot know exactly how the planet will respond to greenhouse gas emissions. The precautionary principle holds that lack of scientific certainty is no excuse for postponing the implementation of measures to prevent environmental degradation. From an ethical standpoint the precautionary principle may be seen as desirable, but is it feasible?

According to the **precautionary principle** lack of scientific certainty is no excuse for postponing the implementation of measures to prevent environmental degradation.

Activity 1.5

Can you think of some problems in interpreting the precautionary principle with respect to climate change? After you have spent a few minutes considering this question read on.

Agreeing that greenhouse gas emissions should be avoided does not provide an indication of the policies that are necessary to reduce emissions. Even if one agrees with the precautionary principle, the fine details of its implementation remain a matter for discussion. So while the precautionary principle is often invoked it is by no means clear what it means in practice. On the one hand, halting all greenhouse emissions immediately, or even over the next decade, is completely unfeasible. On the other hand, taking no action at all to reduce emissions is a high risk strategy that can be seen as unethical. In between these two extremes is a range of possible future emission reduction scenarios that involve different trade-offs between desirability and feasibility. A rapid rate of emissions reductions may be desirable, but unfeasible (Figures 1.13a and 1.13b).

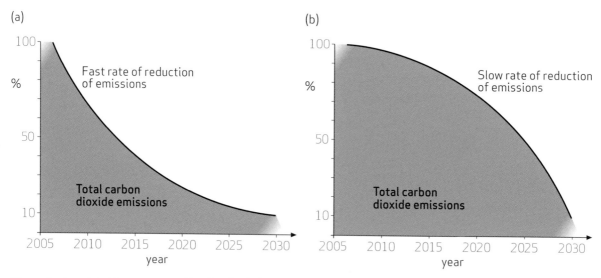

The emissions total is represented by the shaded area under the curve. Note that although the target is met in both cases, the total emissions are lower in Figure 1.13a, which starts with a sharper rate of reduction.

Figure 1.13a and Figure 1.13b Two emission reduction scenarios based on the policy that in order to achieve climatic stability carbon dioxide emissions should be reduced to 10 per cent of today's emissions by 2030

5.2 Equity

Another ethical principle that is often raised in international climate policy is *equity*. The principle of equity concerns fairness between different populations, states and generations. To introduce you to this principle, and some of the questions that it raises, I shall focus on one of the Kyoto flexibility mechanisms, namely the CDM (Box 1.3). You will recall that the CDM allows Annex I states and private sector businesses to finance forest planting in other countries, principally developing countries. Carbon dioxide sequestered from the atmosphere by CDM forests can then be offset against the emissions of the Annex I state. CDM projects are designed to generate 'win–win' outcomes. An Annex I state can deduct from its greenhouse gas inventory the carbon that is offset by reforestation, while developing countries gain financially.

However, CDM reforestation projects have attracted criticism. Environmental NGOs have argued that such projects allow an Annex I state to appropriate space in a developing country for carbon sequestration so that the Annex I state can continue polluting. This, so the argument goes, violates the principle of intragenerational equity. **Intragenerational equity** is the principle of fairness over space, that actions should not impose an unfair or undue burden on individuals or groups within the present generation. Critics of CDM projects claim that poor developing countries are pressured into accepting CDM reforestation projects in order to earn foreign exchange (Lohmann, 1999). This generates inequities between different groups of people in the present generation and, so it is claimed, constitutes a new form of

Intragenerational equity is the principle of fairness over space, that actions should not impose an unfair or undue burden on individuals or groups within the present generation.

colonialism: 'ecocolonialism'. Against this it may be countered that money paid by Annex I states to states that host CDM forest projects may be used for the benefit of local people. According to this view, CDM projects can address some existing intragenerational inequities.

A second criticism relates to effectiveness. Proponents of CDM projects argue that reforestation will fix in trees carbon that is emitted from the burning of fossil fuels. However, CDM forests, like any other forest, can come under threat from social pressures (such as illegal logging and forest clearance for agriculture) and natural pressures (such as pest attack). The viability of CDM forest projects as a long-term fix for CO_2 emitted from the burning of fossil fuels that has lain underground in an inert state for millions of years is thus questionable; the carbon stored in these forests is likely to be re-emitted into the carbon cycle in the future, with adverse consequences for future generations. This, it is argued, violates the principle of **intergenerational equity**. This principle focuses on the rights of future generations. Today's generation should not degrade the environment so that environmental harms are passed on to future generations (Figure 1.14).

Intergenerational equity is the principle of fairness over time, that the present generation should not impose unfair or undue burdens on future generations.

Figure 1.14
Intergenerational equity? Environmental degradation may lead to economic benefits, but it will be future generations who bear the ecological costs

5.3 Introducing sustainable development

The principles of intragenerational and intergenerational equity are often invoked in environmental policy making. They are key elements in the concept of **sustainable development** which the World Commission on Environment and Development (also known as the Brundtland Commission after its chair, the then Norwegian Prime Minister, Gro Harlem Brundtland) has defined as 'development that meets the needs of the present without compromising the ability of future generations to meet their own needs' (WCED, 1987, p. 43). Sustainable development seeks to balance the needs of the present generation with those of future generations (intergenerational equity). It recognises that a major cause of environmental degradation is inequities within the present generation, both inequities between different countries and between different groups within and between countries (intragenerational equity). The challenge of attaining sustainable development raises some fundamental questions. How do we give future generations a 'voice' in political processes? What should policy makers do when the pursuit of intergenerational equity conflicts with the pursuit of intragenerational equity, or vice versa? Which is the greater moral wrong: poverty today, or environmental harm tomorrow?

These are some of the questions that policy makers face when seeking to operationalise sustainable development, an idea that fuses the ideas of sustainability and development. *Sustainability* recognises that there are natural limits to the interferences that an ecological system (ecosystem) can withstand before environmental degradation results. Human activity that goes beyond these limits is said to be unsustainable. The concept of development is often conflated with economic growth, although the two are not reducible to the same thing. Economic growth is a measure of the increase of the value of the goods and services produced by an economy. *Development* is a more amorphous and contested concept. It is often equated with growth, although it also encompasses ideas such as social welfare, quality of life and spiritual fulfilment. Although there are different views of development and how it should be attained, most notions are based on socio-economic changes that, in some way, may be seen as progressive.

One problem with interpreting the meaning of sustainable development is that sustainability and development provide different value-based rationales for policy makers. Take for example the tension in UK government policy that you considered in the previous section. The policy to reduce the country's greenhouse gas emissions is logical from the standpoint of sustainability. The plans to expand airport infrastructure and the road network make sense if development is defined in economic terms. Some environmental campaigners argue that

The Brundtland Commission defined **sustainable development** as 'development that meets the needs of the present without compromising the ability of future generations to meet their own needs'.

the expression 'sustainable development' is an oxymoron, and that when development is understood as the growth of the economy it is inherently and unavoidably *un*sustainable. Others argue that whether development can be sustainable depends on the form of development. For example, localised development that is grounded in communities can be sustainable. But most government policy makers frame development in terms of the growth of the national or global economy. They concentrate on achieving a balance between sustainability and development. However, views on what is the 'right' balance vary considerably.

Whether one accepts sustainable development as a guiding principle or not, how development is framed and the relationship between sustainability and development are unavoidable dimensions of environmental policy making. For example, to what extent should trade-offs between sustainability and development be permissible over time and space? Is development that leads to environmental degradation today acceptable if it is compensated for by environmental conservation policies tomorrow? Are carbon emissions in one space acceptable if compensated for by carbon sequestration in another space? The basic premise that underlies CDM reforestation projects is that such trade-offs are acceptable. But as you have seen, CDM projects have been criticised by those who argue that it is ethically wrong for some countries to pursue economic development while, in effect, colonising ecological space in other countries.

Course theme 4
The relationship between sustainability and development

I would now like to consider this concept of ecological space a bit further. Ecological space encompasses nature and the non-living physical environment of the planet. It includes the atmosphere, forests, natural resources, wildlife, rivers, lakes, oceans, fish, agricultural land, mountains, and so on. Humans both inhabit ecological space and are intimately embedded within it. Ecological space can be imagined on various scales. At the global level we may talk of the ecological space of the planet. At a personal level we may talk of the ecological space that we inhabit as individuals. Inequities and environmental conflicts may arise when one group of people infringes upon ecological space that is claimed by another. According to the political philosopher Andrew Dobson, all citizens have the same rights to ecological space. No individual should claim more than his or her fair share. Those who do so are imposing an *ecological footprint* on the ecological space of others and have a moral obligation to reduce their consumption of ecological space (Box 1.4) (Dobson, 2003).

> ### Box 1.4   Ecological footprints and carbon footprints
>
> An ecological footprint may be defined as the ecological space that would be required to support a given human population (Wackernagel and Rees, 1996). The term is often used to describe the impacts upon distant spaces of the consumption patterns of people in developed countries. For example, if a given area of land in Kenya is given over to growing strawberries for consumption in Norway, then that area of land is said to form part of the ecological footprint of Norway. All populations have an ecological footprint. Political conflicts may arise when there are asymmetries in the ecological footprints of different groups or countries, with some occupying more ecological space than others. The concept of environmental sustainability holds that there are limits to the ecological space that humans can occupy before environmental degradation results.
>
> A conceptual cousin of ecological footprint is carbon footprint, defined as the impact upon the climate of human activities in terms of the net greenhouse gases emitted (that is, emissions less sequestration, for example through forests). The carbon footprint of producing strawberries in Kenya for consumption in Norway will include the energy expended in growing and processing the product and in transporting it from Kenya to Norway.

What does this ethical vision suggest for international climate policy? Any policy would be premised on the idea that all citizens have an equal right to the atmosphere. All citizens should therefore be permitted to emit the same quantity of greenhouse gases, but only to the extent that such emissions do not result in an increase in the long-term global mean temperature.

One such proposal is the 'contraction and convergence' scheme proposed by the UK-based Global Commons Institute (GCI). The proposal is based on the principles of fair and equal entitlements to ecological space. It holds that the annual total of worldwide emissions should be allocated to countries on a pro rata basis according to their population size. The GCI proposes a series of phases, with countries agreeing to contract their emissions over time until, in the final phase, the emissions converge at a point where all individuals have the same entitlement. Within countries the allocation of emissions would be handled by the government. Contraction and convergence is a popular idea in the environmental movement and is an agreed policy of the UK Green Party (Green Party, 2005).

Activity 1.6

If contraction and convergence is ethically desirable then why hasn't it been implemented? To consider this question you may like to revisit the various constraints that you examined in Section 4 above.

The proposal has been adopted by the governments of several countries in Africa and Asia, but it has no support from the governments of developed countries which have achieved relative advantages in industrial production and international trade by consuming more than their fair share of ecological space. 'Contraction and convergence' thus faces opposition from some powerful states that would lose economically if the proposal was adopted.

6   Conclusion: working with an analytical framework

You started this heated debate by considering some 'cold facts'. The melting of the polar ice sheets may not be of immediate concern to you or I but it is, I would argue, symptomatic of a fundamental problem that is crucial to the future of the Earth. Climate change has been recognised as a pressing policy problem, but the responses so far have been inadequate. You have started to develop some idea of why this is so, and have considered some of the options for the future. You have gained a good working knowledge of some important aspects of climate change that you will be able to build upon and develop throughout the remainder of this book.

However, that is not all you have gained. You have started working with an analytical framework that will guide your exploration not only of climate change, but also of the other environmental problems that you will work with on this course. There are two sets of components that make up this framework. The first set of components is the four *course questions*. The main sections of this chapter have introduced you in turn to these questions. Each question focuses on a different dimension of environmental policy in an international context. Working with these questions will enable you to develop a broad understanding of environmental problems, why the policy responses to date often fail to maintain environmental quality, and the future options for addressing these problems.

The second set of components that make up the analytical framework of the course is the six *course themes*. As you worked through this chapter you will have noticed margin notes drawing your attention to individual themes. I have highlighted each course theme just once, although you may also have noticed the themes reappearing elsewhere in the chapter. You will find these themes recurring throughout the course. The themes have a different purpose to the course questions. The intention behind the themes is to guide your exploration of environmental problems, politics and policy, and to suggest how you can work with and open up the four questions. In different ways each of the six themes can be used to structure your thinking as you approach individual course questions. 'Thinking thematically' will not provide answers to the course questions, but it will suggest some signposts and lines of enquiry that you can use to help you think through the course questions. Working with the themes will also help you to appreciate some of the similarities and differences between different environmental problems and the policy responses to them.

Together these themes and questions provide an analytical framework that you can bring to bear upon any environmental problem, both those that you will learn about on this course and those that you will encounter in your daily life. Working with the themes and questions in the weeks ahead will, I hope, be a stimulating, enjoyable and rewarding experience as you explore the environmental challenges that the world faces in the early twenty-first century.

Video 1

Now watch Video 1: *Adapting to climate change 1: Khulna district, Bangladesh.*

References

Allison, G. T. (1971) *Essence of Decision: Explaining the Cuban Missile Crisis*, Boston, Little Brown.

Baer, P. with Mastrandrea, M. (2006) *High Stakes: Designing Emissions Pathways to Reduce the Risk of Dangerous Climate Change*, London, Institute for Public Policy Research.

Brown, P. (2006) *Global Warming: The Last Chance for Change*, London, Guardian Books.

Commission of the European Communities (2006) *Limiting Global Climate Change to 2 Degrees Celsius: Policy Options for the EU and the World for 2020 and Beyond*, Brussels, 27 November.

Daily University Science News (2002) 'Collapse of Antarctic's Larsen B ice shelf revealed' [online], 19 March, http://www.unisci.com/stories/20021/0319021.htm (Accessed 27 May 2007).

Dobson, A. (2003) *Citizenship and the Environment*, Oxford, Oxford University Press.

Dow, K. and Downing, T. E. (2006) *The Atlas of Climate Change*, London, Earthscan.

Forsyth, T. (2003) *Critical Political Ecology: The Politics of Environmental Science*, London, Routledge.

Giddens, A. (1984) *The Constitution of Society*, Cambridge, Polity Press.

Gore, A. (2006) *An Inconvenient Truth*, London, Bloomsbury.

Green Party (2005) *Real Progress: Real Choice for Real Change – Green Party Manifesto 2005*, London, Green Party of England and Wales.

Hardin, G. (1968) 'The tragedy of the commons', *Science*, no. 162, pp. 1243–48.

Intergovernmental Panel on Climate Change (IPCC) (2005) *Carbon Dioxide Capture and Storage: Summary for Policy Makers and Technical Summary* [online], http://www.ipcc.ch (Accessed 12 December 2006).

Intergovernmental Panel on Climate Change (IPCC) (2007) *Climate Change 2007: The Physical Science Basis – Summary for Policymakers, Contribution of Working Group I to the Fourth Assessment Report of the Intergovernmental Panel on Climate Change* [online], http://www.ipcc.chSPB2feb07.pdf (Accessed 2 February 2007).

Liberatore, A. (1995) 'The social construction of environmental problems' in Glasbergen, P. and Blowers, A. (eds) *Environmental Policy in an International Context: Perspectives on Environmental Problems*, London, Arnold

Lohmann, L. (1999) *The Carbon Shop: Planting New Problems – Briefing Paper*, Plantations Campaign, Montevideo, World Rainforest Movement.

Lynas, M. (2007) *Six Degrees: Our Future on a Hotter Planet*, London, Fourth Estate.

Marshall, G. J., Orr, A., van Lipzig, N. P. M. and King, J. C. (2006) 'The impact of a changing Southern Hemisphere Annular Mode on Antarctic Peninsula summer temperatures', *Journal of Climate*, vol. 19, pp. 5388–404.

O'Riordan, T. (1981) *Environmentalism* (2nd edn), London, Pion.

Rotstayn, L. D., Roderick, M. L. and Farquhar, G. D. (2006) 'A simple pan-evaporation model for analysis of climate simulations: evaluation over Australia', *Geophysical Research Letters*, vol. 33, L17715.

Travis, D. J., Carleton, A. M. and Lauritsen, R. G. (2002) 'Contrails reduce daily temperature range', *Nature*, no. 418, August, p. 601.

Travis, D. J., Carleton, A. M. and Lauritsen, R. G. (2004) 'Regional variations in U.S. diurnal temperature range for the 11–14 September 2001 aircraft groundings: evidence of jet contrail influence on climate', *Journal of Climate*, vol. 17, no. 5, pp. 1123–34.

USA Congress (1997) 'Byrd Hagel resolution sponsored by Senator Robert Byrd (D-WV) and Senator Chuck Hagel (R-NE)' [online], 105th Congress, 1st Session, S.RES.98, available http://www.nationalcenter.org/KyotoSenate.html (Accessed 12 April 2008).

Wackernagel, M. and Rees, W. (1996) *Our Ecological Footprint: Reducing Human Impact on the Earth*, Gabriola Island, Canada, New Society.

Warnock, M. (2001) *An Intelligent Person's Guide to Ethics*, Croydon, Duckbacks.

World Commission on Environment and Development (WCED) (1987) *Our Common Future*, Oxford, Oxford University Press.

Chapter 2
The role of science in climate change policy

David Humphreys

Contents

1	**Introduction**	**58**
	1.1 Learning outcomes	60
2	**What is science?**	**61**
	2.1 Introducing science	61
	2.2 Science and social values	64
3	**Coping with uncertainty**	**66**
	3.1 What is uncertainty?	66
	3.2 The role of models	68
4	**The IPCC: where science meets politics**	**71**
	4.1 The role of the IPCC	71
	4.2 The institutional design of the IPCC	75
5	**The IPCC as an epistemic community**	**77**
6	**Climate of denial in the greenhouse**	**82**
	6.1 The discourse of denial	82
	6.2 'Atmospheric pressure' in the USA	83
	6.3 The politics of denial	88
	6.4 Climate science and the media	89
7	**Conclusion**	**91**
	References	**93**

1   Introduction

On Friday, 2 February 2007 the world's media assembled in Paris to cover the release of an Intergovernmental Panel on Climate Change (IPCC) report on the physical scientific evidence on climate change (Figure 2.1). Attending the IPCC meeting was Achim Steiner, the executive director of the United Nations Environment Programme (UNEP), who commented that the report should remove any doubt on whether anthropogenic climate change was taking place:

> February 2 will perhaps one day be remembered as the day the question mark was removed. Anyone who would continue to risk inaction will one day in the history books be considered irresponsible
> (Achim Steiner, cited in Smith, 2007, p. 32)

That same day in Houston, Texas the oil company ExxonMobil announced the largest annual profit ever recorded for a USA corporation: $39.5 billion (Macalister, 2007).

These two events, which at first sight are unrelated, each have a bearing on the politics and science of climate change. Whereas the IPCC concludes that there is increasing evidence that anthropogenic climate change is taking place, ExxonMobil has disputed this, claiming that any changes to the Earth's temperature are predominantly natural in origin. How have these two different claims influenced international policy response to climate change? And what role does scientific knowledge play in international climate policy?

A **discourse** is a body of language that is unified by certain ideas, assumptions and understandings.

To help you explore these questions I will introduce you to the idea of discourse. A **discourse** is a body of language – an established way of thinking about things and expressing ideas – that is unified by certain assumptions and understandings. Discourses structure how people think about, interpret and make sense of what happens. When actors agree upon a discourse they can communicate with one another because they share common understandings, ideas and beliefs (Hinchliffe and Belshaw, 2003, pp. 98–100). An understanding of discourse is an important aspect of the study of international environmental policy. How discourses are sustained and challenged influences how actors frame environmental problems and how these problems are handled by policy makers. I will present the story of international climate politics in terms of two competing discourses and will outline the different ways that these discourses have been mobilised by political and economic actors to legitimise their political positions.

The first discourse is based upon scientific knowledge, although it is not exclusively scientific in nature and is, in part, politically negotiated. According to this discourse climate change is taking place, it is primarily

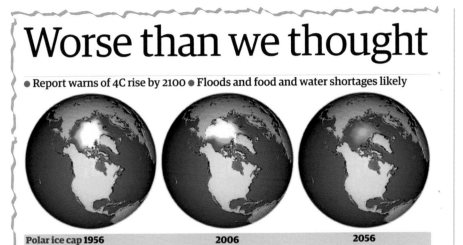

Worse than we thought

● Report warns of 4C rise by 2100 ● Floods and food and water shortages likely

Polar ice cap 1956 | 2006 | 2056

Source: *Guardian* (2007)

New fears on climate raise heat

Source: *The Times* (2007)

FINAL WARNING

According to yesterday's UN report, the world will be a much hotter place by 2100. This will be the impact...

+2.4°	+3.4°	+4.4°	+5.4°	+6.4°
CORAL REEFS ALMOST EXTINCT	RAINFOREST TURNS TO DESERT	MELTING ICE CAPS DISPLACE MILLIONS	SEA LEVELS RISE BY FIVE METRES	MOST OF LIFE IS EXTERMINATED

Source: *The Independent* (2007)

Figure 2.1
The release of the Intergovernmental Panel on Climate Change's Fourth Assessment Report on the physical science basis for climate change was front-page news in the UK

anthropogenic, it is serious and it will get worse. The vast majority of climate scientists adhere to this discourse, although a small minority do not. The second discourse holds that there is so much uncertainty about climate change that no firm conclusions can be drawn about it. According to this discourse climate change is probably due to natural variations and it is unlikely to lead to significant, if any, adverse effects.

For reasons that will become clear I refer to this as the discourse of denial. Unlike the first discourse it is not based on scientific knowledge and is overtly political.

I will introduce you to these two very different discourses, their origins, how they have evolved over time and how they have influenced international climate policy making. As you work through this chapter you will see how the idea of discourse illustrates some important aspects of scientific knowledge, and how such knowledge is used, and sometimes abused, in environmental policy making. You will see that actors who produce discourses that are widely accepted may exert power in social life by shaping how people understand and think about the world. This is a very different approach to power to that of the previous chapter, where you were introduced to power as the capacity of an actor to influence other actors by mobilising and deploying resources, such as technology, finance and human resources. In the conclusion of this chapter I will suggest that these two different aspects of power – as the control and deployment of resources and as the shaping of discourses – should not be seen as separate. In practice the two are often related.

1.1 Learning outcomes

This chapter should enable you to:

■ understand some of the main political responses to climate change as an international environmental problem (*course question 2*)

■ appreciate how knowledge and values may interact in environmental policy making (*course theme 3*)

■ explain how climate scientists and policy makers have sought to deal with uncertainty on climate change

■ explain the functioning of the Intergovernmental Panel on Climate Change as an institution that integrates science and politics

■ discuss environmental policy making as a process that involves contention between different discourses.

2   What is science?

2.1 Introducing science

Figure 2.2
Many people have
strong views on climate
change. How can we
know when these views
are well founded?

Activity 2.1

Figure 2.2 contains some statements you may have heard about climate change. What do the people you know say about climate change, and how do they justify what they say? How do you decide whose views to take seriously, and whose to ignore?

You may have found that thinking about this raises more questions than answers. So how do we decide what, or who, is 'right'? With different people saying different things who should we believe? How do we decide which claims to reject as uninformed and which to accept as authoritative knowledge? And what is knowledge, and how do we know when we have found it?

These questions lie at the core of an area of philosophical study called epistemology. Derived from the Greek words *episteme* for knowledge and *logos* for reason, **epistemology** is the study of how knowledge is

Epistemology is the study of how knowledge is produced, validated and accepted.

produced, validated and accepted. The classical view of scientific knowledge is based on the ideas of the ancient Greek philosopher Plato, who defined knowledge as 'justified true belief'. According to Plato we can only say that there is knowledge if something is true, it is believed to be true (at least by some people) and it has been justified through argument, reason and evidence. We cannot say that there is knowledge if something is true, but which nobody knows or understands to be true. Similarly, mere belief does not constitute knowledge if the belief is untrue. So conviction, opinion and assertion are, on their own, insufficient to constitute knowledge.

My interest in this chapter is in the epistemology of science. The classical view of science as the disinterested pursuit of the truth is expressed through **positivism**, an epistemological approach that holds that knowledge can only be obtained by the testing of scientific theories through observation, measurement and analysis. According to this view, scientists should be detached from the object of their analysis. Their values and beliefs should have no bearing on their research and the results of the hypotheses that they test (Box 2.1). The positivist view holds that values should be kept separate from the facts; scientific knowledge should be value free.

Positivism is the epistemological approach that knowledge can only be obtained by the testing of scientific theories through observation, measurement and analysis.

A **hypothesis** is a proposed explanation for something.

Box 2.1   Hypothesis testing

Much scientific research is conducted through hypothesis testing. A **hypothesis** is a proposed explanation for something. At its simplest a hypothesis posits a relationship between two variables, for example, that increasing A will lead to an increase in X. Here A is said to be the independent variable, while X is the dependent variable. To test the relationship between these variables, scientists may conduct an experiment, varying A and observing and measuring the changes to X in order to investigate whether changes to X are dependent on A. Testing will either confirm or disconfirm a hypothesis. When a hypothesis is disconfirmed scientists have various options. They may slightly modify the hypothesis, and then test that, or they may test a completely different hypothesis: for example, increasing B will cause an increase to X, or increasing A will cause an increase to Y.

Activity 2.2

Look again at the definition of a hypothesis in Box 2.1. The main dependent variable that climate scientists seek to measure is the global mean temperature. Now pause and think back to your work in Chapter 1. What are the independent variables that scientists will need to measure if they are to predict future climate change?

The independent variables referred to in Box 2.1 are the causes of climate change. These changes are both natural and anthropogenic in origin (*course theme 1*). Natural causes include volcanic eruptions and changes to solar activity, while anthropogenic causes are primarily greenhouse gas emissions and the destruction of carbon sinks such as forests.

There are different approaches to scientific reasoning. One common approach is **deduction**. Deductive reasoning moves logically from premises to a conclusion. Here is an example:

Premise: The mean temperature of the Earth will vary according to the atmospheric concentration of greenhouse gases.

Premise: Humans are emitting more greenhouse gases into the atmosphere than can be absorbed by sinks.

Conclusion: The mean temperature of the Earth will rise.

> **Deduction** is a method of reasoning that moves from premises to a conclusion.

According to deductive reasoning, as long as the premises are true then the conclusion will be true (Warburton, 1996, p. 39). Deduction is thus a truth-preserving method of reasoning. Scientists must first be sure that their premises are true, for example by hypothesis testing and experiment, before they can have confidence in their conclusions. Similarly, rejecting a conclusion logically means that one or more of the premises must also be rejected.

Another method of scientific reasoning is **induction**. An inductive theory moves from a series of observations to a conclusion. This is sometimes called the 'white swans' method of reasoning. If an ornithologist were to observe 1000 swans and all were white they might conclude 'All swans are white'. The inductive conclusion serves as a prediction for future events. The ornithologist might predict that the next swan observed will be white.

> **Induction** is a method of reasoning that moves from a series of observations to a conclusion.

Induction may be contrasted with **falsification**, sometimes called the 'black swans' method. If our ornithologist were to observe just one black swan the original conclusion that all swans are white will have been falsified. Falsification is attributed to the philosopher Karl Popper (Figure 2.3), who argued that although the truth exists it is elusive; humans can never really know what the truth is. The testing of

> **Falsification** is the theoretical approach that we can never know the truth, only what is not true through the falsification of hypotheses.

Figure 2.3
Karl Popper argued that humans can never be completely sure what the truth is. Scientists can only falsify hypotheses, not prove them

hypotheses does not yield the truth, argued Popper; it merely tells us what is not false. Each falsified hypothesis takes us closer to the truth, although we can never know what the truth is. To Popper, hypotheses testing does not yield knowledge as Plato defined it, as justified true belief. To Popper, knowledge is always provisional, hypothetical and never fully reliable. The scientific process is the progressive elimination of falsified hypotheses; a good scientific theory is one that can be empirically tested, and thus potentially falsified. The truth cannot be verified, but a wrong hypothesis can always be falsified (Popper, 1979, p. 58).

2.2 Science and social values

In this section I would like to consider the relationship between social values and scientific knowledge (*course theme 3*). Most scientists agree with the positivist view that values should be kept out of science. But can science ever be completely value free? Scientific research has always been driven in part by the curiosities and interests of people who, in turn, will reflect the social values of their particular time and place. Contemporary climate science needs to be understood within a historical context in which social and political concerns about climate change have driven the climate research agenda. More specifically, climate science research reflects in part the social values of policy makers, who indicate to scientists the sort of knowledge that they need. Policy makers may be highly critical of knowledge that is too technical or which is not relevant to policy; they may demand knowledge in very specific areas, such as predictions on future climate change, new technologies to mitigate carbon emissions and climate monitoring systems.

My point here is that the demand for *policy-relevant* research shapes to some degree the work that climate scientists do. The relationship between science and policy is not a linear process whereby environmental scientists feed the latest scientific research to policy makers, who accept the research and then make policy based upon it. Scientific research funding is a scarce resource. It may be ring-fenced so that it can be used only to pursue research questions that have been established by the research funders (such as a government or business).

Knowing this, scientists may consciously choose to specialise in areas that they know to be well funded or that will lead to reputational benefits. So scientific research is always socially situated, and the choice of what gets funded and what does not inevitably favours some areas of research, and therefore some scientists, more than others. So in a *social* sense, therefore, scientific research is rarely completely value free.

Although social values may help determine the science that is researched, can they be kept out of the actual process of scientific research? There are different views here. The positivist view would acknowledge the role of social values in driving research agendas, but would argue that such values should not interfere with the actual process of scientific research. Even if social values help to shape research questions they should not impinge upon the value-free nature of scientific enquiry. According to the positivist view the integrity of science will be eroded if there is social or political interference in the scientific process or if the results of scientific research reflect the personal values or beliefs of scientists.

An alternative view is put forward by sociologists of science. According to this view, social values inevitably creep into the research process. Sociologists of science argue that the distinction between value-laden research agendas and value-free scientific enquiry is hard to maintain in practice. Research funding may not only stipulate certain research questions; it may favour one scientific method over and above another. Sociologists of science ask questions such as who is science for, whose scientific methods are being used, and to what social ends will scientific research be put (Latour, 1999). According to Jerome Ravetz it is time to dispel 'the illusion of scientific objectivity' (2006, p. 77). Views of what constitutes 'sound' scientific practice and 'good quality' research may vary over time as social values change. New scientific research will be judged in part on the extent to which it conforms to an existing 'orthodoxy' or 'wisdom', and is consistent with the scientific views held by establishment institutions and leading scientific experts. On this view, social values inevitably influence the conduct of research, and if scientific integrity is to be maintained scientists, rather than insist that their methods are value free, should instead acknowledge these values and make them explicit.

In one respect these views are opposites yet, perhaps ironically, both contribute to our understanding of international climate science. As you will see in Section 3, on the one hand climate scientists strive to be as value free as possible in their research in order to work out the geophysical processes that lead to climate change. On the other hand, climate science over the last thirty years reflects a particular dominant approach to how the Earth's climate should be modelled. A **model** is a simplified

A **model** is a simplified representation of a complex system or phenomenon.

representation of a complex system or phenomenon. It is impossible to study all the variables at play in the world's climatic system; there are simply too many of them. So climate modellers seeks to represent only those scientific and natural processes that have a bearing on the Earth's temperature. The idea of a model is an important one in the sciences and, as you will see in Chapters 3 and 4 of this volume, of the social sciences.

Before you consider climate modelling I first wish to introduce you to an important concept that will recur throughout the remainder of this chapter: uncertainty.

3   Coping with uncertainty

3.1 What is uncertainty?

Uncertainty is a
condition that arises
when something cannot
be precisely measured,
established or
understood.

Uncertainty is a condition that arises when something cannot be precisely measured, established or understood. There are many sources of uncertainty on climate change. Some uncertainties derive from the limitations of scientific knowledge. For example, scientists know relatively little about the role of the oceans in climate change compared to terrestrial ecosystems. Other uncertainties arise from problems in measurement: accurate measuring of all the independent variables contributing to climate change is impossible, hence climate science is inherently uncertain. Any errors in the data for the independent variables will inevitably lead to an error in the dependent variable. Scientists have an expression for this: 'Garbage in – garbage out' (GIGO).

The term **transcience**
denotes those questions
that can be formulated in
scientific terms but which
cannot be answered with
certainty.

The global climate system can be seen as an example of **transcience**. Alvin Weinberg (1972) used this term to describe those questions that can in principle be formulated in scientific terms – in terms of independent and dependent variables – but which cannot be answered with certainty because science cannot measure all the variables concerned nor are scientists likely to understand how these variables interrelate. So scientific uncertainties on climate change should not necessarily be attributed to imperfections or flaws in the scientific method. Some uncertainties are derived from the very nature of the climate system, which is complex, dynamic and non-linear.

Activity 2.3

A non-linear system is one with feedback effects. Referring back to Chapter 1 can you summarise the main feedback effects that you have learned about so far? Once you have answered this question in your own words read on.

A feedback effect will enhance or diminish the original effect, in this case changes to the Earth's temperature. One important climate change feedback that you may have recalled from Chapter 1 is the melting of the world's ice. Scientists are unsure exactly how fast the world's ice is melting, although they do know that this process will increase the rate of climate change. The complexity and non-linearity of the Earth's climatic system does not mean that it is not amenable to scientific inquiry, although it does add to the difficulties of accurate prediction. Uncertainty is thus an inescapable aspect of climate policy making, which must be based on probabilities rather than firm proof.

Scientists and policy makers have very different approaches to uncertainty. For scientists the identification of uncertainty is not necessarily a problem; it can point towards areas where future research is needed. For policy makers, who seek reliable knowledge so that they can make clear policy, uncertainty can lead to indecision and disputes in the policy-making process. Scientists who work at the science–politics interface thus find themselves pulled in different directions. From policy makers and politicians, who do not want their policies to lead to unintended or adverse consequences, they face demands for knowledge that is as certain, accurate and reputable as possible. But from their training and from colleagues in the scientific community scientists will face pressure not to express more certainty than the scientific evidence can justify (Harrison, 2004, p. 118).

When scientists do claim certainty it is usually in one of two situations. The first is where they have an opportunity to make repeated observations of a phenomenon or phenomena, so that they can establish patterns and make accurate predictions. The example usually cited is the movement of planets in the solar system. So regular are these movements that astronomers can use precise mathematical equations to predict eclipses thousands of years into the future (Figure 2.4). The second situation is when scientists run a control experiment. For example, let us assume that scientists hypothesise that changes to a dependent variable X depend upon changes to three independent variables – A, B and C. They wish to measure the effect just of A. To do this they have to 'isolate' A, in other words to measure the effects of A that are independent of B and C. Two experiments are then run. In the first experiment A is varied, while B and C are held constant. In the second experiment – the control – all variables, including A, are held constant. Assuming there are no other independent variables then any difference to X between the two experiments would be attributed to A.

Although climate scientists can conduct laboratory experiments that help them to understand how the climate system may behave, the empirical study of climate change takes place in a vast open system – the Earth and

Figure 2.4
Something in the air! A time-lapse sequence of the total eclipse of the Sun on 29 March 2006, photographed from Antalya, Turkey. Scientists can predict eclipses thousands of years in advance, but predicting climate change is far more complex

its atmosphere. We only have one planet, so a control experiment to measure how anthropogenic greenhouse gas emissions may change the Earth's climate is not an option. By adding huge volumes of greenhouse gases to the atmosphere humans are, in effect, running a massive uncontrolled experiment. With no control experiment possible, anthropogenic climate change remains, in scientific terms, a hypothesis. However, it is a hypothesis for which there is a substantial and growing body of confirmatory evidence that is consistent with knowledge of how the climate system has behaved in the past.

3.2 The role of models

Because the global climate is a vast, complex system climate scientists attempt to map the various independent variables through computer-driven models called general circulation models (GCMs). A GCM simulates how the climate will change over time. A GCM cannot replicate the global climate system in its entirety – there are far too many variables – so climate modellers disaggregate the Earth's climatic system into small, constituent parts that can be easily analysed. These include, for example, changes in carbon sinks due to deforestation, increased radiative forcing due to greenhouse emissions, changes in albedo due to changes in land use, emissions from industrial agriculture, and so on. This is an example of **reductionism**, the scientific method of analysing a complex phenomenon by reducing it down into smaller, less complex, constituent parts. Modellers then use complex mathematical equations to reassemble these constituent parts in a way that represents the complexity of the Earth's climatic system, including the various positive and negative feedback effects. Climate models are intended to be holistic mathematical representations of the climatic system, although they cannot capture all the relevant variables. They are approximate, rather than accurate, representations that can predict broad patterns and general trends.

Reductionism is the scientific method of analysing a complex phenomenon by breaking it down into smaller, less complex, constituent parts.

Online Exercise 2

Can you think how general circulation models might be tested to ensure their accuracy? Once you have thought about this question log on to the course website and click on Online Exercise 2: *Climate modelling*. When you have completed this activity continue reading below.

GCMs are hugely expensive. The design of these models varies; there is no 'right' way of designing a climate model. Model design will vary according to the training of the modellers, where they have been educated and the colleagues with whom they associate. The group of scientists designing a GCM will negotiate and deliberate on the design of the model, the variables to be included, the data sets to be used and how the evidence should be interpreted. Stephen Bocking has noted that those who criticise science may argue that because scientists negotiate and deliberate that there must be something wrong in the scientific process. So if there are two views to a scientific argument then it might be assumed that 'one side may be incompetent or fraudulent, or one (or both) sides may have fallen prey to ideology or the influence of economic or political interests' (Bocking, 2006, p. 28). However, it is rarely as simple as that. Different scientists may interpret the same evidence differently. Often debates on how the evidence should be interpreted are unavoidable due to the complexity of biophysical processes and the limitations of science in understanding them. All climate scientists have to grapple with uncertainty, seeking to eliminate it when they can, but acknowledging it when they cannot.

Inevitably, therefore, there is a degree of subjectivity in model design. Let me be quite clear about how I am using the term 'subjectivity' here. I am not using it in a pejorative way to denigrate climate modellers or to suggest that they are biased or prejudiced. A climate scientist will draw from the methods and model designs that, in their judgement, are best able to 'get at' the truth. I call this *disinterested subjectivity*, as the intention in subjectively choosing one approach over another is to be as objective as possible. The dividing line between subjectivity and objectivity can thus be very fine. In this sense, and contrary to what positivists would suggest, climate scientific knowledge is not *entirely* value free. Some element of subjective choice in the scientific research method is unavoidable.

How do scientists control for subjectivity? Clearly 'too much' subjectivity in research design and the interpretation of results is undesirable; it can introduce bias. Before a paper is published in a scientific journal it is subject to peer review. A number of experts will be asked to comment on the paper to assess its competence, originality and impartiality. These experts will assess whether the paper's conclusions can be supported from the work carried out. The peer review process is not flawless. A peer reviewer might not be fully objective and might judge scientific research within the conventional practices and wisdoms of a scientific community at a given moment of time, thus reinforcing and perpetuating certain established ways of 'doing science'. GCMs have now become the dominant approach to climate science. Peer review does not always guarantee accuracy, nor does it mean that a paper that survives the process has 'found' the truth. The conclusions of peer-reviewed scientific papers may later be challenged or overturned by new scientific developments. Despite these weaknesses peer review generally leads to scientific papers that are more authoritative than many non-peer-reviewed papers. They are based on methods and research designs that other scientists accept as trustworthy.

Peer review is an important part in the design of GCMs and in the assessment of the results that GCMs yield. Although the design of different GCMs vary, as do their specific predictions, all models are now conveying the same basic message: that the climate is warming due to anthropogenic activities and it will continue to warm far into the future unless action is taken to reduce greenhouse gas emissions. None suggest that global temperature changes over the last two centuries are due solely to natural factors.

You now have a grasp of how scientists carry out their work. But what happens when science meets politics? In the next section the interactions between science and politics will be illustrated using the IPCC as a case study.

4 The IPCC: where science meets politics

4.1 The role of the IPCC

The relationship between scientists and politicians is often difficult. To be influential, scientists need high-level political recognition, while resisting political interference in the research process. Politicians need clear scientific inputs to policy making, although they will invariably assert that policy should be made by policy makers, not scientists. In this section you will explore how the relationship between these two different groups is managed at the international level.

In the 1980s, a growing body of scientific knowledge on climate change was being produced by research institutes and universities around the world, but there was no international institution in place to assess and synthesise this knowledge. So a new organisation was created within the United Nations (UN) system. In 1988 the World Meteorological Organisation and the United Nations Environment Programme created the IPCC. The IPCC is an example of a 'boundary organisation'. This is a term that is often used to refer to organisations where scientists meet non-scientists, although it can refer to any organisation that brings together people from two or more disciplines or different organisational cultures.

The IPCC was designed in order to meet two key objectives. The first was to allow scientists to demonstrate to politicians the veracity of scientific knowledge on climate change. If politicians are to accept scientific knowledge they first need to understand it. Scientific knowledge in its pure form is laden with technical terms and language, so part of the work of the IPCC is to 'translate' the technical jargon of climate science into an idiom that can be readily understood by politicians, policy makers and other non-scientific audiences. Second, the IPCC enables politicians to accept this knowledge as authoritative. The IPCC has been remarkably successful at meeting this objective in a way that avoids *significant* political interference with the scientific knowledge although, and as you will see later, sometimes politically motivated changes are made to scientific conclusions. So the knowledge that the IPCC produces is not *pure* scientific knowledge; there are some political inputs too. This knowledge is one example of a discourse, a particular way of thinking and understanding. I refer to the consensual knowledge that the IPCC produces as the 'IPCC discourse'.

The IPCC is not a research body. It carries out no original research, although its conclusions may suggest areas of uncertainty where future research is needed. As an intergovernmental body the IPCC's membership is comprised of government delegations. These delegations include both scientists and policy makers. Scientists are appointed by governments because they have an international reputation in climate science. Policy makers are appointed by governments because they are trusted to represent the national interests of their government. So both within individual IPCC delegations, and within the organisation itself, the IPCC is characterised by an inherent tension between these two very different professional cultures.

There are three IPCC working groups:

■ *Working Group I* assesses the physical science of climate change and its causes, and estimates future climate change.

■ *Working Group II* assesses the impacts and vulnerabilities of climate change, including the adaptation possibilities.

■ *Working Group III* assesses the mitigation possibilities.

How do climate scientists deal with uncertainty? Like other scientists they do so by qualifying their conclusions with probabilities that convey different levels of uncertainty. As the climate scientist Barrie Pittock writes, 'It is common in the physical sciences to say that something is "true", "certain" or "well established" if the evidence suggests that there is less than a 5 per cent chance (1 in 20) of it being wrong' (Pittock, 2005, p. 65). The IPCC works with a scale of descriptive judgements. These vary between working groups. Here I would like to focus on the descriptions used in the Working Group I Fourth Assessment Report published in 2007. This agreed two ways to communicate different levels of uncertainty: a description of the levels of confidence of the IPCC experts in the correctness of the underlying science; and a description of the likelihood, or probability, that a defined outcome has occurred or will occur (Box 2.2).

Box 2.2   Communication of uncertainty expressed by IPCC Working Group 1, Fourth Assessment Report, 2007

Levels of confidence used to express expert judgements on the correctness of the underlying science

Terminology	Degree of confidence in being correct
Very high confidence	At least 9 out of 10 chance of being correct
High confidence	About 8 out of 10 chance
Medium confidence	About 5 out of 10 chance
Low confidence	About 2 out of 10 chance
Very low confidence	Less than a 1 out of 10 chance

Assessed likelihood, using expert judgement of an outcome or result	
Terminology	**Assessed likelihood**
Virtually certain	> 99% probability
Extremely likely	> 95% probability
Very likely	> 90% probability
Likely	> 66% probability
More likely than not	> 50% probability
About as likely as not	33–66% probability
Unlikely	< 33% probability
Very unlikely	< 10% probability
Extremely unlikely	< 5% probability
Exceptionally unlikely	< 1% probability

Note:
> indicates greater than, so > 99% indicates a probability that is greater than 99%

< indicates less than, so < 1% indicates a probability that is less than 1%

Activity 2.4

Once you are familiar with the statements in Box 2.2, read through Box 2.3. This contains excerpts from the policy makers' summaries from the first four IPCC assessment reports from Working Group I. What can you conclude about the level of certainty or uncertainty in the scientific knowledge on climate change when these reports were published?

Box 2.3　IPCC assessments of climate change 1990–2007

These are extracts from the first four summaries on the physical science basis for climate change, which were produced for policy makers by the IPCC's Working Group 1.

First Assessment Report, 1990

> The size of this warming is broadly consistent with predictions of climate models, but it is also of the same magnitude of natural climate variability. Thus the observed increase could be largely due to this natural variability ... The unequivocal detection of the enhanced greenhouse effect is not likely for a decade or more
>
> (WMO, UNEP and IPCC, 1990)

Second Assessment Report, 1995

> The balance of evidence suggests a discernible human influence on global climate
>
> (IPCC, 1996)

Third Assessment Report, 2001

> In the light of new evidence and taking into account the remaining uncertainties, most of the observed warming over the last 50 years is likely to have been due to the increase in greenhouse concentrations
>
> (IPCC, 2001)

Fourth Assessment Report, 2007

> The understanding of anthropogenic warming and cooling influences on the climate has improved since the Third Assessment Report (TAR), leading to *very high confidence* that the globally averaged net effect of human activities since 1750 has been one of warming ... Most of the observed increase in globally averaged temperatures since the mid-twentieth century is *very likely* due to the observed increase in anthropogenic greenhouse gas concentrations [emphases in original].
>
> (IPCC, 2007)

The First Assessment Report in 1990 was cautious, offering no clear conclusion. Note that the Fourth Assessment Report uses the expression 'very likely', thus denoting a stronger judgement on likelihood than the Third Assessment Report, which used the softer expression 'likely'. The use of the expression 'very high confidence' in the Fourth Assessment Report is the strongest that the IPCC can deliver regarding the correctness of the science. The IPCC's conclusions have thus grown firmer over time.

4.2 The institutional design of the IPCC

You have seen what the IPCC has been saying, but how does the IPCC agree such language? Tora Skodvin, a political scientist who has analysed the institutional design of the IPCC, argues that it has succeeded in agreeing a consensual diagnosis of climate change because it both *separates* and *integrates* science and politics. Separation is necessary so that political values do not 'contaminate' the science, but complete separation is undesirable. A high level of integration at the science–politics interface is also necessary, as without it a common understanding between scientists and politicians could not be reached (Skodvin, 1999, 2000).

How does the IPCC as an institution manage these two seemingly contradictory objectives? 'Separation and integration' is achieved over a three-stage process (Figure 2.5). First, scientific peer review and synthesising of the science literature is conducted in meetings of the scientific core of the three working groups. The published scientific literature is subjected to further peer review and the findings are summarised. These meetings are attended only by scientists. Although members of the scientific core are appointed by governments they are not expected to represent political interests. The scientific core will seek to identify those areas on which there is a general scientific consensus, for

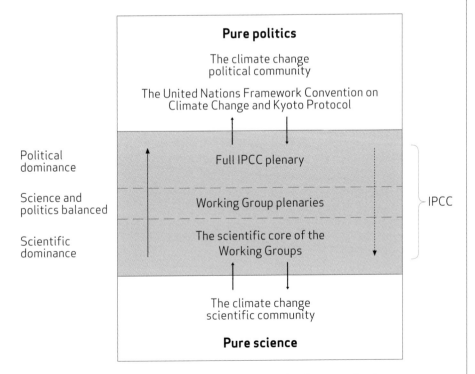

Figure 2.5
The institutional design of the Intergovernmental Panel on Climate Change (Source: Skodvin, 2000, p. 152)

The arrows indicate the formal and informal channels of communicating.

example, where a conclusion has been reached by several scientists. If different scientists have reached different conclusions the scientific core will agree conclusions that accord with the 'general' scientific view. Lead authors are appointed to prepare the first drafts of the IPCC's policy makers' summary.

Second, each working group holds a series of plenary meetings attended by both government delegates and scientists to continue the drafting of the policy makers' summaries. Finally, the full IPCC plenary will meet to finalise the drafting of the policy makers' summaries. The full IPCC plenary meets at the end of an assessment cycle, which lasts five or six years.

In the final two stages the policy makers' summaries are negotiated line by line, with any government delegate being free to propose changes. However, major changes to the scientific content cannot be made without the agreement of the lead authors of the chapter under negotiation. The lead authors thus play a key role in maintaining the integrity of the science at the science–politics interface. A purely political process would see the scientific results weakened through political bargaining. The final two stages usually see a 'tug of war' between scientists and government delegates. A government delegate may insist that a particular phrase is unacceptable; a lead author may respond that the phrase cannot be deleted or weakened. The lead authors will guard against weakening of the scientific conclusions, while accepting that some change is inevitable. This is the price of political acceptance; pure scientific knowledge on climate change is worthless if politicians do not accept the knowledge as authoritative. As Sir John Houghton, the former chair of Working Group I notes, if governments were not involved in the IPCC its documents 'would be treated like any old scientific report. They would end up on the shelf or in the waste bin' (cited in Skodvin, 1999, p. 30). The IPCC plenary negotiations thus reach a consensus that is politically negotiated while retaining a high degree of scientific integrity (Skodvin, 1999, pp. 20–1, 2000).

The involvement of government delegates representing political interests in the process inevitably involves some weakening of the text. For example, in the Fourth Assessment Report of 2007 the European Union agreed with the scientific core that the report should state it is 'extremely likely' that human activity was causing global warming, an assessed likelihood of greater than 95 per cent (Box 2.2 above). China, one of the world's largest carbon dioxide emitters, opposed this, after which 'very likely' was agreed (ABC News, 2007). One commentator, David Wasdell, compared the draft text presented by the scientific core with the IPCC's Fourth Assessment Report submitted in 2007. Wasdell found that there was a general softening of any language that could suggest climate change is accelerating. Scientific statements on strong positive feedbacks that could suggest major climatic disturbances did not survive the political negotiations. The result, to Wasdell, is a document which is 'profoundly dependable albeit inevitably conservative' (Wasdell, 2007, p. 8).

Wasdell views the IPCC editorial and drafting process as a cultural struggle in which scientists resist government delegates representing a fossil-fuel addicted political culture with an interest in continued greenhouse emissions. Collectively, he suggests, the world's governments have an interest in emphasising scientific uncertainty. This serves a political purpose: states that do not want to take strong action against climate change can then cite IPCC statements as evidence of uncertainty (Wasdell, 2007). Brazil, Russia, Saudi Arabia and the USA were among those countries that emphasised uncertainty during the negotiation of the IPCC's Fourth Assessment Report (*Earth Negotiations Bulletin*, 2007; Smith, 2007). Some political leaders appear to have an ambiguous relationship with the IPCC. Collectively, politicians use the IPCC to adopt the latest scientific findings. However, some politicians may then resist some of the stronger conclusions that they see as counter to their interests, particularly those that suggest urgent measures to reduce greenhouse gas emissions are necessary.

It is clear that the IPCC language on uncertainty is a hybrid. The IPCC discourse is based predominantly upon scientific knowledge, but it is not pure science; the final text of the policy makers' summary contains statements that are expressed scientifically as probabilities, but are also shaped by political values (Bocking, 2006). Many conclusions are filtered out, first by the scientific core, which emphasises only findings on which there is a high degree of certainty, and then during the political negotiations. Overall the IPCC produces conservative reports, with strong provisional conclusions often discarded during the drafting process.

Despite its weakness the IPCC has achieved a scientific consensus that is trusted and accepted by the governments of the world as authoritative. It is this consensus that has led to international cooperation to address climate change, as the next section shows.

5 The IPCC as an epistemic community

Over the weeks ahead you will work with various theories of international cooperation. Theories of international cooperation make claims about the conditions under which states are likely to negotiate a political agreement. In this section, I shall introduce you to a cognitive theory of international cooperation. Cognitive theories hold that international cooperation is more likely when policy makers share similar perceptions and lines of reasoning, for example on the diagnosis of a problem and on shared policy principles.

An **epistemic community** is a knowledge-based community of experts that agree on the causes of an environmental problem and how it can be solved.

Where does scientific knowledge in general, and the IPCC discourse on climate change in particular, fit into this literature? One cognitive explanation of international cooperation is the theory of the **epistemic community**. Developed by the political scientist Peter Haas, the theory of the epistemic community holds that international environmental cooperation on global environmental issues is more likely when a knowledge-based community of experts, which agrees on the causes of an environmental problem and how the problem can be solved, leads key states to redefine their interests (Haas, 1990, p. 349). To Haas the members of an epistemic community share:

> (1) a shared set of normative and principled beliefs, which provide a value-based rationale for the social action of community members; (2) shared causal beliefs, which are derived from their analysis of practices leading or contributing to a central set of problems in their domain and which then serve as the basis for elucidating the multiple linkages between possible policy actions and desired outcomes; (3) shared notions of validity – that is, intersubjective, internally-defined criteria for weighing and validating knowledge in the domain of their expertise; and (4) a common policy enterprise – that is, a set of common practices associated with a set of problems to which their professional competence is directed, presumably out of the conviction that human welfare will be enhanced as a consequence.
>
> (Haas, 1992, p. 3)

Let us pause here and consider the word *intersubjective* in point (3) of this definition. This refers to shared understandings between a community of people. You have seen that there may be contention between scientists on what constitutes valid knowledge. There may be deliberations on which results should be accepted as 'close to the truth' and which are more tentative and provisional. So different scientists may have different subjective criteria on how knowledge can be validated; when the subjective understandings of a group of people coincide we may talk of *intersubjective* understandings. So in point (3) of his definition Haas claims that a transnational epistemic community is more likely to form when the different views of scientists on what constitutes valid knowledge converge, leading to 'shared notions of validity'.

Activity 2.5

Look again at the definition of an epistemic community proposed by Haas. Based on your understanding over the last two chapters of climate science and the IPCC, to what extent do you think that the IPCC constitutes an epistemic community? Organise your response according to the four features of an epistemic community provided by Haas. When you have done this read on.

I have filled out my responses in Table 2.1. They are not exhaustive, and you may be able to add to what I have written.

Table 2.1   The Intergovernmental Panel on Climate Change as an epistemic community

Haas' definition of an epistemic community	Application with respect to the IPCC
1. A shared set of normative and principled beliefs	A normative belief is a belief that something should happen or, alternatively, should not happen. A shared normative belief of the IPCC is that anthropogenic climate change and its social and environmental consequences should be avoided. Those with principled beliefs point to certain principles which, they claim, should guide human behaviour. A shared principled belief of the IPCC is the *precautionary principle*: scientific uncertainty in some areas of climate science is no excuse for inaction. (The precautionary principle was introduced in Chapter 1.)
2. Shared causal beliefs	The IPCC has concluded that contemporary climate change is caused by anthropogenic emissions of greenhouse gases and the destruction of carbon sinks. The IPCC's conclusions on the causes have grown stronger over time (Activity 2.4).
3. Shared notions of validity	There has been debate in the IPCC and elsewhere on what should be accepted as valid knowledge. The IPCC's results are largely based on general circulation models (GCMs). The peer-reviewed knowledge and predictions produced by GCMs are accepted as valid.
4. A common policy enterprise	The IPCC has agreed that the knowledge it has produced should be acted upon and future greenhouse gas emissions should be limited. The IPCC has recommended a combination of mitigation and adaptation measures.

The IPCC is consistent with the Haas definition and may be considered the organisational locus of the climate change epistemic community. Note that an epistemic community is not necessarily the same as a formal organisation. Prior to the creation of the IPCC the epistemic community existed, although it was very much an informal, or at best a semi-formal, grouping within the science community. It acquired a formal organisational status with the creation of the IPCC in 1988. However, the current climate change epistemic community is more than just the IPCC: there are scientists who may be said to be part of the epistemic community in that they agree with its knowledge claims, but who are not members of the IPCC in a formal sense. This epistemic community has emerged despite a minority of scientists disagreeing with the scientific view that anthropogenic climate change is taking place.

The status and authority of the climate change epistemic community cannot be seen to be in the service of any particular country, ideology, organisation or interest group. The epistemic community has developed more or less simultaneously, albeit at an uneven rate, through different scientific research enterprises in different countries (Paterson, 1996, p. 139). Different scientists, many of them working in isolation from each other, have arrived at the same, or very similar, conclusions. This has generated the consensual knowledge that makes up the IPCC discourse. An influential discourse can help shape common understandings and may lead actors to reframe how they see a particular issue.

The IPCC discourse is not static; it has evolved over time and, as you have seen, its confidence that humans are causing climate change has grown stronger. The increasing political concern about climate change can be attributed to this growing confidence. The IPCC has led many states to reframe their interests, so that state power is harnessed in a new policy direction. The resources that states have directed towards the development of GCMs, renewable energy, carbon capture and storage (CCS) and climate monitoring technology can, in large part, be understood as a consequence of the reframing of state interests in response to the consensual scientific knowledge that the IPCC has produced.

Activity 2.6

Epistemic communities can thus influence international environmental policy. It may then be asked why the work of the IPCC has not led to stronger international climate policies. Can you think of any reasons why this is so? To begin considering this question look again at Figure 2.5. You may also find it helpful to review your work in Section 3 of Chapter 1.

The knowledge that an epistemic community produces will not influence all states in the same way. While consensual knowledge may lead states to reframe their interests, this does not mean that all states will then have identical, or even similar, interests. Consensual scientific knowledge is one input to the policy-making process, but as you saw in Chapter 1, other factors may contribute to how states frame their interests. Scientific knowledge cannot *prescribe* policy. In Figure 2.5 you can see that the IPCC represents just one part of the international climate policy-making process. The political agreements are made in that part of the diagram labelled 'pure politics' where negotiations take place between the states that have ratified the Framework Convention on Climate Change (FCCC) and the Kyoto Protocol. The balance between science and politics is very different here compared to the IPCC. In the IPCC science dominates, with politics present, or at least overtly present, only towards the end of an IPCC assessment cycle. But in the FCCC and Kyoto Protocol negotiations science retreats to the background, and policy making is overtly political. While most delegations to the FCCC and Kyoto Protocol included climate scientists, their role is purely advisory. They have no voice in policy making other than the discretionary role granted by the heads of individual government delegations.

One critic of the epistemic community approach is Reiner Grudmann, who argues that it is not scientific knowledge per se that shapes the political responses to international environmental problems; it is how this knowledge is interpreted and understood (Grudmann, 2001). Different actors will understand and interpret science in different ways. Knowledge on climate science may *mean* different things to different actors in different social contexts. Science does not determine environmental policies, although it may help to shape them. Radoslav Dimitrov makes a similar point. The perceived risks and consequences of climate change will vary over time, from country to country and from one actor to another. Different political actors have different prior understandings of the world. They will process and mediate new knowledge in line with these understandings (Dimitrov, 2006, p. 24).

So understanding how the consensual knowledge of the IPCC is produced gives little insight into the different ways that this knowledge is understood by different policy makers in different countries. The IPCC has provided a shared *scientific* understanding of the problem of climate change, but it cannot provide a shared *political*, *social* or *cultural* understanding. Scientific knowledge about an international environmental problem should be seen as a necessary, but not a sufficient, condition for international political cooperation. This knowledge may be framed in different ways by different states, and thus lead to different policy prescriptions.

An epistemic community need not necessarily result in strong environmental policies. It *may* do so, when it causes a majority of states to redefine their interests. However, international cooperation will be difficult if several states – or a small number of powerful states – ignore or dispute the knowledge that an epistemic community produces. As Lawrence Susskind has argued, an epistemic community may not generate international cooperation if its findings and recommendations run counter to the interests of important groups (Susskind, 1994, pp. 73–5). This is the case within the USA, where there has been long-standing opposition against policies to reduce greenhouse gas emissions from some powerful groups. The USA has signed up to all the assessment reports produced to date by the IPCC, where the institutional design enables scientists to resist overt interference from political interests. But, outside the IPCC, where the science–politics relationship is very different, the USA has been able to stall international agreement to tackle climate change.

Under the George W. Bush administration, the USA government framed climate change as a threat to core economic interests, questioning the scientific basis for limiting CO_2 emissions. Many political leaders in Washington agreed with this. However, elsewhere in the USA political leaders accepted the IPCC's findings and adopted greenhouse gas reduction policies. In 2005 nine states in the north-east of the country agreed to reduce CO_2 emissions from power plants by 10 per cent by 2020. By 2007 mayors from over 600 cities and towns in the USA had stated that they considered themselves bound by the USA's Kyoto target (Seattle.Gov, 2007). It is fair to conclude that the climate policies of the Bush administration were not a fair reflection of the 'political climate' of the country at large, where policies to reduce emissions enjoyed a large measure of support. This serves to remind us that environmental policy making may take place in different institutions and in different layers of government in any one country. Different policies within a country are not always internally consistent with each other.

6 Climate of denial in the greenhouse

6.1 The discourse of denial

So far you have considered how the scientific knowledge produced by the IPCC has influenced international climate policy. In this section I wish to introduce you to a second discourse: the discourse of denial. Like the IPCC discourse, the discourse of denial has helped to shape how many people understand and think about climate change. Although this discourse has now been discredited scientifically, it has been very influential politically.

By the mid 1970s there was a sizeable scientific literature on climate change and a genuine scientific debate on the subject, with some scientists convinced that anthropogenic climate change was happening while others argued that there was insufficient evidence to support such a conclusion. During this period there was a large body of sceptics. I define a *sceptic* as a scientist who objectively seeks the truth but who has yet to be convinced that the available scientific evidence supports a particular claim or hypothesis, in this case that human behaviour is changing the climate. Sceptics can play a useful role in questioning scientific evidence and identifying areas where future research is needed to eliminate uncertainty. Sceptics stand in contrast to deniers. Unlike a sceptic a *denier* does not seek the truth. A denier will ignore or undermine scientific evidence for political ends.

By the mid 1980s scientific evidence was accumulating that climate change was, at least in part, human induced. Many of the earlier scientific predictions, for example on melting glaciers, were now confirmed by empirical data. Some uncertainties on the central thesis of anthropogenic climate change had been settled (although scientific research had revealed new uncertainties). Many former sceptical scientists had now accepted that anthropogenic climate change was happening. This growing consensus was a key factor in the creation of the IPCC. The publication in 1995 of the IPCC's Second Assessment Report also led some deniers to accept that the scientific evidence on anthropogenic climate change was well founded. However, some influential deniers remained, and their political resistance to the scientific consensus subsequently grew more robust.

6.2 'Atmospheric pressure' in the USA

In this section I will focus on climate denial in one country, the USA. A full account of all the activities of climate deniers in the USA is well beyond the scope of this chapter, so I will confine myself to introducing some illustrative examples. My argument is that the climate deniers have constructed and successfully promoted a second discourse – what I call the discourse of denial – that, like the IPCC discourse, has been influential in shaping global climate politics. The intellectual origins and claims of this discourse are, however, fundamentally different to those of the IPCC discourse. This discourse of denial emphasises that the science on climate change is unclear and unsettled, recent climate change could be entirely due to natural factors, the role of humans in causing climate change is unproven, and any social and environmental consequences of climate change are unlikely to be serious.

Organised lobbying by business corporations against strong international policies to address climate change dates back to the 1980s. In 1989 a group of transnational corporations, mainly from the oil sector, founded the Global Climate Coalition (the so-called 'carbon club') to lobby against binding targets for greenhouse gas emissions. For over a decade the coalition queried the scientific basis for climate change. It was disbanded in 2002 after some corporations, such as BP, Dupont and Shell, accepted the scientific evidence on climate change and left the coalition. Despite the demise of the coalition, organised denial of the scientific consensus on climate change in the USA became increasingly widespread during the presidency of George W. Bush (2001–09). There was active denial of the scientific evidence within certain precincts of the Republican Party (although it should be stressed that many Republican Party members do not agree with or support the deniers) and within certain USA business corporations. However, on an international scale the number of business corporations that deny anthropogenic climate change is happening dwindled considerably during the Bush presidency. Indeed, in 2007 over 150 transnational business corporations signed the Bali Communiqué, calling for international, legally binding targets to address climate change. The signatories stated 'it is our belief that the benefits of strong, early action on climate change outweigh the costs of not acting' (Bali Communiqué, 2007).

One oil business that did not sign the Bali Communiqué was ExxonMobil. ExxonMobil has been active in undermining climate science, funding a number of reports and publications that deny anthropogenic climate change is taking place. In February 2001 a fax from ExxonMobil was leaked to the press. Addressed to the Council on Environmental Quality (CEQ) at the White House the fax detailed a list of concerns from ExxonMobil

Figure 2.6
The former chair of the Intergovernmental Panel on Climate Change, Dr Bob Watson. Watson failed to gain re-election as IPCC chair in 2002 after the US government refused to support him

about the preparations for the IPCC's Third Assessment Report, and sought the support of the Bush administration to replace the chair of the IPCC, Dr Bob Watson (Figure 2.6). The fax alleged that Watson had a 'personal agenda' on climate change and was using his position with the IPCC 'to get media coverage of his views'. The fax asked 'Can Watson be replaced now at the request of the U. S.?' (ExxonMobil, 2001). In 2002 the Bush government refused to support Watson's re-election, as a result of which he lost his chairmanship of the IPCC (Figure 2.7).

Figure 2.7
The close relationship between Exxon Mobil and the George W. Bush White House has been satirised by political cartoonists in the USA

In 2006, Exxon's activities attracted the attention of the UK's most eminent scientific institution. The Royal Society took the unusual step of writing to ExxonMobil to tell it that its statements on climate science are 'very misleading', providing 'an inaccurate and misleading impression of the evidence on the causes of climate change that is documented in the scientific literature'. The Royal Society noted that some of the organisations that ExxonMobil has funded have engaged in 'outright denial of the evidence that greenhouse gases are driving climate change' (Royal Society, 2006). That same year two USA Senators – the Republican Olympia Snowe and the Democract Jay Rockefeller – called upon ExxonMobil to stop funding climate change denial, saying that Exxon's funding of an 'echo chamber' of 'non-peer reviewed pseudo science' had raised questions about the legitimate science of climate change (Snowe, 2006). The two senators wrote to the chief executive officer of ExxonMobil, stating that 'Climate change denial has been so effective because the "denial community" has mischaracterized the necessarily guarded language of serious scientific dialogue as vagueness and uncertainty' (Snowe, 2006).

Shortly after the Bush administration came to power it announced, in line with the USA Senate's Byrd–Hagel resolution, that it would not be bound by the USA target for emission reductions agreed by President Clinton under the Kyoto Protocol. Bush stated that the Kyoto Protocol was not in the USA national interest. The administration received advice from various consultancies on how to justify its position to the American public. In 2003 an adviser to the Republican Party, Frank Luntz, produced a memorandum that explicitly advised the Republicans

The Byrd–Hagel resolution was introduced in Chapter 1

to emphasise that there was scientific uncertainty on climate change. I have reproduced some excerpts from this in Box 2.4.

Box 2.4   Public relations advice given to the USA Republican Party from Luntz Research Companies

The scientific debate remains open. Voters believe that there is *no consensus* about global warming within the scientific community. Should the public come to believe that the scientific issues are settled, their views about global warming will change accordingly. Therefore, *you need to continue to make the lack of scientific certainty a primary issue in the debate,* and defer to scientists and other experts in the field...

Emphasise the importance of *'acting only with all the facts at hand'* and *'making the right decision, not the quick decision'*.

Source: Luntz Research Companies, 2003. All emphases in original.

There is other evidence that the Bush administration played a major role in undermining climate science and climate scientists. In 2007 a House of Representatives committee heard that the White House had systematically altered established scientific conclusions before issuing White House statements. Under questioning before the committee, a political appointee called Philip Cooney admitted that he and other members of the Council on Environmental Quality made 181 edits to a White House report to emphasise scientific uncertainties on climate change, and a further 113 edits to de-emphasise the role of humans in climate change. Cooney told the committee 'My sole loyalty was to the president and advancing the policies of his administration' (Goldenberg and Randerson, 2007, pp. 18–19; Goode, 2007). Cooney was no longer working for the White House when he gave testimony. He was working for ExxonMobil.

Activity 2.7

You have seen that much of the work of the IPCC involves the editing of language. It could be claimed that there is little difference between what the IPCC does and what White House staff were doing during the Bush presidency. Is this a view with which you would agree? Once you have considered this question read on.

It seems to me that we need to draw a clear distinction between editing scientific reports in order to improve the clarity of the science for policy makers and other non-scientific audiences, and editing in order to distort the scientific consensus for political ends. It should also be noted that at the IPCC scientists have a voice in the changes made to the policy makers' summaries, whereas the approval of scientists to the changes made to the White House report was neither sought nor given.

The same House of Representatives committee also heard further evidence of political tampering with the scientific evidence on climate change during the Bush presidency. It considered a survey from the Union of Concerned Scientists and the Government Accountability Project in which 58 per cent of federal scientists (in other words, scientists employed by the USA government) reported that they had 'personally experienced' political interference with climate science 'over the past five years' (Donaghy et al., 2007, p. 2). Scientists not employed at federal agencies reported a much lower level of political interference in science (22 per cent) (Figure 2.8). The report concluded that 'science has been increasingly tailored to reflect political goals rather than scientific fact' (Donaghy et al., 2007, p. 1).

Figure 2.8
In 2007 a House of Representatives committee heard from the Union of Concerned Scientists and the Government Accountability Project that 58 per cent of federal climate scientists had experienced political interference in their work

Climate denial can have some important political effects. It can leave policy makers and the general public with the impression that the science is more obscure than it really is, so that policy lacks a firm scientific basis. Denial thus interferes with the science–politics interface. USA climate scientist James Hansen commented that White House editing of the reports on climate change has contributed to 'a substantial gap between the understanding of global warming of the relevant scientific community and the knowledge of the public and policy makers' (Goode, 2007). The journalist and activist George Monbiot concludes that 'I think it is fair to say that the professional denial industry has delayed effective global action on climate change by several years' (2006, p. 39).

6.3 The politics of denial

You have now considered a few examples of how some political and economic actors in the USA have undermined the scientific evidence on climate change. These actors seek to change the language people use when thinking about and discussing climate change. The intention is to change the assumptions and understandings of people so that they refuse to accept that climate change is a problem. Deniers have established an alternative discourse that often surfaces in political discussions on climate change. This discourse stresses uncertainty, unsettled science and the natural causes of climate change. It has challenged and undermined the IPCC discourse and led some actors to believe that climate change is not a pressing problem. The result has been a weakened social demand for strong international policies to limit greenhouse gas emissions, which was precisely the intention. Organised denial has thus acted as a major constraint on more effective responses to climate change (*course question 3*).

Why do deniers deny? I would like to offer two possible explanations. The first concerns political values, in particular the view that business works best when it is free of regulation and legislation that impedes economic efficiency. This view forms part of a political philosophy known as *neoliberalism* which will be introduced in Chapter 3. In many countries, in particular the country where denial has taken deepest root – the USA – the argument that business should be free to operate in the market place without state intervention (or bureaucratic 'red tape' as it is sometimes pejoratively called) is widely accepted. The view that there should be heavy cuts in greenhouse gases to deal with a problem such as climate change that may be seen as distant and remote has yet to attract widespread political support in the USA, especially when this would affect economic growth which, it is claimed, will yield more benefits to the population at large than stringent measures to curb emissions. On this view USA climate change policy needs to be understood in terms of the contested relationship between sustainability and development (*course theme 4*).

The second explanation is much less charitable to the deniers. According to this view deniers are not interested in the common good. They deny because they believe that doing so will enhance their own narrow interests, such as increasing party political support and maximising shareholder value. If this view of deniers and their motivations is right then the argument against them will be won only if they can be persuaded that funding denial and disputing science will materially harm their interests; for example, political parties find that engaging in organised climate denial costs them votes at the ballot box, and businesses find that denial loses customers. This is not the case at present. Denial of scientific evidence is a political strategy. Organised climate denial is only likely to cease when it attracts widespread moral opprobrium and harms the interests of the deniers. Whereas sceptics can be persuaded with new scientific findings, deniers cannot because for them the science is not their main concern.

6.4 Climate science and the media

The discourse of denial has found expression in some television programmes and newspapers, although it has not succeeded in penetrating climate science journals. A study that reviewed 928 peer-reviewed journal articles on climate science published between 1993 and 2003 found that not one disagreed with the IPCC view that human activities are causing global warming (Oreskes, 2004). However, many non-peer reviewed articles questioning or denying global warming were published elsewhere during this period and continue to be published. The system of peer reviewing used by the editors of science journals is not a requirement for publication in the media. Newspapers use very different criteria for publication from science journals.

Scientific research aims to produce impartial and disinterested knowledge about biophysical realities that exist independently of human cognition. Scientific research is only published when it uses methods and models that other scientists accept as rigorous. Impartial journalism is very different. Whereas scientists aim to ensure objectivity through peer review, journalists aim to provide impartiality by giving media space to different sides of a debate. Science and journalism also have different views of bias. An example of bias in science would be if a scientist were to use dubious methods and interpretation of results in order to produce research that fitted preconceived beliefs. The journalist's view of bias is very different; bias can be seen as giving more media space to one side of a debate at the expense of another.

Jules and Maxwell Boykoff have surveyed media reporting of climate change in the USA, and found that 53 per cent of the articles they surveyed were structured as 'balanced reporting'. Equal prominence was given to the views of those arguing that climate change is due to human activities and to those who claim that climate change is, or could be, entirely due to natural fluctuations (Boykoff and Boykoff, 2004). If a member of the IPCC is invited to present their views, a climate denier is then also consulted in order to provide 'balance'. Boykoff and Boykoff used statistical analysis to show that the content of these articles differed significantly from the IPCC consensus. By giving equal coverage to unequal views media reporting has misleadingly left readers with the impression that there is a genuine scientific debate on the causes of climate change. Somewhat ironically, therefore, the result of 'balanced reporting' is 'biased coverage'.

Some deniers have been vociferous in demanding the right to state their views, arguing that unless they are given media space they are being 'silenced', with the media favouring one view over another. Presenting competing arguments and different opinions in the press is an important check against bias when social and political issues are under discussion on which there are many differing opinions, but, you will recall, there is a difference between knowledge and opinion. Climate science is not a matter of opinion; it is a matter of knowledge. While this knowledge is uncertain and contested in some areas, it is settled and uncontroversial on the main hypothesis: that humans are causing global warming, and unless greenhouse gas emissions are greatly reduced over the next ten to twenty years the problem will worsen. The main disagreements among climate scientists are over the scale and speed of global warming, not whether it will happen. As the divergent views within the climate science community have slowly converged since the 1970s the scientific debate has slowly settled, at least on the central thesis that humans are causing climate change. During this same period the deniers have grown more assertive, responding with what is, in effect, a disinformation campaign so that in the minds of many members of the public the scientific debate remains open and unresolved.

Activity 2.8

Would Peter Haas describe those who subscribe to the discourse of denial as an epistemic community? You might like to revisit the four features of an epistemic community that you considered in Activity 2.5 when considering this question.

The discourse of denial is a political discourse rather than a knowledge-based discourse. It is based upon claims and assertions that do not pass the test of peer-reviewed knowledge. The deniers may share certain causal beliefs, but they do not share notions on what constitutes valid knowledge (the third point of Haas' definition). Deniers make the claims they do for political reasons, not because they have evidence that their claims correspond to the truth. They cannot therefore be considered an epistemic community.

What I hope Sections 4, 5 and 6 have demonstrated is that climate politics and climate science are interrelated. Sheila Jasanoff (1996) and Tim Forsyth (2003) argue that science and politics should be seen as *co-produced*, with each shaping the other. By 'co-produced' they mean that actions in one domain will impact upon the other. Scientific findings will generate new political developments, and political processes may help to shape which scientific questions are researched and which are not.

7 Conclusion

This chapter has introduced the idea of discourse in order to analyse the relationship between climate science and climate politics. A discourse is a body of language that embodies certain understandings and ideas. It is a generic term that covers a wide range of ways of thinking. Discourses regulate the production of meaning in social life; they help to structure how people think and act. An understanding of discourses is an important part of the study of environmental policy. No discourse is static; discourses evolve, and over time they may be replaced by new discourses that articulate new knowledge or alternative ways of thinking. The most effective discourses are those that are taken for granted as 'common sense'. Actors often frame their interests in part using the language and assumptions of commonly accepted discourses. They may draw from discourses to legitimise their positions and to provide their statements with authority. As the environmental sociologist Martin Hajer has argued, 'Interests cannot be taken as given *a priori* but are constituted through discourse' (1997, p. 51). So discourses do not exist only in the abstract. What matters is where discourses settle. In what countries or social spaces do discourses become dominant? Which actors are influenced by which discourses? What set of interests may a particular discourse serve?

Chapter 6 of this book examines the different discourses that enter into energy policy

You have seen that where an established discourse, such as the scientific knowledge produced by the IPCC, runs counter to the perceived interests of powerful actors then these actors may respond by setting out to create an alternative discourse that promotes their interests. In this sense discourses are said to be *socially constructed*; they are created by groups of people. The discourse of denial can be explained in this vein. Until the mid 1980s this discourse did not exist; at this time there was a lot of scepticism about whether humans were driving climate change so there was no need for organised denial. As the scientific evidence on climate change has grown stronger so too has the denial. However, this trend is unlikely to continue indefinitely. At some stage the discourse of denial, already scientifically discredited, is likely to become politically untenable.

This illustrates two broader points. First, not all discourses are equal. The IPCC discourse has a firm epistemological basis and counts as legitimate knowledge. The discourse of denial has no such status and comprises assertion, manipulation and dishonesty. Nonetheless, it would be a mistake to dismiss it because of that. An awareness of the discourse of denial informs our understanding of how climate science is used and abused politically. Second, an important part of environmental policy making – and of politics more generally – is that actors engage in *discursive struggles*, seeking to use words and vocabularies that will gain acceptance from other actors. The IPCC discourse is highly authoritative; no government has openly said that the knowledge produced by the IPCC is unreliable. Instead, those governments that wish to deny the science acknowledge that while the IPCC is saying one thing, other actors are saying something different, so it is difficult to know who to believe.

In political terms the discourse of denial matters because it has been articulated, and is invoked, by some powerful actors. It would matter less if it were supported only by more peripheral actors who have less power. You first encountered the concept of power in the previous chapter where you were introduced to the idea that an actor has power if it can mobilise and deploy material resources. However, another view in the social sciences is that the power of an actor depends, at least in part, on whether the actor can produce and shape discourses that other actors accept as legitimate. According to the French philosopher Michel Foucault (1994), the production of discourse and the production of power are not separate processes; they are one and the same thing. To Foucault a discourse is not just words; it is a particular expression of power. The more dominant a discourse is, the more it 'makes sense' to think within it. On this view the leading scientists in the IPCC may be seen as powerful people. The removal of Dr Bob Watson as chair of the IPCC can be explained as part of a discursive struggle in which some powerful actors in the USA sought, as they would see it, to protect their interests through undermining one discourse and promoting another.

What this suggests is that there is an iterative relationship between the two types of power that you have worked with in these first two chapters of the course: power as the mobilisation of resources, and power as the construction of discourses. First, discourses matter when they influence actors that control significant resources. Note that Haas' theory of epistemic communities holds that consensual knowledge is only a pre-condition for international environmental cooperation; cooperation will only occur when states, and especially powerful states, accept this knowledge as authoritative and redefine their interests as a result. Second, actors that can mobilise resources can play an important role in discursive formation; in other words, in the construction of new discourses. You have seen that a full understanding of international climate policy requires an understanding of the ways in which these two types of power interact.

Audio 1

Now listen to Audio 1: *Climate science and policy.*

Activity 2.9

So what do you believe now? Imagine that you have been invited to join a group of people discussing the topic 'Climate change: should we be concerned?' You wish to make a brief speech of five to ten minutes. Jot down the main points you would make. Include the following concepts:

- discourse

- knowledge

- power

- uncertainty

- values.

References

ABC News (2007) *Human Activity to Blame for Global Warming: Report* [online], http://www.abc.net.au/cgi-bin/common (Accessed 22 June 2007).

Bali Communiqué (2007) [online], http://www.balicommunique.com/communique.html (Accessed 21 December 2007).

Bocking, S. (2006) *Nature's Experts: Science, Politics and the Environment*, New Jersey, Rutgers University Press.

Boykoff, J. and Boykoff, M. T. (2004) 'Balance as bias: global warming and the U.S. prestige press', *Global Environmental Change*, vol. 14, no. 2, pp. 125–36.

Dimitrov, R. (2006) *Science and International Environmental Policy: Regimes and Non-regimes in Global Governance*, Lanham, MD, Rowman and Littlefield.

Donaghy, T., Freeman, J., Grifo, F., Kaufman, K., Maassarani, T. and Shultz, L. (2007) *Atmosphere of Pressure: Political Interference in Federal Climate Science*, Cambridge, MA, Union of Concerned Scientists and Government Accountability Project.

Earth Negotiations Bulletin (2007) 'Eighth Session of Working Group II of the International Panel on Climate Change: 2–6 April 2007', *Earth Negotiations Bulletin*, vol. 12, no. 320.

ExxonMobil (2001) 'Regarding: Bush team for IPCC negotiations', memorandum accompanying signed fascimile from Arthur G. Randol, ExxonMobil, Washington to John Howard, Council for Environmental Quality, 6 February, 10 a.m.

Forsyth, T. (2003) *Critical Political Ecology: The Politics of Environmental Science*, London, Routledge.

Foucault, M. (1994) *The Archaeology of Knowledge*, London, Routledge.

Goldenberg, S. and Randerson, J. (2007) 'Bush appointees "watered down greenhouse science"', *The Guardian*, 20 March, pp. 18–19.

Goode, D. (2007) 'Ex-Bush aide defends changes to global warming reports' [online], http://www.govexec.com/story_page.cfm?articleid=36402&printerfriendlyVers=1& (Accessed 20 March 2007).

Grudmann, R. (2001) *Transnational Environmental Policy: Reconstructing Ozone*, London, Routledge.

Guardian, the (2007) 'Worse than we thought', 3 February.

Haas, P. M. (1990) 'Obtaining international environmental protection through epistemic consensus', *Millennium: Journal of International Studies*, vol. 19, no. 3, pp. 347–63.

Haas, P. M. (1992) 'Introduction: epistemic communities and international policy coordination', *International Organization*, vol. 46, no. 1, pp. 1–35.

Hajer, M. (1997) *The Politics of Environmental Discourse*, Oxford, Oxford University Press.

Harrison, N. E. (2004) 'Political responses to changing uncertainty in climate science' in Harrison, N. E. and Bryner, G. C. (eds) *Science and Politics in the International Environment*, Lanham, MD, Rowman and Littlefield.

Hinchliffe, S. and Belshaw, C. (2003) 'Who cares? Values, power and action in environmental contests' in Hinchliffe, S., Blowers, A. and Freeland, J. (eds) *Understanding Environmental Issues*, Chichester, John Wiley/Open University.

Independent, The (2007) 'Final warning', 3 February.

Intergovernmental Panel on Climate Change (IPCC) (1996) *Climate Change 1995: The Science of Climate Change*, Cambridge, Cambridge University Press.

Intergovernmental Panel on Climate Change (IPCC) (2001) *Climate Change 2001, Working Group 1: The Scientific Basis, Summary for Policy Makers*, Geneva, IPCC.

Intergovernmental Panel on Climate Change (IPCC) (2007) *Climate Change 2007: The Physical Science Basis – Summary for Policymakers, Contribution of Working Group I to the Fourth Assessment Report of the Intergovernmental Panel on Climate Change* [online], http://www.ipcc.ch/ipccreports/ar4-wg1.htm (Accessed 2 February 2007).

Jasanoff, S. (1996) 'Beyond epistemology: relativism and engagement in the politics of science', *Social Studies of Science*, vol. 26, no. 2, pp. 393–418.

Latour, B. (1999) *Pandora's Hope: Essays on the Reality of Science Studies*, Cambridge, MA, Harvard University Press.

Luntz Research Companies (2003) 'The environment: a cleaner, safer, healthier America' [online], http://www.luntzspeak.com/graphics/LuntzResearch.Memo.pdf (Accessed 15 March 2007).

Macalister, T. (2007) 'Profits up a fifth but Shell emits more CO_2 than most countries', *The Guardian*, 2 February, pp. 28–9.

Monbiot, G. (2006) *Heat: How to Stop the Planet Burning*, London, Allen Lane/Penguin.

Oreskes, N. (2004) 'Beyond the ivory tower: the scientific consensus on climate change', *Science*, vol. 306, no. 5702, p. 1686.

Paterson, M. (1996) *Global Warming and Global Politics*, London, Routledge.

Pittock, A. B. (2005) *Climate Change: Turning up the Heat*, London, Earthscan.

Popper, K. L. (1979) *Objective Knowledge: An Evolutionary Approach* (revised edition), Oxford, Oxford University Press.

Ravetz, J. (2006) *The No-Nonsense Guide to Science*, Oxford, New Internationalist Publications.

Royal Society (2006) Letter from Bob Ward, Senior Manager, Policy Communication, Royal Society, London to Nick Thomas, Esso UK/ExxonMobil, Leatherhead, UK, 4 September.

Seattle.Gov (2007) 'USA mayors climate protection agreement' [online], http://www.seattle.gov/mayor/climate (Accessed 8 April 2007).

Skodvin, T. (1999) 'Science-policy interaction in the global greenhouse: institutional design and institutional performance in the Intergovernmental Panel on Climate Change (IPCC)', Center for International Climate and Environmental Research (CICERO) Working Paper 1999, no. 3, Oslo, University of Oslo.

Skodvin, T. (2000) 'The Intergovernmental Panel on Climate Change' in Andresen, S., Skodvin, T., Underdal, A. and Wettestad, J. (eds) *Science and Politics in International Environmental Regimes*, Manchester, Manchester University Press, pp. 146–80.

Smith, L. (2007) 'New fears on climate raise heat', *The Times*, 3 February, p. 32.

Snowe, O. J. (2006) 'Rockefeller and Snowe demand that Exxon Mobil end funding of campaign that denies global climate change' [online], 30 October, http://snowe.senate.gov (Accessed 23 January 2007).

Susskind, L. E. (1994) *Environmental Diplomacy: Negotiating More Effective Environmental Agreements*, New York, Oxford University Press.

Times, the (2007) 'New fears on climate raise heat', 3 February.

Warburton, N. (1996) *Thinking from A to Z*, London, Routledge.

Wasdell, D. (2007) 'Political corruption of the IPCC Report? Changes in the Final Text of the "Summary for Policy Makers of the Fourth Assessment Report", WG1: the Physical Science Basis' [online], http://www.meridian.org.uk/_PDFs/IPCC.pdf (Accessed 19 June 2007).

Weinberg, A. (1972) 'Science and transcience', *Minerva*, vol. 10, pp. 209–22.

World Meteorological Organisation, United Nations Environment Programme and Intergovernmental Panel on Climate Change (WMO, UNEP and IPCC) (1990) *Scientific Assessment of Climate Change*, Geneva, WMO/UNEP/IPCC.

Chapter 3
Climate change: economic valuation and policy

Graham Dawson

Contents

1	**Introduction**	**98**
	1.1 Learning outcomes	99
2	**The social cost of carbon**	**100**
	2.1 Global warming as market failure	100
	2.2 Calculating the social cost of carbon	108
3	**The matrix of policy instruments**	**116**
	3.1 Green taxes	118
	3.2 Regulation or 'command and control'	121
	3.3 Carbon trading	122
4	**Physical limits to growth? Ecological economics**	**127**
5	**Conclusion**	**130**
	References	**130**

1 Introduction

Never make predictions – especially about the future.

Attributed to Samuel Goldwyn, Hollywood producer

Chapter 2 reviewed the scientific evidence for climate change. The Intergovernmental Panel on Climate Change (IPCC) has concluded that it is 'very likely' that human activity is responsible for most of the observed increase in global mean surface temperature since the mid-twentieth century (IPPC, 2007, p. 10). So it seems appropriate to ask: how bad are the consequences of climate change likely to be, and what are we (humans) going to do about it? My intention is to examine some of the answers that economists have given to these questions. Rephrased in economic terms the questions may be put as: what is the cost of climate change, or, remembering that carbon dioxide (CO_2) is the main greenhouse gas, what is the social cost of carbon; and what policy instruments should be deployed to reduce that cost? The answer to the first question, which will be explored in Section 2, depends in part on scientific models of the causal links between increases in greenhouse gas emissions and increases in global mean surface temperature – but only in part, because it also depends upon economic models of the causal links between economic growth and greenhouse gas emissions.

Economics, in particular neoclassical economics, has its own language and analytic techniques, which set it apart from the other social sciences that contribute to this course. **Neoclassical economics** is the study of the price mechanism in a competitive market system. To neoclassical economists the market is in most circumstances the best way of allocating resources so as to maximise the well-being of members of society. Section 2 introduces environmental economics as the application of neoclassical economics to pollution in order to explain the idea of market failure. **Market failure** occurs when market competition fails to bring about an allocation of resources that maximises the well-being of members of society. Pollution is a standard example of market failure, where market transactions between people impose costs on other people. For example, acid rain caused by sulphur dioxide (SO_2) emissions from industrial production in one country may fall on lakes in another, causing the death of fish and threatening the livelihood of the local population that depends upon the fishing industry. To Lord Nicholas Stern, the author of a major review on *The Economics of Climate Change* commissioned by the UK government, climate change is 'the greatest market failure in history' (Stern, 2006, 2007). What Stern means is that the costs that climate change will impose on people will exceed those of any other single market failure.

Neoclassical economics studies the price mechanism in a market economy.

Market failure occurs when a market fails to allocate resources to the greatest possible benefit of society.

The second question, 'What are we going to do about reducing these costs?', is the subject of Section 3. What policy instruments should be deployed? Environmental policy consists of a range of policy instruments, including regulation such as government directives and standards, and market-based instruments such as taxes, subsidies and tradable emission permits (in other words the trading of pemits to emit carbon dioxide). In reviewing the use of these policy instruments, you will learn about some of the main political responses to climate change (*course question 2*).

I will also suggest some ways that you can begin to answer the questions 'What are the constraints on more effective policy responses?' (*course question 3)* and 'What can be done for the future, and what should be done?' *(course question 4).* In order to do this I will discuss the advantages and disadvantages of different policy instruments, in particular the market-based instruments that have become prominent following the Kyoto Protocol and which the Stern Review concludes should have a crucial role in mitigating climate change. Both 'green taxes' and regulation are products of the neoclassical approach. However, carbon trading, which is central to Kyoto, is neoliberal in inspiration. I will introduce you to neoliberalism, a theoretical perspective which has its roots in libertarian political thought as well as in economics.

Finally, I will set up a signpost for later in the course by briefly introducing ecological economics. Ecological economics holds that because economic processes are part of the physical world there are physical limits to growth. Climate change can be interpreted as the consequence of a physical limit, namely the limited capacity of the atmosphere to absorb greenhouse gases without affecting the global temperature. The existence of physical limits to growth is a potential threat to the living standards of future generations. Some economists believe that the current generation should do more to safeguard the prospects for future generations than put taxes or carbon trading in place. Deeper changes to affluent lifestyles might be required. This suggests that a more radical approach to *course question 4* may be necessary.

1.1 Learning outcomes

This chapter should enable you to:

■ understand environmental economics as an application of neoclassical economics to environmental issues

■ appreciate the difficulties in estimating the economic and social impacts of climate change, that is, the social cost of carbon

- understand neoliberalism as a theoretical perspective that informs carbon trading

- evaluate the strengths and weaknesses of the main policy responses to climate change

- discuss the argument from ecological economics that there are physical limits to growth.

2   The social cost of carbon

2.1 Global warming as market failure

In October 2006 Lord Nicholas Stern, then the UK government's chief economist, presented his review, *The Economics of Climate Change* (Stern, 2006, 2007), which had been commissioned by the then UK Prime Minister Tony Blair and Chancellor of the Exchequer Gordon Brown. Figure 3.1 is taken from the Stern Review and shows the linkages between rising emissions, the consequent temperature increases and the various impacts of higher temperatures.

Figure 3.1 illustrates the types of impacts that could be experienced as more and more greenhouse gases are emitted into the atmosphere. 'CO_2e' means 'CO_2 equivalent' and is a measure of the radiative forcing potential of greenhouse gas emissions (see Chapter 1). The top panel shows the range of temperatures projected at stabilisation levels between 400ppm and 750ppm CO_2 equivalent. The five solid horizontal lines indicate the ranges based on recent climate sensitivity estimates from the IPCC and the Hadley Centre. The bottom panel illustrates the range of impacts expected at different levels of warming. Note that the relationship between global average temperature changes and regional climate changes is very uncertain, especially with regard to changes in precipitation. This figure shows potential changes based on the current scientific literature.

Activity 3.1

Examine Figure 3.1 carefully. Think about how CO_2e emissions are associated with temperature change and with different impacts. In what ways does Figure 3.1 suggest that there might be a role for economic modelling in predicting the impacts of global warming?

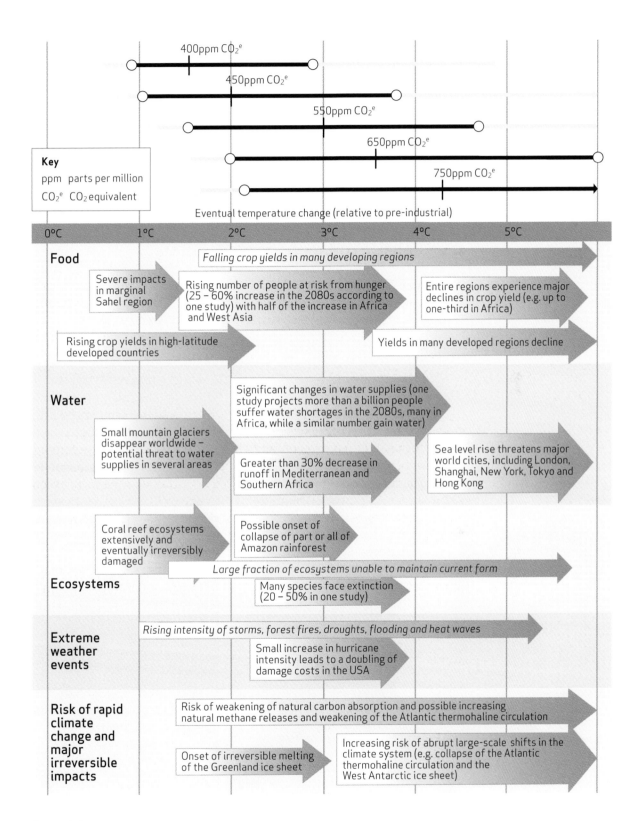

Figure 3.1
CO_2 emissions, temperature change and impacts (Source: Stern, 2006, p. v)

The impacts of a rise in temperature of 1 °C will be less severe than those of a rise in temperature of 5 °C; for example, at 1 °C there is a 'potential threat to water supplies in several areas' while at 5 °C there will be more widespread changes to water availability and sea level rise will threaten major coastal cities. So the impacts depend upon the extent of temperature change. The top part of Figure 3.1 shows that these temperature changes are associated with different atmospheric concentrations of greenhouse gases. The future path of greenhouse gas emissions depends on future world economic activity and how carbon intensive this activity is. So predicting the future path of greenhouse gas emissions involves modelling the future rate of growth of the world economy; this is a task for economics. The impacts of climate change are analysed in economics as a case of market failure. Indeed, according to the Stern Review:

> Climate change presents a unique challenge for economics: it is the greatest and widest-ranging market failure ever seen (p.1).

> A significant amount of economic activity involves the emission of greenhouse gases (GHGs). As GHGs accumulate in the atmosphere, temperatures increase, and the climatic changes that result impose costs (and some benefits) on society... However, the full costs of GHG emissions, in terms of climate change, are not immediately carried by the producers or emitters, and are unlikely ever to be. Similarly, emitters do not have to compensate those who lose out because of climate change. They therefore have little or no economic reason, or incentive, to reduce emissions (p.24).

(Stern, 2006)

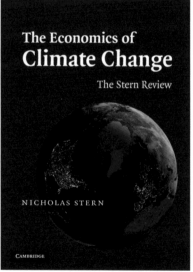

Figure 3.2 (a) and (b)

Sir Nicholas (now Lord) Stern presented his report *The Economics of Climate Change* to the UK government in 2006

The economic costs predicted by the Stern Review attracted the most headlines. By 2100 the damage wrought by climate change might reduce the value of the world economy by up to 20 per cent. Yet, Stern concluded, this catastrophe could be prevented at a cost of only 1 per cent of the value of the world economy. On the face it, Stern's call for urgent policies to reduce greenhouse gas emissions presented governments across the world with what might colloquially be called a 'no brainer', a decision so obvious that no thought is needed to make it. But is it really as simple as that? This section will first explain the idea of market failure and apply it to climate change and then move on to assess Stern's estimates of the costs of climate change and of mitigating its effects.

The key principle of the mitigation strategy advocated by the Stern Review is that 'GHG emissions should be priced to reflect the damage they cause' (2006, p. 309). Climate change is analysed in neoclassical economics as a market failure of the kind associated with a negative externality and since this is the approach that Stern takes, it is important to understand the main principles of neoclassical economics. A **negative externality** occurs in a market when the actions of a producer or consumer lead to an adverse influence upon the well-being of people who are not involved in the market transaction. A negative externality is therefore an example of market failure. (For example, the damage caused by acid rain is a negative externality.)

A market transaction causes a **negative externality** when it reduces the well-being of someone who is neither the buyer nor the seller in the transaction.

My argument will now move through two stages: the first setting out the basic case for resource allocation through a lightly regulated market, and the second making the neoclassical argument for a greater degree of government intervention in response to negative externalities. In making this argument I will introduce you to **environmental economics**, namely the application of the neoclassical paradigm to environmental issues.

Environmental economics is the application of neoclassical economics to environmental issues.

Neoclassical economics developed out of the liberal tradition of political thought. The core liberal principle is to protect the individual from threats and force from other individuals and social groups by demarcating a private area within which individuals can do as they please, free from interference from the rest of society. This prioritising of the rights of individuals grew out of an acknowledgement of the diversity of people's opinions, religious beliefs, ethical principles, ethnic and cultural identities, sexualities, economic roles, talents, skills, tastes and preferences. The state responded to such diversity by embodying, in its constitution and laws, toleration of diverse beliefs, identities and social and economic activities. In the liberal tradition the state has an essential, but limited, role in establishing and enforcing laws that will enable different groups of people to live together, respecting one another's right to pursue their own way of life. These laws must be neutral or impartial with respect to each particular social group or way of life.

The principles of liberalism have been applied to the economic world as well as the political realm. Some liberal theorists saw an affinity between the neutral state and the free or competitive market, which came to be interpreted as an impartial arena for settling competing claims on economic resources. There is a diversity of consumer wants, leaving no obvious way of reaching agreement on what to produce. There is individual autonomy in that producers and consumers in a competitive market make their own decisions about what to buy and sell. There is liberal neutrality, too. For, in the absence of a central authority ordering people to produce certain goods rather than others, those goods that are produced in a competitive market will not favour any one source of consumer demand over any other. The competitive market is therefore a neutral arbiter in the allocation of resources.

It is, however, a central proposition of neoclassical economics that markets can fail as well as succeed. Can the state intervene to correct market failures, cutting back on negative externalities without putting too many obstacles in the way of market transactions? In order to weigh the value of the costs (negative externalities) that are imposed on other people against the benefits that a consumer or producer derives from market transactions, environmental economists have developed a technical, diagrammatic form of analysis.

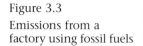

Figure 3.3
Emissions from a
factory using fossil fuels

For neoclassical economics the optimum level of production is the level
that maximises the well-being of members of society. The neoclassical
analysis of the optimum level of production can be applied to the
'production' of pollution and hence to carbon emissions (Figure 3.3). It
is tempting to assume that the optimum level of pollution must be zero.
Why contemplate anything other than zero tolerance for something
that damages people's well-being? The answer is that until we can devise
new technology that allows pollution-free production, some pollution is
an unavoidable side effect of the production of things we would not
want to be without, such as domestic heating and lighting (see below
and the discussion of ecological modernisation in Chapter 6). Ideally,
the production of goods and services would take place in a low- or non-
carbon economy. However, technological change on the required scale
takes time and meanwhile damage is being done. The second best or
interim solution is therefore to reduce the level of production of goods
and services in order to reduce the harm caused by carbon emissions.
This approach to pollution reflects the origins of neoclassical economics
in liberal neutrality; it is not a question of taking sides with either the
polluter or the victim of pollution, but of devising procedures that
enable both to live together without either inflicting too much harm on
the other.

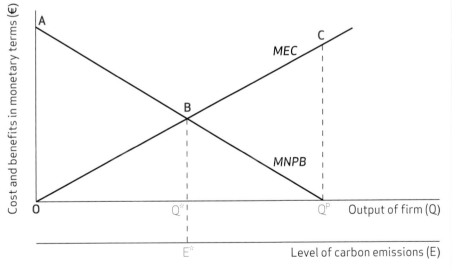

Figure 3.4
Optimum level of
carbon emissions for a
firm producing goods
using fossil fuels

I would now like to express this approach to pollution in more formal
and technical terms, in order to identify the benefits and harms
contingent upon production using fossil fuels so that we can then
quantify them. This exposition has been adapted from David Pearce
(2003), who would see climate change as a negative externality caused
by industrial production. Suppose that a firm is producing goods using
fossil fuels and hence also producing carbon emissions. In Figure 3.4 this

dual aspect of the firm's activities is represented by two horizontal axes. The top one shows the level or quantity of output Q of a firm whose production processes are responsible for carbon emissions. As the quantity of output Q increases (reading from left to right from the origin O), so too does the level of carbon emissions E shown along the bottom horizontal axis. The vertical axis measures the costs and benefits of production in monetary terms, say euros (€). The lines *MNPB* and *MEC* will take a little more explaining.

MNPB stands for 'marginal net private benefit' where 'net private benefit' is best understood as the polluting firm's profit, which is the firm's reward for producing goods that consumers choose to buy. 'Marginal' means 'extra' or 'additional', so, by sloping downwards, the *MNPB* line shows that the polluting firm's extra profit earned on each extra unit produced declines as output increases. Adding up each extra increment of profit on each extra unit of output gives the firm's total profit and is shown by the triangular area underneath the *MNPB* line. At output Q^P total profit is maximised at OAQ^P, because any further units of output would take the *MNPB* line below zero, indicating *negative* extra profit or a loss.

MEC stands for 'marginal external cost' where 'external cost' is the negative externality caused by the carbon emissions. Identifying the adverse effects of carbon emissions on human well-being is complicated and subject to substantial uncertainty. For example, the people who experience those effects may be spatially distant from the firm whose emissions they suffer from, and they may not suffer from these emissions immediately. So the cause and effects of these emissions may be separated across space and time (*course theme 5*). Despite such uncertainties economists have invested a lot of effort and ingenuity in trying to quantify and even to put a monetary value on 'the social costs of carbon'. The *MEC* line represents these costs in marginal terms, in other words as the extra damage caused by an extra unit of carbon emissions. This line slopes upwards as each extra unit of carbon emissions causes more and more extra damage. The total external cost of a given level of emissions is given by the area underneath the *MEC* line up to the relevant output.

Let us see if we can use the diagram to discover whether there is an optimal level of output Q, and hence a level of emissions E. The optimum level of output is one that achieves the best possible balance between the interests both of the firm (and by implication its customers) and of those who bear the costs of carbon emissions.

Activity 3.2

Spend some time studying Figure 3.4 carefully and reading the explanation above. When you think you understand what Figure 3.4 represents, try to answer the following question:

How much damage from carbon emissions should be permitted?

Neoclassical economists use the concept of **equilibrium** to denote a situation in which the choices made by agents are consistent with each other so that everyone's interests are taken into account. In Figure 3.4 the private equilibrium is at Q^P, where the firm carries out its plan by maximising its profits. However, that level of output is not optimal for society because it imposes excessive damage on third parties. Diagrammatically, when the firm maximises its profits of OAQ^P, it imposes a total external cost of OCQ^P on the rest of society. Taking the size of the respective triangles OAQ^P and OCQ^P as a 'rough guide' to the monetary value of profit and external cost, that is, of gain and loss to society, it is clear that at output Q^P, the firm's profit is earned at an external cost of approximately equal monetary value. This is fine for the firm but it is definitely not optimal for society as a whole. (Note that there is a difference between what is optimal for society in economic terms, and what some non-economists might feel is *desirable* for society. What is desirable requires some consideration of ethics, a subject that will be considered in Chapter 6.)

> A firm is in **equilibrium** when it maximises its profits.

The optimum level of output is lower, at Q^* with a correspondingly reduced level of carbon emissions E^*. The area OBQ^*, being under both the *MNPB* and *MEC* lines, is both profit and external cost and is therefore disregarded, leaving a surplus gain to society (the firm being part of society) in the profit shown by area OAB. At output levels below Q^*, the marginal gain to the firm is greater than the marginal cost to the rest of society, that is, the *MNPB* line is above the *MEC* line. Output should be expanded until the *MNPB* and the *MEC* lines intersect at which point there is no longer a net gain to society and output should not be increased further.

Summary

Environmental economics suggests that market failure occurs when transactions between a producer and a consumer lead to a sub-optimal allocation of resources, in that resources are allocated to the over-supply of a good whose production has an adverse effect upon the well-being of people who are not party to the market transaction. Because market failure occurs there is a case for government regulation of or intervention in markets in order to reduce output to the level that maximises total well-being, both of the firm and of the victims of the pollution (in this case those who suffer the damage caused by climate change). The optimum level of output is neither zero nor that which the firm would choose if left to its own devices but, in keeping with the tradition of liberal neutrality, represents an equilibrium where neither party achieves everything they want, whether it is maximised profits or a life completely free from pollution, but both parties achieve something of what they want. In practice there is no easy decision procedure but a complicated empirical question of measuring the profit and the external cost in each case. In this section you have seen how the use of diagrammatic analysis can represent this puzzle much more economically than it could be explained in words. The next stage is to move on to the measurement of monetary values by estimating the social cost of carbon and the cost of reducing it.

2.2 Calculating the social cost of carbon

The monetary value of global warming impacts

The standard assumption in economics about assessing the economic impact of an event or a process is that it means putting a monetary value on its costs and benefits. There is good reason for this approach in that economists often advise governments on how best to spend money. Using monetary analysis enables policy makers to assess whether the benefits will outweigh the costs.

From this perspective, estimating the economic impact of climate change helps to answer the question: how much should we pay to mitigate climate change? The answer depends on two things: how much it will cost us to do so, and what the costs will be if we do nothing. The benefits of climate change abatement are the costs of climate change that will thereby be avoided. Economic analysis of the costs and benefits of climate change abatement has been very influential but it is controversial and may fail to reflect accurately the full impact of climate change on the world's population.

Activity 3.3

Read the extract from the Stern Review in Reading 3.1. You might also find it helpful to look back at Figure 3.1. The standard economic approach to calculating 'the social cost of carbon' entails putting a monetary value on the impacts of global warming summarised below and in Figure 3.1. Take a few minutes to think about the following questions:

1 Can you see any impacts which it might be relatively easy to 'cost' in monetary terms?

2   Are there any impacts on which it seems difficult or impossible to put a monetary value?

3   Do you have any misgivings about the idea of quantifying the impacts of climate change in monetary terms?

Reading 3.1

An edited extract from Stern Review, *The Economics of Climate Change*, 2006

How Climate Change will Affect People Around the World

On current trends, average global temperatures will rise by 2–3 °C within the next fifty years or so, leading to many severe impacts, often involving water:

- Melting glaciers will initially increase flood risk and then strongly reduce water supplies, eventually threatening one-sixth of the world's population, predominantly in the Indian sub-continent, parts of China, and the Andes in South America.

- Declining crop yields, especially in Africa, could leave thousands of millions without the ability to produce or purchase sufficient food. At mid to high latitudes, crop yields may increase for moderate temperature rises (2–3 °C), but then decline with greater amounts of warming. At 4 °C and above, global food production is likely to be seriously affected.

- In higher latitudes, cold-related deaths will decrease. But climate change will increase worldwide deaths from malnutrition and heat stress. Diseases such as malaria and dengue fever could also become more widespread.

- Rising sea levels will result in tens to hundreds of millions more people flooded each year with warming of 3 or 4 °C. There will be serious risks and increasing pressures for coastal protection in South East Asia (Bangladesh and Vietnam), small islands in the Caribbean and the Pacific, and large coastal cities, such as Tokyo, New York, Cairo and London. According to one estimate, by the middle of the century, 200 million people may become permanently displaced from their homes due to rising sea levels, heavier floods, and more intense droughts.

- Around 15–40% of species potentially face extinction after only 2 °C of warming. And ocean acidification, a direct result of rising carbon dioxide levels, will have major effects on marine ecosystems, with possible adverse consequences on fish stocks.

- Warming may lead to sudden shifts in regional weather patterns that would have severe consequences for water availability and flooding in tropical regions and threaten the livelihoods of millions of people.

- A number of studies predict significant drying in the Amazon rainforest.

- The melting or collapse of ice sheets would eventually threaten land which today is home to 1 in every 20 people.

Source: Stern, 2007, p. 65

Figure 3.5

The effects of climate change will vary over time and space. Some areas will suffer from increased drought while others will be more prone to flooding

It seems to me that it is relatively easy in principle to put a monetary value on some impacts. For example, there is a lot of expensive real estate with known market prices in major coastal cities such as London, New York and Tokyo. Moreover, without offices or factories for people to work in, output (which has a monetary value when it is sold) will fall, at least for a while. Other things being equal, declining crop yields (adjusted for higher prices) and fish stocks will lead to a reduction in the value of world output. Further, all of these impacts would cause distress and hardship, perhaps over a long period, for the people affected. Standard economic practice is to estimate the loss of output consequent upon people's incapacity for paid and unpaid work and use this as a proxy for the cost of hardship.

However, there are some impacts on which it seems very difficult to put a monetary value. In industrialised nations the existence of market prices makes it easy to quantify many, but certainly not all, of the economic effects of global warming. For example, if agricultural land is lost to rising sea levels, we can refer to its previous market value to calculate the cost of its loss. But even in industrialised nations climate change may damage aspects of the environment that do not have a market value; for example, the inundated land might have had cultural value for its beautiful landscape. Nevertheless, a monetary estimate of such value can be made indirectly by examining the earnings of the tourism industry for information about how much people were willing to pay to enjoy the beautiful landscape. Outside industrial countries climate change

Figure 3.6
How should economists value the future possible consequences of climate change, such as coastal erosion and the loss of species such as polar bears?

might deprive subsistence farmers of the ability to make an independent livelihood from traditional land. Economists would try to estimate the monetary value of any such land lost or degraded by climate change by examining data on the cost of food in nearby markets.

The difficulty of evaluating non-market impacts is particularly acute when trying to assess the damage inflicted by climate change on ecosystems over and above their value as resource inputs to economic activity. Monetary values have been put on the loss of biodiversity through species extinction, but if animal and plant species are thought to possess intrinsic value or dignity that ought to be respected, their degradation under climate change might seem to be a loss that cannot possibly be evaluated. Even here economists have devised methods of putting a monetary estimate on existence value, in other words the intrinsic value that a part of the natural environment has simply for its very existence as distinct from its use as a resource, by using time spent by volunteers on biodiversity conservation projects as an indicator of willingness to pay through earnings forgone (Ninan et al., 2007, p. 106).

The concept of intrinsic value was introduced in Chapter 1

You might have misgivings about thinking of the impacts of climate change in monetary terms. The incidence or burden of the impacts is expected to fall disproportionately on the populations of low income countries. Assessing the severity of impacts in terms of the loss of output available for consumption will devalue those impacts on the most vulnerable victims of global warming, unless the estimates for low income countries are weighted to bring them up to the world average. As you will see below, the Stern Review weighted the estimated costs for low income countries for this reason.

Modelling the costs of global warming

The earliest studies of the economic impact of global warming assumed a doubling of atmospheric concentrations of CO_2 and estimated the costs of the resulting warming at about 1–2 per cent of world gross domestic product (GDP), that is, the monetary value of world output of goods and services available for consumption. The costs of mitigation were estimated to be 1–3 per cent of GDP. So the estimated costs of mitigation exceeded the estimated costs of global warming, which ostensibly called into question the wisdom of mitigation as a strategy. Both estimates are, however, subject to deep uncertainty and are also open to doubt about their comprehensiveness. They typically fail to take account of non-market impacts.

The IPCC does not offer firm predictions of future temperature increases and their impacts but prepares a number of illustrative scenarios, using integrated assessment models (IAMs). These integrate models of world economic growth and consequential greenhouse gas emissions with climate science models of the links between those emissions and temperature change. Chris Hope (2005) reviews 29 IAMs but I will examine how just one of them was used in the Stern Review.

The Stern Review (2007, pp. 161–2) decided to use PAGE2002, a British IAM designed for government use that can readily be adapted to include estimates of non-market impacts. First, the review estimated 'that if we don't act, the overall costs and risks of climate change will be equivalent to losing at least 5% of global GDP each year, now and forever' (Stern, 2006, p. vi). I will return to this reference to 'now and forever' in a moment.

Second, Stern departed from most other models by adding 'non-market' impacts on the environment and human health. This increased the total cost from 5 per cent to 11 per cent of global GDP. The inclusion of estimates on the costs of non-market impacts is subject to considerable uncertainty and has been dismissed by some commentators as 'conjectural' (Byatt et al., 2006). Third, Stern included estimates of the positive feedback effects of climate change, including the risk of catastrophic climate change. This further increased the potential total cost from 11 per cent to 14 per cent of global GDP. Finally, Stern addressed the concern about the expectation that a disproportionate burden of climate change will fall on poor regions. Stern argued that this burden should be given a stronger relative weight, which would take the estimated total cost of climate change to 'around 20%' of global GDP.

Now let us return to the phrase 'now and forever'. The effects of climate change are expected to accrue year by year over a very long period of time. Some of the catastrophic effects that Stern included are not expected to occur for several hundred years (Nordhaus, 2007, p. 158). If you add up each year's costs and then average them out over the number of years climate change is expected to last, you would be only one step away from knowing the 'present value' of those future costs (the other step being discounting, which is explained below). The present value measures the importance of the future costs of climate change to policy makers in the present. The Stern Review made this kind of calculation for the costs of climate change, averaging the total costs over the number of years the model runs. The costs for the short-to-medium term are relatively low, and it is the extremely high cost of catastrophic events over the long term that drives up the annual average (Nordhaus, 2007).

Activity 3.4

Look back over the previous section and think about this question:

What do you think are the main strengths and weaknesses of the economic analysis presented in the Stern Review?

It seems to me that the Stern Review has advanced the debate about the social cost of carbon in two ways: by adding to estimates of the loss of GDP a figure for non-market impacts, and by increasing the weight given to damage in low income countries. No doubt researchers in years to come will contest the actual values that Stern assigned to non-market impacts and to income inequality adjustment but that is the price you pay for setting a research agenda. The main issue for me is the importance Stern attached to catastrophic damage in the remote future. So much can happen in even a hundred years. It is to this subject that we now turn.

Evaluating long-term effects

For most people £100 is worth more today than £100 next year because there is a degree of uncertainty about what might happen between now and next year; they would prefer to spend £100 rather than postpone consumption to an uncertain future. True, many people save for 'a rainy day', a holiday or their children's education. But most people choose to save with the bank that offers the highest interest rate rather than keep the cash in a shoe box under the bed. The interest paid on your savings compensates you against the risk you take in not spending your money now and having something tangible to show for the exchange. For example, inflation would gradually erode the purchasing power of the cash in the shoe box, while interest should guard your savings against a sustained rise in prices. The greater the risks to your savings, the higher the interest rate will need to be today to persuade you to postpone consumption until tomorrow.

A similar line of thought underlies the idea that the future costs of an event or occurrence should be discounted or reduced in value. Many economic impacts of climate change are not expected to occur until decades or even centuries into the future and their occurrence is inevitably subject to a degree of uncertainty. Catastrophic climate change impacts may never happen so economists discount, or reduce the value of, their costs. So as you add up the costs of climate change year by year, you might want to adjust downwards those expected in later years, that is, you might want to discount them to reflect the uncertainty of their occurrence.

Discounting is a mathematical technique for converting future costs (or benefits) into an equivalent present value.

By how much, you might be wondering, should we reduce costs that might be incurred so far into the future? The technique of discounting is intended to help us to think clearly about this question. **Discounting** is a technique for converting future costs (or benefits) into an equivalent value in the present. But by how much should you discount distant future costs? By 1 per cent, 5 per cent, 10 per cent or more? The choice of discount rate may do more to influence the results of running a model than any other assumption in the model. As Richard Tol and Gary Yohe (2006) put it, 'low discount rates produce high estimates of discounted damages' (p. 238). Similarly, high discount rates produce low estimates of discounted damage.

Online Exercise 3

Now log on to the course website and complete Online Exercise 3: *Discounting future costs and benefits.*

There is no single 'right' answer to the question of what discount rate to use, because it is ultimately a matter of ethical attitudes about how to treat current and future generations fairly. Evaluating impacts over the long term raises issues of intergenerational equity. The concept of intergenerational equity underpins the argument for sustainable development, and hence the arguments about what can and should be done about climate change (*course question 4*). Intergenerational equity is the obligation to ensure a fair distribution of resources between the current generation and future generations. This concept has been debated at length by philosophers, political scientists, economists and environmentalists. The basic problem, as the economist and philosopher John Broome (1992) points out, is how to assess and compare the benefits and costs that occur at different times. One approach is to draw upon the theory, advanced by the philosopher John Rawls (1973), of justice as impartiality between individuals. This impartiality might be extended over time, suggesting that the well-being of each generation should be equally valued. This is particularly relevant to climate change, which scientists have estimated will continue for seventy years as a consequence of past emissions even if CO_2 emissions were to cease today. Mitigation is therefore inescapably altruistic, and intended to benefit people who do not yet exist.

However, there is no agreement about the appropriate discount rate that should be used. One view is that the discount rate applied by society to further the well-being of future generations should be zero. Any discount rate greater than zero will, it can be claimed, unfairly devalue the interests of future generations. This is the basis of Stern's approach, on the grounds that 'if a future generation is present, we suppose that it has the same claim on our ethical attention as the current one' (Stern, 2007, p. 31).

Figure 3.7
The Scottish philosopher David Hume (1711–76)

Stern has been criticised for considering only 'a narrow range of plausible ethical approaches' (Beckerman and Hepburn, 2007, p. 188). In particular, Beckerman and Hepburn suggest that agent-relative ethics should have been considered. The origin of agent-relative ethics can be traced to the thought of Aristotle (384–22 BC) and was also expounded by David Hume (1711–76) during the Scottish Enlightenment (Figure 3.7). The essence of agent-relative ethics is captured in this quotation from Hume:

> A man naturally loves his children better than his nephews, his nephews better than his cousins, his cousins better than strangers, where everything else is equal ... Our sense of duty always follows the common and natural course of our passions.
>
> (Hume, 1969 [1740], p. 462)

John Kay, a contemporary economist, expresses a similar view and uses it to criticise Stern's approach as unworkable:

> Why should I do anything for posterity? What has posterity ever done for me? ... The problem of weighing the present and the future equally is that there is a lot of future. The number of future generations is potentially so large that small and permanent benefit to them would justify great sacrifice now ... No government advocating it would ever be elected. The burden of caring for all humanity, present and future, is greater than even the best-intentioned can bear.
>
> (Kay, 2007)

The differences between Rawls, Broome and Stern on the one hand and Hume and Kay on the other reflect differences of attitude towards temporally remote strangers among the current generation. These are ethical issues on which reasonable minds may differ.

Activity 3.5

In Chapter 6 you will examine further the ethical aspects of intergenerational equity. To help you think about the issues now, write a few sentences explaining whether you agree with Kay's approach to future generations or Stern's.

3   The matrix of policy instruments

Four general types of policy instruments can be identified on the basis of how prescriptive the government is about the goal of policy and the method of trying to achieve it. They are summarised in Figure 3.8.

	Government specifies goal	Government does not specify goal
Government specifies how goal is to be achieved	Regulation 1: Command and control	Regulation 2: Technology-based standards
Government does not specify how goal is to be achieved	Most voluntary agreements	Most market-based instruments and public information programmes

Figure 3.8

Matrix of environmental policy instruments

Command and control policy measures are government directives to polluters to reduce pollution.

Technology-based standards require producers to use a specified technology.

Voluntary agreements are pledges by polluters to achieve a specified reduction in pollution.

Command and control designates policy measures that instruct the polluter about what emissions reduction target should be achieved and how it should be achieved; this form of regulation has not so far been used in climate change policy. **Technology-based standards** would specify a method of reducing emissions, such as using the least carbon-intensive production technology, but would not specify a particular emissions reduction target. Again, this type of policy instrument has not been deployed in climate change policy, although it is commonly used in other areas of environmental policy. **Voluntary agreements** typically set a goal or target but leave it to the polluter to choose the method of achieving it. For example, the European Union (EU) agreement with car manufacturers set a maximum limit of 140g/km (grams per kilometre) for CO_2 emissions from cars but allowed individual car makers to decide how to achieve it (for example, by reducing the emissions of all engines, by introducing hybrid vehicles or by withdrawing high-emissions vehicles from sale).

Market-based instruments aim to raise the price of the good whose production causes pollution in order to reflect the damage done. In the case of global warming, the basic principle of market-based instruments is carbon pricing or setting a price for carbon (in addition to the goods that are produced using fossil fuels). Market-based instruments comprise 'green' taxes, emissions trading systems (ETSs) (in the context of climate change, carbon trading) and subsidies (for example to the renewable energy industry). In recent years market-based instruments have been assigned a greater role in some areas of environmental policy, including climate policy. The EU has discussed a *carbon tax* and the UK has introduced an *energy tax*, the climate change levy, which might develop into a carbon tax (Box 3.1).

Market-based instruments raise the price of a good whose production or consumption causes pollution.

Box 3.1   Energy tax and carbon tax

An **energy tax** is a tax on energy use irrespective of the source of the energy. For example, the UK climate change levy is an energy tax in that it is a tax on each kilowatt-hour of coal, gas or electricity used (even if the electricity was generated from nuclear or renewable sources).

A **carbon tax** is a tax on carbon use or CO_2 emissions; it would tax energy only if it was generated by burning fossil fuels. The Kyoto Protocol includes several market-based instruments, most notably the aspiration towards a global carbon trading system.

An **energy tax** taxes the use of energy irrespective of its source.

A **carbon tax** taxes carbon emissions from industry or households.

Carbon trading, the policy instrument favoured by Kyoto and the EU, is neoliberal in inspiration. **Neoliberalism** is based in part on a resurgence of the classical liberal idea that government should have a very limited role, being concerned only with assigning and defending property rights, leaving the greatest possible freedom to individuals to engage in market transactions. However, neoliberalism differs from classical liberalism in some important respects. First, neoliberalism emphasises an enhanced role for the private sector in achieving government policy. Second, rather than using regulation (such as command and control or technology-based standards) to change the behaviour of private actors, both of which are interventions in markets, neoliberalism tends to favour voluntary agreements and market-based instruments. Third, neoliberalism conceives of markets as global in scope, advocating the liberalisation of international markets in trade and finance. Since the 1970s neoliberalism is seen by many as the dominant ideology of our age (Harvey, 2005). As you will see throughout this course, many

Neoliberalism holds that government should have a very limited role in economic activity, which should be left to the private sector and the market.

environmental policies reflect neoliberal assumptions. In this section I will set aside ideological considerations and examine policy instruments on their merits.

What are the advantages and disadvantages of the different policy instruments that have a crucial role to play in mitigating climate change?

3.1 Green taxes

The most influential economic argument for government intervention in markets that cause greenhouse gas emissions is based on the neoclassical analysis of market failure (Section 2). Government intervention has traditionally taken the form of regulation or taxes, which are alternative policy instruments for achieving the same goal. I will explain the analysis underlying government intervention in terms of a 'green' tax but it is worth remembering that neoclassical analysis could also be used to make the case for regulation. The effects of global warming are analysed in environmental economics as a negative externality (or an external cost). A free market overproduces goods causing negative externalities such as the effects of carbon emissions. So the aim of a tax is to shift the market towards the *social optimum*, namely the lower level of output that maximises the benefits of all members of society. The diagrammatic analysis of a negative externality can be developed to explain the environmental economics case for taxes on carbon emitting activities (Figure 3.9).

The social optimum is a concept that is also used in models of international cooperation

Figure 3.9

Optimal tax on production for a firm producing goods using fossil fuels

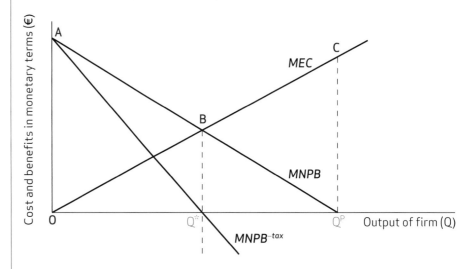

The neoclassical analysis of pollution taxes was developed by a British economist, Arthur Pigou, in the early years of the twentieth century and such taxes are therefore called Pigovian. In Figure 3.9 a Pigovian tax is levied on the firm whose production activity causes carbon emissions

(for simplicity, the bottom horizontal axis shown in Figure 3.4 above is omitted from Figure 3.9). The aim is to reduce output to the optimum at Q* and the line $MNPB^{-tax}$ from A through Q* represents the tax. The reason output exceeds the optimum is that the firm does not have to take account of the costs its carbon emissions inflict on third parties. In order to force the firm to take account of those costs the tax is set equal to the monetary value of the marginal external costs of the firm's production. If the firm continues to produce at its previous profit-maximising output Q^P, it will pay tax on the last extra unit of output equal to Q^PC. The tax 'internalises' the externality in that the previously external cost is now subtracted from the profits of the firm, just like any other cost of production. The firm will not choose to avoid the tax entirely by reducing output to zero; that would mean going out of business. The rational decision for the firm is to maximise its profits net of the tax, which it does at Q*, where the line $MNBP^{-tax}$ intersects the horizontal axis. Increasing output beyond Q* will incur losses (negative profits) to offset the profits earned on output up to Q*.

What are the difficulties in implementing a Pigovian tax? The biggest problem is the cost of gathering information on negative externalities (external costs). This is not always an insuperable obstacle. In fact the UK taxes on landfill and on the extraction of aggregates such as sand and gravel are Pigovian. However, the external costs of landfill and aggregate extraction are mainly local, consisting in loss of tranquillity and landscape value to people living near the sites, and hence relatively easy to quantify through standard procedures such as house price comparisons and surveys. A Pigovian tax on production causing carbon emissions is a very different matter, because, as we saw in Section 2, the external costs are spread over time and space and are therefore difficult to quantify (*course theme 5*).

Nevertheless, policy makers seem to be taking a more pragmatic approach, being less interested in ensuring that polluters pay for the external costs they impose – 'not a penny more, not a penny less' (to borrow the title of one of Jeffrey Archer's novels) – and more in designing incentives to change their behaviour in roughly the right direction. Rather than taxing the output of goods whose production causes carbon emissions, they have become interested in devising a carbon tax, which penalises carbon emissions directly. The advantage of a carbon tax is that it does not require producers to reduce output provided that they can reduce carbon emissions for an unchanged level of output by switching to a less carbon-intensive, or ideally a carbon-neutral, production process (see Chapter 6 on ecological modernisation). The information costs of a carbon tax designed to encourage innovation and the uptake of new energy technologies are much lower than those of a Pigovian tax. Policy makers need to know enough about the cost structure of firms to be able to calculate the level of tax necessary to persuade them to invest in new, less carbon-intensive technology.

The EU has so far failed to agree to impose a carbon tax but Norway, Sweden, Finland and Denmark introduced carbon taxes in the early 1990s. In practice the success of a carbon tax in reducing emissions depends on several factors. First, carbon taxes are not a 'quick fix' but 'are typically effective in the medium to longer term. In the short run, demand for carbon-creating activities, such as electricity generation and transport, tends to be "inelastic" [that is, unresponsive to changes in price]' (Helm et al., 2005, p. 305). In the UK the Royal Commission on Environmental Pollution estimated that petrol would need to increase in price by 9 per cent (in real terms) a year for ten years to meet the government's CO_2 reduction targets (Figure 3.10).

Figure 3.10

Taxing petrol consumption is a policy option for governments that wish to reduce carbon emissions

Second, a carbon tax should ideally be internationally harmonised. Otherwise, firms in high-tax countries will be placed at a competitive disadvantage and might relocate to low-tax countries. This would reduce the effectiveness of the tax, which is intended to reduce carbon-intensive activities rather than redistribute them across countries. Unfortunately, the four Scandinavian countries that introduced carbon taxes in the early 1990s 'have not been able to harmonise their approaches – demonstrating the difficulty of co-ordinating tax policy internationally, even among a relatively small group of countries' (Stern, 2007, p. 386). The USA policy stance is not sympathetic to taxes, while the developing countries are unwilling to take action because they see climate change as the product of carbon emitted by industrial countries in the past. Harmonising a carbon tax on a global scale is achievable only in the long term, if at all.

Third, many voters do not like taxes but the public acceptability of a carbon tax may be enhanced by the prospect of revenue recycling. In the short run a carbon tax will raise revenue as firms and households pay to emit carbon for as long as it takes to switch to low- or non-carbon energy sources. There is a risk that a carbon tax would be perceived as a stealth tax rather than a tax with a genuine environmental purpose.

This risk can be reduced by revenue recycling, which requires the government to use carbon tax revenues to reduce other taxes. For example, using carbon tax revenues to cut income tax would reduce the tax burden on an economic good, in the form of work effort and skills, by increasing it on an economic bad, namely carbon emissions.

It seems that carbon taxes in some form are very likely to play a central role in climate change policy for the foreseeable future. However, there are some political constraints to carbon taxation (*course question 3*). Many countries subsidise fossil fuel consumption.

> Removing price subsidies in China, India, Indonesia, Iran, Russia, Kazakhstan, South Africa and Venezuela alone would reduce global energy usage by an estimated 3.5 per cent and reduce global CO_2 emissions by 4.6 per cent.
>
> (International Energy Agency, 1999, pp. 9–10)

Some members of the EU also subsidise fossil fuel, particularly coal. For example, in Germany 'coal remains untaxed under the ecological tax reform introduced in 1999' (European Environmental Agency, 2004, p. 14); this subsidy was worth about €3.5 billion in 2001. The economic purpose of a subsidy is to increase the output of a good that provides positive externalities or public benefits, such as vaccinations against infectious diseases and education. On economic grounds, and assuming a substantial anthropogenic contribution to climate change, there is an unanswerable case for phasing out subsidies to fossil fuel industries. However, such a policy recommendation would meet vigorous resistance on political grounds, because fuel subsidies are typically a form of employment protection without which jobs would be at risk.

3.2 Regulation or 'command and control'

As you have seen, neoclassical economics makes the case for reducing the output of carbon-intensive production to the social optimum either by taxing such production or by regulating it. The USA introduced legislation on vehicle fuel efficiency following the oil price rises of 1973–74. Porsche and BMW are paying fines 'at the cost of millions of dollars a year, for exceeding average fuel-economy standards [in the USA]' (*The Economist*, 2007). Car manufacturers and the EU reached voluntary agreements in 1998 and 1999 to reduce the CO_2 emissions of the average car to 140g/km by 2008. Most car makers were expected to fail to

Figure 3.11
At present the Ferrari Mille Chili hybrid car is just a concept – but does it point the way to the future?

reach this target and in 2007 the EU announced plans to introduce legislation to impose stricter emissions targets on car manufacturers. It is hoped that manufacturers will respond by developing hybrid vehicles which combine petrol and electric motors to cut emissions (Figure 3.11).

Regulation will continue to play an important role in climate change mitigation policy in some countries but it is unlikely to be at the forefront of internationally coordinated policy approaches. Many governments will be unwilling to increase the legislative burden on industry and consumers. In any case regulation has been most effective against pollution with different characteristics from greenhouse gas emissions. Consider, for example, the UK Clean Air Act of 1956 and USA legislation requiring the fitting of catalytic converters to vehicle exhausts, since adopted in many other countries. In both cases there was a single source of pollution, coal smoke or vehicle emissions of nitrogen oxides (NO_x) and carbon monoxide (neither of which are greenhouse gases, as it happens). The pollution was localised, limited to smog in London causing many deaths from respiratory diseases. In California the problem was the pollution caused by the interaction of emissions and sunlight. In both countries polluters were also among the victims of pollution, whose self-interest contributed to the acceptability of the legislation. Finally, there was a fairly straightforward 'end-of-pipe' technological solution to the problem, enforcing the use of smokeless fuel or the fitting of catalytic converters, which turn the toxic emissions into water and – of all things – CO_2.

At present these conditions do not hold for climate change. It might take only a few severe impacts in the main greenhouse gas emitting countries for world policy makers to turn to the complex regulations that would be needed to cover all the main sources of greenhouse gas emissions.

3.3 Carbon trading

Carbon trading has been advocated by some neoliberal economists as an application of free market principles to climate change; it is regarded with suspicion by other economics theorists for the same reason. However, ideas often transcend their political genealogy. Road pricing was regarded in the 1980s as a radical free market theory that would never work in practice. Yet in 2003 a left-wing mayor, Ken Livingstone, introduced the London congestion charge.

Neoliberalism revisited

Let us recall that a core proposition of neoclassical economics is that markets can fail. One of the ways in which a market can fail is that it imposes external costs such as pollution and the adverse effects of climate change on people who are not engaged in transactions in that market. According to the neoliberal view, markets never fail. Things can and do go wrong in markets but they are always cases of *government failure*. This may strike you as a paradoxical view, especially after working through the technical details of the neoclassical analysis of market failure (Section 2.1). To understand the neoliberal point of view we need to trace it back to its origins, which lie in libertarian political thought as well as in economics.

Libertarianism is essentially a contemporary restatement of **classical liberalism**, which held that each individual should enjoy as much freedom as anyone else. The intention is to devise a society which minimises coercion of individuals by other people and by the state. The duty of the state is to protect individual rights to life, liberty and the pursuit of happiness. But although individual rights are central to the libertarian view these rights are limited. There are no rights to education or health care because the state can guarantee them for all individuals only by funding them from taxation. But libertarians are hostile to taxation on the grounds that it entails coercion, in that paying taxes is compulsory on pain of a fine or imprisonment. To libertarians the state should defend the right to private property and enforce contracts. This is enough to enable markets to work and provide goods and services including education and health care.

Libertarianism is a rich tradition of thought with several different strands (Machan, 2006). To give one example, libertarians disagree among themselves about the ideal society. Some see it as involving complete freedom from the state, while others see a role for a minimal state concerned only with defending the security of individual life and property (*Journal of Libertarian Studies*, 2007). What is common to all libertarians is the aim of reducing the size and scope of government to a very limited role, namely allocating and defending property rights.

The neoliberal explanation of climate change is that it is a consequence of government failure to establish a complete allocation of property rights, by omitting to allocate the right to use the atmosphere as a receptacle for greenhouse gas emissions. According to this view, the atmosphere should be treated as property; firms or nations must buy or be allocated the right to use this property as a receptacle for carbon emissions up to a limit that does not result in a rise in the global mean temperature. Moreover, once property rights have been allocated, trade can take place. As with any other market, the government defines who owns what and enforces the contracts people make. The state sets the market in motion, so to speak, and then stands back to allow it to operate freely. In the case of carbon trading, once the permits have been allocated, trading can take place and the price mechanism will not only achieve a reduction in carbon emissions but will do so at least cost to the economy.

Libertarianism is a contemporary restatement of the view that individuals should enjoy as much liberty as possible.

Classical liberalism developed in Great Britain in the nineteenth century and held that each individual should enjoy as much liberty as any other.

Emissions trading and the Kyoto Protocol

The Kyoto Protocol envisages a major role for market mechanisms, in particular carbon emissions trading, in achieving greenhouse gas emissions reduction targets at the lowest possible cost. A number of models have been used to estimate the costs of achieving the Kyoto 2012 targets, as negotiated in 1997. The average cost for the USA was 1.3 per cent of GDP without emissions trading, falling by more than half with emissions trading for Annex 1 (industrialised) countries and to only 20 per cent of the no-trading estimate with global emissions trading (Golub et al., 2006, p.254).

The Kyoto targets apply only to the Annex 1 countries, the major industrialised economies which are historically the major emitters. Despite the prospect of much lower emissions reduction costs from carbon trading, the US presidency of George W. Bush resisted any mandatory emissions reduction targets, while China and India expressed resistance to mandatory targets for the post-Kyoto period (after 2012). In contrast the EU established a multinational emissions trading system (ETS). If the EU ETS proves to be effective in reducing emissions at least cost, a similar scheme may be introduced by other countries, possibly incorporating all of the major emitters which are responsible for 80 per cent of global emissions (Figure 3.12).

The EU ETS is a *cap and trade* scheme. The EU, as a supranational organisation, establishes property rights to the atmosphere by setting a limit, in other words *capping* emissions, for a given period of time and allocating permits to firms in carbon-intensive industries to emit carbon up to this limit. The firms can then *trade* the permits. Some firms will emit less carbon than their allocation allows, perhaps because they have installed low or non-carbon technology, and can recoup some of the investment costs by selling their surplus permits. Other firms will want to emit more carbon than the permits allocated to them allow, perhaps because their carbon-intensive capital equipment is not yet due to be retired. Until they can invest in cleaner technology, they will need to buy permits to cover their excess emissions.

Neoclassical economics assumes that firms are well-informed about their costs. Trading permits (whose prices will change in response to their relative scarcity) is therefore an efficient way of making use of all this knowledge spread among firms. In principle, a cap and trade system is the least-cost method of reducing emissions because it mobilises the decentralised knowledge of costs. Each firm can choose to invest in new technology at a pace that suits it, minimising its costs and its prices to consumers.

Figure 3.12
The European Union is a strong proponent of an international market in CO_2 emisisons

Nevertheless, whether carbon emissions are reduced at all, never mind at least cost, depends crucially on the quality of government decision making in the design of the ETS. Three key decisions need to be made: about the limit to be placed on emissions, the coverage of the system and the method of allocating permits among participating firms.

First, the level of emissions should be consistent with the long-term objective of policy, such as avoiding dangerous climate change (the agreed goal of the Kyoto Protocol). This can only be based on scientific evidence and a prediction about future 'business as usual' emissions; such predictions inevitably introduce uncertainty into the trading system, and this may compromise its acceptability to participating firms. The EU ETS began with a *baseline and credit* approach. The EU set the trading system in motion with an allocation of permits that reflected a generous baseline of predicted near-term future usage in order to win acceptance among participating firms. However, there was a risk that this approach might end up crediting firms with enough permits to cover their expected emissions, thus failing to provide any incentive to move to low carbon technology. The UK ETS began in this way but it has proved difficult to manage the transition to a genuine cap and trade system (Smith and Swierzbinski, 2007). If the baseline and credit approach is too generous in its initial allocation, the carbon price will collapse and firms can easily afford to buy extra permits, in which case there is no incentive to introduce new technology to reduce emissions.

Second, the coverage of the trading system may, at least in its early stages, be limited to carbon-intensive industries that are not at immediate risk from competition in international markets. Industries that are granted exemption are protected and, in effect, subsidised. The UK ETS and EU ETS both include significant exemptions.

Third, the choice of the method of allocating the first permits, between free distribution or auction or a mix of the two, is crucial. Free distribution may be an essential part of a strategy to win acceptance from sceptical firms, but it has its risks. One is that free distribution can act as a barrier to the entry of new firms, undermining the degree of competition in industries covered by the scheme. Incumbent firms receive a free allocation of permits when the trading system begins, but new entrants have to purchase permits at the prevailing market price. The implication is that 'the free distribution system imposes a bias against new users in the sense that their financial burden is greater than that of an otherwise identical existing user' (Tietenberg, 2005, p. 184).

The combination of baseline and credit approach and free distribution of permits can have unwelcome effects on the distribution of income. For example, firms such as electricity producers may increase prices in anticipation of receiving insufficient permits and having to purchase extra permits at the predicted market price. If the quota is sufficient to cover actual emissions for most firms, the carbon price (the price of permits) will collapse and the funds raised for purchasing will become windfall profits. The distributive effects on society as a whole are likely to be regressive, with money being redistributed from electricity customers, many of whom will be on low incomes, to shareholders, who may be expected on average to be more affluent. The EU ETS in its first phase experienced some major problems surrounding the setting of the national quotas, which were too generous. However, it is possible that the second phase will be more effective in setting more stringent targets that persuade more firms to invest in low carbon technology.

The EU ETS has to meet several difficult conditions if it is to become part of an effective international carbon trading scheme. The number of permits allocated by free distribution must be limited, and at least some permits should be auctioned. The scheme should cover all carbon emissions with no industries exempt. And the carbon market should be reasonably competitive. An effective international trading scheme also requires international political agreement on an emissions reduction target and a schedule for reaching it. The prospects for international collaboration will be discussed in Chapter 4.

It would take a very brave policy maker to bet the future of the world on just one policy for mitigating global warming, rescinding all others. A mix of policy instruments seems sure to be retained. Political responses to climate change are not restricted to the deployment of policy instruments by governments. Some people give a more radical interpretation of the question: What can be done for the future and what should be done? (*course question 4*). Among them are some ecological economists.

4 Physical limits to growth? Ecological economics

Environmental economics, understood as the application of neoclassical economics to environmental issues, is by far the most important theoretical framework for analysing the economics of climate change. However, it is not the only one. Ecological economics is perhaps a work in progress compared to the long-established principles of neoclassical economics, and it has not yet made a substantial contribution to the mainstream climate change policy debate. I explained in Section 1 that neoclassical economics (and hence environmental economics) uses a language and analytic techniques that sets it apart from the other social sciences. By contrast ecological economics has a greater interdisciplinary appeal and is associated with more environmentally committed ethical standpoints. In this section I will introduce you to some of the key principles of ecological economics.

Ecological economics holds that economic processes must be understood as part of the physical world and that there are physical limits to economic growth. From this perspective, climate change can best be understood as an example of a problem that occurs when the physical limits to economic growth are exceeded. Neoclassical economists assume that the physical world does not impose any limits on growth. Until the 1970s this way of thinking was unchallenged in economics. A key assumption behind the neoclassical approach is that if one natural resource ran out, it could always be replaced with another that would maintain the rate of economic growth. Ecological economics denies that this is possible. This is the key difference between ecological economics and neoclassical economics.

In neoclassical economics, all goods or services that are exchanged for money count towards the value of GDP. This assumes that there is nothing unique and irreplaceable about any particular component of

Ecological economics holds that there are physical limits to economic growth.

economic growth, or about any particular resource used in producing goods and services. Neoclassical economists believe that productive resources can always be substituted one for another. For example, it is not unusual for a firm to substitute new technology for unskilled labour. Similarly, for the neoclassical economist economic growth can always be sustained, even if environmental capital (raw materials) is lost, because it can be replaced with human capital (skills and knowledge) and manufactured capital (machinery). However, the view that growth can be maintained indefinitely is denied by ecological economists.

Figure 3.13

A model of the economy embedded in the environment

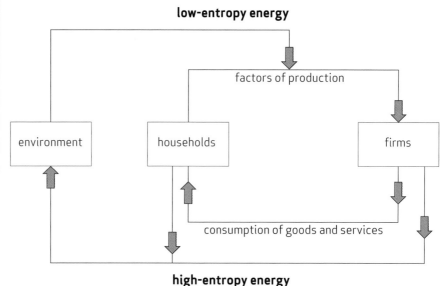

For ecological economists, the economy must be situated in the physical world (Figure 3.13). In this view, economics is based on the second law of thermodynamics and the concept of entropy. Entropy denotes the property of disorder or dissipation of energy, which physicists believe is a fundamental property of any thermodynamic system. Placing a mug of hot coffee in a cold room provides an everyday example of entropy. The coffee and the air in the room will eventually reach the same temperature as the heat from the coffee dissipates throughout the room. The increase in the ambient temperature of the room can also be described as the dissipation of heat and hence also as an increase in entropy.

Physics tells us that matter and energy are governed by the laws of thermodynamics, or the 'science of energy'. The first law of thermodynamics states that matter and energy can neither be created nor destroyed. The second law of thermodynamics, which is also known as the 'law of entropy', states that in a thermodynamic system the unchanging quantity of energy undergoes a qualitative change from available or low-entropy energy to unavailable or dissipated high-entropy energy. In other words, entropy always increases. In a thermodynamic system the unchanging quantity of energy undergoes a qualitative change from available, concentrated or low-entropy energy to unavailable, dissipated or high-entropy energy.

Nicholas Georgescu-Roegen (1971) introduced the concept of entropy into economics, claiming that economic processes are entropic; that is, they transform low-entropy energy into high-entropy energy, or available energy into unavailable or waste energy. For example, oil is found in the Earth's crust in a state of low entropy. When it is turned into fuel it emits CO_2, which is dissipated throughout the atmosphere in a state of high entropy. Since low entropy is a necessary condition of usefulness, the entropy law is essential to understanding the idea that there are physical limits to economic growth. Natural resources are used in the manufacture of goods and eventually transformed into pollution, thus depleting the available energy. So, for the ecological economist, the terrestrial stock of these natural resources represents a physical limit to economic activity.

What light does this understanding of the physical limits to growth shed on the specific issue of global warming? Recall the example given above of an entropic process, in which low-entropy oil in the Earth's crust is turned into high-entropy CO_2 emissions. For the ecological economist, climate change is therefore the outcome of an entropic process. As such, climate change exemplifies the effects of resource depletion. The atmosphere's capacity for absorbing waste greenhouse gases is a natural resource and so an example of environmental capital, and climate change can be interpreted as stemming from the exhaustion of this capacity (the depletion of this resource). Climate change may reach a point at which its impacts are irreversible, because the pressures of growing populations and economic growth push greenhouse gas emissions to concentrations associated with a temperature increase of 5 °C or more (Figure 3.1). Population growth increases the pressure on natural resources, while economic growth may increase resource requirements per head of the population. Both result in increased energy use and, as more fossil fuels are burnt, an increase in the emissions of greenhouse gases. Ecological economics implies a more pessimistic assessment of the prospects for avoiding dangerous climate change by using policy instruments that impose only low costs on society.

5   Conclusion

The project of estimating the social cost of carbon and the search for effective policy instruments to reduce it has been powerfully influenced by neoclassical economic analysis. In this chapter I have first placed that analysis in a wider context of economic analysis and political thought. Second, I have examined in some detail the Stern Review's modelling of the monetary value of the predicted impacts of climate change. The main conclusion of my analysis was that, beneath all the technical complexity of an economic model, the results depend crucially on the ethical judgements, mainly about intergenerational equity, that inform the choice of the discount rate. Discounting might look like accountancy, but it is really applied ethics in the sense that the process reflects different valuations of the future. Third, my reading of the policy analysis literature is that there is no single policy instrument that alone will reliably reduce carbon emissions, and global warming mitigation policy will need to rely upon a mix of policy instruments, with global carbon trading likely to become a major policy instrument. Finally, it seems clear that policy has to involve international collaboration, otherwise progress will be slowed by concerns about damaging the international competitiveness of national industries in some countries. Chapter 4 will now discuss the opportunities for international collaboration and the obstacles that may impede it.

References

Beckerman, W. and Hepburn, C. (2007) 'Ethics of the discount rate in the Stern Review', *World Economics*, vol. 8, no. 1, January–March.

Broome, J. (1992) *Counting the Cost of Global Warming*, Cambridge, The White Horse Press.

Byatt, I., Castles, I., Goklany, I. M., Henderson, D., Lawson, N., McKitrick, R., Morris, J., Peacock, A., Robinson, C. and Skidelsky, R. (2006) 'The Stern Review: A dual critique, Part II: Economics aspects', *World Economics*, vol. 7, no.4, October–December.

Economist, The (2007) 'The big-car problem' [online], 22 February, http://www.economist.com/business/PrinterFriendly.cfm?story_id=8738865 (Accessed 24 February 2007).

European Environmental Agency (EEA) (2004) *Energy Subsidies in the European Union: A Brief Overview*, EEA Technical Report 1/2004, Luxembourg, Office for Official Publications of the European Communities.

Georgescu-Roegen, N. (1971) *The Entropy Law and the Economic Process*, Cambridge, MA, Harvard University Press.

Golub, A., Markandya, A. and Marcelino, D. (2006) 'Does the Kyoto Protocol cost too much and create unbreakable barriers for economic growth?', *Contemporary Economic Policy*, vol. 24, no. 4, pp. 520–35.

Harvey, D. (2005) *A Brief History of Neoliberalism*, Oxford, Oxford University Press.

Helm, D., Hepburn, C. and Marsh, R. (2005) 'Credible carbon taxes' in Helm, D. (ed.) *Climate-change Policy*, Oxford, Oxford University Press.

Hope, C. (2005) 'Integrated assessment models' in Helm, D. (ed.) (2005) *Climate-change Policy*, Oxford, Oxford University Press.

Hume, D. (1969 [1740]) *A Treatise of Human Nature*, Harmondsworth, Penguin.

Intergovernmental Panel on Climate Change (IPCC) (2007) *Climate Change 2007: The Physical Science Basis. Contribution of Working Group I to the Fourth Assessment Report of the Intergovernmental Panel on Climate Change*, Cambridge and New York, Cambridge University Press; also available online at http://www.ipcc. chSPB2feb07.pdf (Accessed 14 January 2008).

International Energy Agency (IEA) (1999) *World Energy Outlook: Looking at Energy Subsidies*, Paris, International Energy Agency.

Journal of Libertarian Studies (2007) 'Symposium: market anarchism, pro and con', vol. 21, no. 1, Spring.

Kay, J. (2007) 'Climate change: the (Groucho) Marxist approach', *Financial Times*, 28 November.

Machan, T. (2006) *Libertarianism Defended*, Aldershot, Ashgate Publishing.

Ninan, N. K., Jyothis, J., Babu, P. and Ramakrishnappa, V. (2007) *The Economics of Biodiversity Conservation: Valuation Tropical Forest Ecosystems*, London, Earthscan.

Nordhaus, W. D. (2007) *The Challenge of Global Warming: Economic Models and Environmental Policy*, New Haven, CT, Yale University Press.

Pearce, D. (2003) 'Environmental policy' in Artis, M. and Nixson, F. (eds) *The Economics of the European Union: Policy and Analysis* (3rd edn), Oxford, Oxford University Press, pp. 213–39.

Rawls, J. (1973) *A Theory of Justice*, Oxford, Oxford University Press.

Smith, S. and Swierzbinski, J. (2007) 'Assessing the performance of the UK emissions trading scheme', *Environmental and Resource Economics*, vol. 37, no. 1, May, pp. 131–58.

Stern, N. (2006) *The Economics of Climate Change: The Stern Review* [online], HM Treasury, http://www.hm-treasury.gov.uk/independent_reviews/ stern_review_economics_climate_change/sternreview_index.cfm (Accessed 14 July 2008).

Stern, N. (2007) *The Economics of Climate Change: The Stern Review*, Cambridge, Cambridge University Press.

Tietenberg, T. (2005) 'The tradable-permits approach to protecting the commons: lessons for climate change' in Helm, D. (ed.) *Climate-change Policy*, Oxford, Oxford University Press.

Tol, R. S. J. and Yohe, G. W. (2006) 'A review of the *Stern Review*', *World Economics*, vol. 7, no. 4, October–December, pp. 233–50.

Chapter 4
Collective action or collective failure?: the international politics of climate change

William Brown

Contents

1	**Introduction**	**134**
	1.1 Learning outcomes	135
2	**Dilemmas of collective action**	**135**
	2.1 Public goods	137
	2.2 The Prisoners' Dilemma	139
	2.3 Models and metaphors	142
	2.4 The constraints of the international system	146
3	**Towards cooperation?**	**147**
	3.1 Positive-sum games	148
	3.2 Side payments	151
	3.3 Power and threat points	153
	3.4 The story so far	155
4	**Behind and beyond the games**	**156**
	4.1 The politics of state preferences	157
	4.2 Ratification, implementation and agenda formation	160
5	**Conclusion**	**162**
	References	**164**

1   Introduction

In previous weeks you have seen how effective responses to climate change are difficult to agree because of uncertainties about the precise effects of climate change and contention over knowledge and values (*course theme 3*). You have also seen that differences exist among economists about the costs and benefits of different courses of action and inaction. This chapter focuses on the problems of achieving international cooperation on climate change and poses a distinct and provocative analytical problem: even if the science around global warming was absolutely certain about causes and effects, and economists were united in their valuation of the various costs and benefits of mitigation, it still may not be possible to achieve the necessary international cooperation. In this chapter you are going to investigate why.

In unpicking the several interwoven strands of this issue I will engage with two course questions: what have been the political responses to climate change (*course question 2*) and what are the constraints on more effective policy responses (*course question 3*)? The answer to these questions lies in *course theme 2*, that we are seeking solutions in a world that is politically divided and highly unequal, with power unevenly dispersed across the international political system. My analysis will also touch upon the relationship between sustainability and development (*course theme 4*) and the dimension of time (*course theme 5*). Developing your critical understanding of these issues will involve a number of key steps. In Section 2 you will deepen your understanding of international environmental problems as 'collective action problems'. You will consider why international collective action problems are particularly difficult to address compared to collective action problems that occur within a single society. By analysing international climate politics you will also, therefore, develop an awareness of the different character of politics *between* states, as compared to politics *within* states.

Attempts to address problems such as climate change engage states in processes of bargaining in which relations of power and interdependence play a crucial role in determining outcomes. In Section 3, I present some basic ideas used in the discipline of international studies (although also widely shared among other social sciences) which help to throw some light on the particular political challenges posed by environmental problems. Much of the politics of climate change revolves around attempts to forge international treaties, namely legally binding agreements between states, such as conventions and protocols. I give considerable attention to this subject. However, my discussion of politics *between* states also inevitably leads back to issues of social and political power *within* states. In Section 4, therefore, I return to the issue of the relationship between domestic and international politics to assess the power of social actors in determining the politics of climate change.

1.1 Learning outcomes

This chapter should enable you to:

- develop your knowledge and understanding of the contributions of the discipline of international studies to the analysis of environmental policy in an international context, particularly some of the key concepts used to analyse international collective action

- develop your critical understanding of key concepts, models, theories and debates relevant to the study of global environmental problems and our responses to them, particularly those used in studying international cooperation

- develop your knowledge of the range of agencies, processes, institutions, organisations and areas of interaction that shapes environmental policy making.

2 Dilemmas of collective action

I shall begin by thinking through how to characterise the problem of climate change in terms of the kinds of interaction that it involves between political actors. As you have learned, climate change is caused by a multitude of natural and human factors including the actions of billions of people across the world involved in commerce, industry, trade and transport, as well as in their domestic lives; by firms and governments; and the many processes and structures within which they operate. The effects are widespread and will be increasingly dramatic if the prognoses of climate scientists are correct. Climate change is one very important example of a *collective action problem*, that is, a problem which actors cannot solve or prevent by individual action alone. If any state, firm or individual decides that it wants to prevent climate change, it simply cannot achieve this without complementary action by others. This is one reason why climate change, like many other environmental problems, inevitably becomes highly political: it demands collective decisions. One reason why effective action has not been taken in response to climate change lies in the way that international political divisions complicate efforts to make collective decisions at the international level.

The problem of collective action is introduced in Chapter 1

As you have seen in Chapter 1, the history of attempts to tackle global warming is a story of difficult, halting, partial steps forward. In the early negotiations around climate change the European Union (EU) and some northern European states argued for a binding commitment to reduce carbon dioxide (CO_2) emissions to 1990 levels by 2000. The USA led a group of states opposing targets and timetables while large developing countries like China and Brazil campaigned for industrialised countries to take on the initial burden of reducing emissions. In the event, agreement was reached in the shape of the United Nations (UN) Framework Convention on Climate Change (FCCC), signed at the 1992 UN Conference on Environment and Development, the so-called 'Earth Summit'. However, what many perceived as the weakness of the FCCC – vague commitments to avoid 'dangerous climate change' and to stabilise emissions of CO_2 at 1990 levels – led advocates of a more stringent agreement to push for a new agreement. The result was the Kyoto Protocol agreed in Japan in 1997 (Figure 4.1). This introduced the first targets and timetables for reducing greenhouse gas emissions, with different states agreeing to different commitments:

- The Annex 1 group of industrialised countries and countries in transition from communism agreed to an average 5.1 per cent reduction from 1990 levels of emissions of CO_2 equivalents, to be achieved by 2012.

- Among the Annex 1 group, commitments varied from an 8 per cent cut by the EU to a 10 per cent increase on 1990 levels for Iceland.

- Developing countries were exempt from any binding commitments.

The Kyoto Protocol remains highly controversial. Some environmental campaigners and many scientists dismissed the targets as inadequate while powerful groups in the USA and elsewhere claimed they were too costly. Others saw Kyoto as a useful first step towards more significant cuts in the future. Contrary to the expectations of some commentators, the protocol entered into force in 2005 but without participation of the USA and with no emissions reduction commitments from the largest developing countries. Australia did not ratify the protocol until 2007.

Activity 4.1

Reflecting on what you have learned of international climate negotiations so far on the course, can you use the course themes to identify some preliminary reasons as to why agreement has proved difficult to achieve?

You might pick out a number of issues. Three stand out for me. The first relates to international political divisions and inequality (*course theme 2*). Collective agreement at the international level is necessary because the world consists of numerous, and very different, independent states. In

Figure 4.1
The Kyoto climate
conference of 1997

Section 2.2 I will consider why this presents difficulties. Second, one of the problems of international climate change negotiations is that of time: agreement requires politicians today to undertake actions which may only deliver benefits far in the future (*course theme 5*). Part of the criticism of Kyoto by the USA resides in a scepticism about whether the agreement will deliver enough future benefits to justify the costs today. Third, the reluctance of developing countries to undertake binding cuts in greenhouse gas emissions lies in part in contestation over the relationship between sustainability and development (*course theme 4*). Some of these ideas will be developed further in what follows.

2.1 Public goods

My starting point for beginning to think systematically about the politics of climate change revolves around the idea of public goods. Public goods benefit everyone. Once a public good is created it is impossible to prevent anyone from benefiting from it. Furthermore, one person's consumption of a public good does not diminish what is left for others. Examples of public goods include street lighting, a police force and public radio. The provision of many environmental services and resources may have the character of public goods. A slightly more technical way of putting this, and the classic definition of **public goods**,

A **public good** is one that is non-excludable, non-rival and jointly supplied.

is to say that they are those goods and services which are *non-excludable* and *non-rival*, and additionally, which are *jointly supplied*. In reality, many public goods do not perfectly fit this neat definition.

Let me unpack this rather technical definition in terms of climate change. A stable climate is in many respects a pure public good. First, maintaining a stable climate by mitigating greenhouse gas emissions would provide something which is available to everyone. No one can be excluded from benefiting from a stable climate, so the good is said to be *non-excludable*. Second, consumption of a stable climate is *non-rival*, that is, when one person or nation benefits from a stable climate this does not reduce the benefits to others. Finally, the supply of a stable climate is a joint endeavour. It cannot be provided by one person or state alone, but is *jointly supplied*. Climate change poses special challenges to cooperation as it is a truly *global* public good. By the same token, damaging climate change can be defined as the reverse of this: a public bad. No one can be excluded from the effects of climate change.

Activity 4.2

Why might the provision of environmental public goods present difficult political problems?

There are perhaps two ways in which one might answer this. The first, more general, problem is that organising the provision of public goods requires collective decisions and thus some form of political process by which decisions are made. If all have to contribute, then some agreed basis for contributing is needed. Because public goods are non-excludable they cannot be priced in the market; if you cannot stop someone using something it is difficult to charge them for using it. Instead, environmental public goods are provided either by command and control policies by governments which ban undesirable activities such as pollution, or by market incentives such as taxes which seek to deter environmentally undesirable activities. Choosing between these different policy options is a political matter. Because climate change is a truly global environmental public good, these political challenges are cast at a very high level: that of international politics.

The second problem is that whatever mode of action is decided upon, provision of the public good has to counteract the temptation of individual actors to take the benefits of public goods provision without contributing to the supply. This is the problem of **free-riding**. Because public goods are non-excludable, once they are provided they are available for all to use. So some actors may conclude that if the good is going to be provided anyway, and no one can be excluded from the benefits, then they would be better off not contributing to its supply. At

Free-riding is where an actor in a collective action problem seeks to benefit from the provision of a public good by others while avoiding bearing the costs of provision.

the international level the free-rider problem might take the form of states not undertaking actions to cut greenhouse gas emissions while continuing to enjoy the climatic benefits of the emissions cuts of others. The inherent danger is that all actors will reason in this way, thus undermining the provision of the public good. Supplying public goods in ways that overcome the problem of free-riding is a major political challenge.

To summarise, many environmental problems are politically difficult because they require us to overcome the collective action problems associated with the provision of public goods. Climate change is a highly complex example of a collective action problem. In the analysis that follows, I want to delve a bit deeper into the problems of international environmental cooperation by introducing you to a number of analytical models. Models form part of the intellectual toolkit for addressing other international environmental problems too. The first step is to look at a model known as the Prisoners' Dilemma.

2.2 The Prisoners' Dilemma

Chapter 1 introduced you to the parable of the tragedy of the commons, which shows how individual rational action can lead to common ruin; in seeking to maximise individual gain, individual herdsmen produced an outcome that harmed them all collectively. Preventing a tragedy of the commons is an example of a collective action problem because it cannot be achieved by individual action alone. The idea of the Prisoners' Dilemma shares the same emphasis on individual behaviour leading to a collective action problem as the tragedy of the commons, although it presents it in a different way. The Prisoners' Dilemma draws on a body of thought, used by many social scientists, known as game theory, which uses the metaphor of games in order to represent some of the patterns of interaction involved in collective action problems. The Prisoners' Dilemma is one kind of 'game'; indeed, it is a cornerstone model in debates on international cooperation. The dynamics which it describes allow us to understand some, although by no means all, of the important features of collective action situations. Game theory is also used by academics and other policy advisers to governments. For example, the Stern Review which was discussed in the previous chapter makes some use of game theory. In numerous other scenarios, from nuclear war planning to trade negotiations, game theory is part of the 'toolkit' both for policy makers and policy analysts. I will say a bit more about the usefulness, and limitations, of such models later on in this section before looking at some ways in which states might overcome Prisoners' Dilemma scenarios in Section 3.

In the original Prisoners' Dilemma story two people are arrested and accused of a crime. Unable to be sure that the other prisoner will not make a police statement, both seek a more lenient prison sentence by confessing to the crime. This ensures that rather than go free (if neither had made a statement) both are found guilty. Individual decisions thus lead to collective ruin. A number of assumptions about the prisoners and their situation need to be noted. The original model uses two individuals who can make rational choices about their situation. In applying it to the international political arena it is often assumed that states can also be analysed as unitary, rational actors. I stick with this idea for now, but will question it in Section 4. Other assumptions are that neither prisoner knows how the other will act: they cannot communicate with each other, and even if they could they cannot trust each other. The outcome for each player depends on the choices of the other as well as their own. However, because they cannot trust what the other says, they have to act in a situation where the other's choices are unknown. In these circumstances the two prisoners cannot agree a binding deal that both will keep quiet. The game also assumes that each will act in his or her own self-interest, not in their mutual interest; that is, they make their decisions thinking 'What is best for me?', not 'What is best for us both?' Finally, a feature of this version of the game is that it is a 'one-shot game'; it is only played once, so the prisoners cannot learn from each other's behaviour, nor punish each other if the other 'cheats' by breaking their promise not to make a statement. Similar assumptions are made when applying this game to international climate change politics although, as you will see later, all of these assumptions can be questioned.

So let's take a look at how this idea might be applied in a basic way to the efforts to fashion cooperative agreements to tackle climate change. Like the original dilemma, I'll assume there are just two actors or 'players': the USA and China. (In 2007 these countries were the two biggest emitters of greenhouse gases.) Games are often represented in a matrix, like that in Figure 4.2. Each player has a choice between two courses of action: to cooperate and cut CO_2 emissions, or to 'cheat' and not to cut them. As you can see, the game allows for four possible outcomes, based on the four possible combinations of cut/don't cut.

The matrix represents a hypothetical example, where all the costs and benefits involved in cutting or not cutting greenhouse gases can be rolled up into a single monetary value. The numbers in the matrix – known as pay-offs – serve this purpose and represent hundreds of billions of US dollars. Of course, things aren't this simple in real life, but note that analysts often do make these kind of calculations. For this illustration, I have used the number 5 in the matrix to represent the idea that if both states cooperate and cut CO_2, then each will gain

US\$500 billion from preventing damaging climate change. If, however, both states do not cut CO_2 emissions they may gain in the short term (from higher economic growth, say), but eventually will face larger costs of dealing with unchecked climate change. I have used the figure of –1 (US\$–100 billion) to represent these net losses. If one state acts to cut CO_2 but the other state does not, then the first state will suffer in two ways: it will have expended resources to tackle climate change yet, because the other state has not acted, it will still have to face costs from increased climate change. I have used the figure of –3 in the matrix (US\$–300 billion) to represent this circumstance. Finally, if a state does not cut CO_2 emissions and the other does it will gain in two ways: it will not face any costs from making emissions reductions (and thus gain from higher economic growth as a result), and it will also benefit from the emission reductions of the other state in slowing the pace of climate change. I use the figure of 8 (US\$800 billion) to represent these gains.

In reading a matrix, the convention is that the first number in any cell refers to the gains or losses of the player on the rows (in this case China) and the second to the player on the columns (in this case the USA).

		USA	
		Cut CO_2	Don't cut CO_2
China	Cut CO_2	5, 5	–3, 8
	Don't cut CO_2	8, –3	–1, –1

Figure 4.2
A game theory matrix representing the choices available to the USA and China over whether to cut carbon dioxide emissions

Numbers represent net gains (or losses) as hundreds of billions of US dollars.

To work out the likely outcome of this game, start by putting yourself in the place of one player and thinking about how that player would act. Let's first consider China's position. China knows that the USA has two choices – cut CO_2 and don't cut CO_2 – and must decide what its best response is in either case. If the USA chose to cut emissions, China would gain 5 (first number in the upper left cell) for also cutting emissions, or 8 for not cutting emissions (first number in the bottom left cell). So under these circumstances China's best response would be to not cut emissions as 8 is a higher pay-off than 5. If on the other hand the USA chose not to cut emissions, China would receive –3 for cutting emissions, or –1 for not cutting emissions. Again, China's best response would be to not cut emissions as –1 is a less severe loss than –3. So whichever course of action the USA takes, China will be better off not cutting emissions. In the game depicted here, the gains are symmetrical, so the USA would undergo exactly the same reasoning as China and conclude that whatever China chooses to do, the USA too would be best off not cutting emissions. If both follow through on this reasoning, neither country will cut emissions.

Pause for a moment and consider the combinations of pay-offs in each cell. If each player acts in its own individual self-interest, then neither will cut emissions, climate change is not mitigated and both suffer –1 as a result, giving a joint pay-off of –2. But contrast this with the upper left hand cell where both players cut CO_2 emissions: here each gains 5, giving a joint pay-off of 10. In the other two cells (top right and bottom left) one player gains 8 and the other –3 giving a joint pay-off of 5. These combinations of pay-offs reveal that the best collective outcome is if both players cut CO_2. Economists call this the **social optimum** (see Chapter 3). However, and as shown, the likely outcome is that neither will cut CO_2 emissions and the social optimum will not be achieved.

Social optimum in a collective action game occurs when the sum total of the players' pay-offs is maximised.

But if players know this, why don't they choose to cut CO_2? The answer lies in the assumptions of the Prisoners' Dilemma. Neither player can be certain what the other will do. Even if the other says they are going to cut CO_2 they may 'cheat'. So if a player cuts CO_2 emissions it runs the risk that the other will not, leaving it with –3 as a result. Players are tempted to cheat because they want to maximise their own individual gains, not joint gains. Pursuit of individual self-interest thus leads neither actor to cut CO_2 emissions.

What is most important to note is not the actual numbers used here, which are hypothetical, but instead to note the central dynamic that is explained. In situations which have a similar structure to a Prisoners' Dilemma (that is the net gains and losses are distributed in a similar way), rational pursuit of individual gains results in an outcome which is collectively irrational. The next time you hear an environmentalist declaiming that the world has 'gone mad', using up the Earth's resources with no thought to what would be good for the world as a whole, you might think of this powerful and very influential explanation of what might be happening.

Activity 4.3

Pause here and go back through the explanation of the matrix in Figure 4.2 and the likely outcome to ensure that you understand the reasoning in this explanation. Consider whether this suggests some real features of the climate change problem.

2.3 Models and metaphors

Before reading on, you might like to return to the treatment of models in Chapter 2, Section 3.2

The Prisoners' Dilemma is a theoretical model, and you need to be aware of some of the potential uses and misuses of models as analytical tools. Indeed, it is in questioning the applicability of some of the assumptions on which such models are based that you might begin to arrive at a more optimistic view of the potential for cooperation over climate change.

Models are used in many different ways in the social and natural sciences to reduce the complexity of a situation in order to highlight particular features of the world around us. They are not, nor are they intended to be, exact descriptions of reality. They are rough, sometimes very rough, stylised representations. Models are sometimes also referred to as metaphors. The idea of a 'game' in this context is a metaphor for a particular kind of interaction. A different way that you might imagine this is to think of the difference between meeting a person compared to seeing a photograph. Now move from the photograph to seeing a portrait painting, to a caricature or cartoon of a person. At each stage you become more distant from the reality and focus on fewer features. By doing this, a caricature can convey some of the important distinctive features of the person but it is not an exact replication of them. In some ways analytical models are like that: they are designed to focus on particular aspects of a situation, particular actors and relationships between them.

In her influential book, *Governing the Commons*, Elinor Ostrom warned against taking 'models as metaphors' too literally and arriving at overly pessimistic conclusions about the chances for cooperation. Speaking of the Prisoners' Dilemma Ostrom noted:

> What makes these models so interesting and so powerful is that they capture important aspects of many different problems that occur in diverse settings in all parts of the world. What makes these models so dangerous – when they are used metaphorically as the foundation for policy – is that the constraints that are assumed to be fixed for the purpose of analysis are taken on faith as being fixed in empirical settings
>
> (Ostrom, 1990, p. 6)

Models are useful ways to convey important parts of the problem at hand. Rather than a world gone mad, models can help us to realise that the failure to cooperate over climate change may lie in quite reasoned, if self-interested, calculations by states. However, in order to make these simplified pictures of reality, modellers have to make a series of assumptions, and it is important that such assumptions are made explicit. In the discussion above I made three assumptions: that players do not know how each other will act before having to choose their course of action; that players will act in their self-interest; and that the game is only played once. I now wish to explore these assumptions in the context of climate change.

First, in the original Prisoners' Dilemma the inability to know what the other will do is enforced by the separation of the prisoners into different cells. In today's world of international politics an absolute lack of communication between states would be abnormal. In the case of China and the USA, both countries exchange statements directly with one another, and more indirectly through policy announcements and the media. However, by itself, the information about the other's actions cannot ensure cooperation as even if players know they can gain by cooperating and even if each were to promise to cooperate, without a means of ensuring that players will do as they say, each player will still be tempted to 'cheat'. So if the USA has no means of ensuring that China will cooperate it will always reckon on the possibility that China may cheat; and China will reason in a similar way.

Second, we have the assumption that the players act in their own individual self-interest rather than the collective or common good. If they did the latter, then both players would seek to achieve the social optimum. However, because they are concerned more with their own gains than collective gains, they fail to cooperate. However, you might like to pause and consider whether you think this is accurate; the political rhetoric commonly used by political leaders often speaks both of national self-interests and of common interests. Indeed, in many instances it amounts to more than rhetoric since states are sometimes prepared to act in the common interest, for instance in responding to catastrophes. Acting to protect future generations from disaster may reflect an altruistic motive as well as self-interest. For most of the rest of this chapter I will continue with the idea that self-interest is at least the dominant, if not the only, motive behind states' actions, although in Section 4.1 I do address the question of what determines states' national self-interest.

Chapter 6 considers some of the ethical issues involved in policy making for the future

Finally, the fact that the game is only played once becomes an important limitation on this model. As you know, climate change negotiations have taken place over many years, making it possible for states to learn something about the past behaviour of others. 'Repeated plays' of a Prisoners' Dilemma game can change the pessimistic conclusion of the one-shot game played above. This makes time, or the longevity of the interaction, an important aspect of the analysis. I will return to the question of time in Section 3.

Figure 4.3

An industrial plant in China and a freeway in the USA. Both countries will face short-term economic costs in cutting carbon dioxide emissions

Activity 4.4

Consider the following quotations. China's 2007 National Climate Change Plan argued that:

> developed countries should take the lead in reducing greenhouse gas emissions as well as providing financial and technical support to developing countries. The first and overriding priorities of developing countries are sustainable development and poverty eradication. The extent to which developing countries will effectively implement their commitments under the [FCCC] Convention will depend on the effective implementation by developed countries of their basic commitments.
>
> (People's Republic of China, 2007, p. 24)

By comparison, George W. Bush argued in 2001:

> Our country, the United States is the world's largest emitter of manmade greenhouse gases. We account for almost 20 percent of the world's manmade greenhouse gas emissions ... We recognise the responsibility to reduce our emissions. We also recognise the other part of the story – that the rest of the world emits 80 percent of all greenhouse gases. And many of those emissions come from developing countries.
>
> This is a challenge that requires a 100 percent effort; ours, and the rest of the world's. The world's second-largest emitter of greenhouse gases is China. Yet, China was entirely exempted from the requirements of the Kyoto Protocol.
>
> (White House, 2001)

How far, do you think, the quotations fit with the assumptions of the Prisoners' Dilemma explanation of the impasse in climate change negotiations?

The Prisoners' Dilemma draws our attention to some aspects of these two statements. The key one is that neither is prepared to act unless the other does so too. This is a major stumbling block. There are also allusions to the national interest in China's statement about priorities of development. With respect to the public goods discussion we see a recognition from the USA that supply of public goods is a joint endeavour. However, other features and motivations not captured by the model are also alluded to. Bush talks of 'responsibility' while China's statement about the need for developed countries to take action first is based on the principle of equity.

2.4 The constraints of the international system

Collective action problems like that depicted in the Prisoners' Dilemma can occur in many different situations such as households, communities, nationally and internationally. A variety of ways of tackling such problems can be found. Within a country attempts might be made to address free-riding by enforcing tax laws so that tax payers contribute to the supply of the public good. Something like this idea lies behind the discussion of the pricing of carbon in Chapter 3. However, and as Ostrom notes, typically most of the available solutions require some kind of agency which has the ability to regulate actors' behaviour and impose sanctions on those who try to free-ride (1990, p. 14). For problems located within established politically-governed communities such action is normally supplied by the state, a state-backed local authority, or by some other agreed means of upholding collective decisions. Yet in my version of the Prisoners' Dilemma applied to international cooperation, there is no such actor above the contending parties to play this role.

Here, crucially, you have arrived at a fundamental aspect underlying the discussion so far. Solutions to environmental problems which are within a particular state can in principle be addressed by the government of a state formulating and imposing laws, using its authority, judicial system and police force to directly ban certain kinds of activities, to create incentives such as carbon taxes, or use ideology, persuasion and education to alter behaviour. Environmental problems which are international cannot be addressed as easily in this way. The political division of the world into sovereign states means that there is no state-like authority or 'world government' able to force states to act in a certain way. Indeed, it is for this reason that international relations scholars often characterise the international system as an **anarchy**: a system in which political authority is dispersed among the 192 states of the world and in which the coercive force needed to uphold collective decisions is also dispersed among these states. It is important to note that used in this way, the term anarchy does not equate to chaos or total disorder. Rather, it means that in formal political and legal terms, relations between states are not governed by a single over-arching authority. Whereas within states, actors (whether individual citizens, corporations or interest groups) are subject to the laws of the state, in relations between states there is no unified system of government.

Anarchy is the dispersal of political authority and of the coercive means to uphold collective decisions. Internationally this equates to the absence of a 'world government'.

For international environmental problems, this absence of a state-like actor or 'world government' at the global level lies at the heart of many difficulties in agreeing international environmental policy; solutions which might work within states may not easily apply internationally. Indeed, for international environmental problems, as well as for many other issues, anarchy means that states have to find other ways to try to arrive at solutions to collective action problems. They can do this by a variety of means: by trying to persuade each other to act in certain ways, or by trying to coerce each other whether by using financial or other incentives or, sometimes, force. For many international collective action problems, states seek to formulate agreements and sometimes to create international organisations. Agreements like the Kyoto Protocol, and organisations like the UN, are important examples, but note that they are made necessary because of anarchy, because collective action problems cannot be solved by the actions of any single state alone.

However, these thoughts imply some important constraints on what can be done, in particular the principle of **state sovereignty**. This principle is an important one in international law. It holds that states have the exclusive right to determine their own domestic and foreign policies. The principle of state sovereignty means that states do not have to sign up to an agreement to cooperate if they do not want to, can fail to implement an agreement they have signed or can leave agreements they no longer wish to support. This notion is a crucial one underlying the actions of China and the USA in the model used above: sovereignty gives states the right to choose whether to cooperate or not. Given this context the next section seeks to look at ways in which states might fashion cooperative agreements.

State sovereignty is the principle that an individual state has the exclusive right to determine its domestic and foreign policies.

3 Towards cooperation?

The global commons – the oceans, the atmosphere, outer space – belong to all the world's people. So, ruling out war, the only way to govern their use is through international agreements ... [W]hen considering a treaty, the questions we must ask ourselves are: do the costs outweigh the benefits? Does signing a treaty amount to a net loss or a net gain in terms of our national interests?

Frank E. Loy, Under Secretary for Global Affairs, US Department of State and head of the US delegation to the FCCC negotiations in The Hague, 2000 (cited in Barrett, 2003, p. 195)

By this stage you might be thinking that the chances of finding a cooperative solution to international environmental problems like climate change will always evade us, especially if national interests continue to dominate in the way indicated by Frank Loy in the above quotation. The troubled history of the Kyoto Protocol gives some reason to support this view, but there are reasons for optimism. Ostrom shows that in some rural communities groups and individuals can find cooperative solutions to collective problems of natural resource management. And in international environmental politics, despite the obstacles, there have been numerous international environmental

You will analyse the problem of ozone depletion in Book 2, Chapter 7

agreements of varying scope, size and effectiveness. Some are limited, amounting to agreements between just two states on specific issues. Others, such as the Montreal Protocol on protecting the ozone layer, are nearly global in scope. On one estimate by 2000 the number of multilateral environment treaties (that is, involving three or more states) in force or likely to enter into force was around 300, not including several hundred EU directives and hundreds of bilateral agreements. Indeed, as Figure 4.4 makes clear, the pace of multilateral environment treaty-making has accelerated. Only four such treaties had been agreed by 1945 (Barrett, 2003, p. 135).

Figure 4.4

The number of multilateral environmental treaties increased significantly between 1945 and 2000 (Source: Barrett, 2003, p. 135)

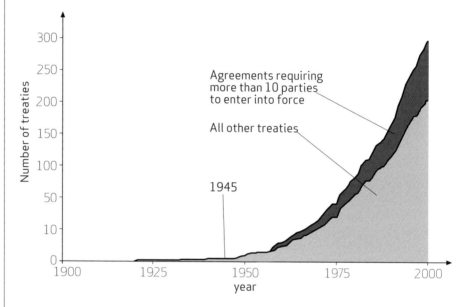

So despite the apparent pessimism of the Prisoners' Dilemma, and although not all international agreements are effective in achieving their aims, international cooperation can happen. In this section I want to think more positively about how cooperation arises and, more specifically, consider what makes agreement more or less likely. The conclusion I come to is that although international cooperation over climate change may be possible it nevertheless remains difficult.

3.1 Positive-sum games

You have seen that states will only enter agreements if it is in their interests and that despite the increase in the number of multilateral environmental agreements there is no external body that can enforce agreements. Consequently, any agreements made between states must be self-enforcing. For this to be so, environmental treaties have to be attractive to states by offering net gains, either immediately or in the future; and they have to include provisions which dissuade states from withdrawing from, failing to implement or cheating on, the agreement (Barrett, 2003).

The presentation above of the Prisoners' Dilemma as a one-shot game emphasises the temptations for states to cheat, which has the effect of undermining the incentive to cooperate. However, as I also noted, negotiations over climate change are not one-off events; they will run indefinitely into the future. This can have significant implications for cooperation. By looking into the future, the pay-offs from different courses of action may alter. In particular, the benefits of mitigating climate change are likely to increase and the prospect of 'repeated plays' of the game may lead states to re-evaluate the temptation to cheat. States will know that if they cheat it is likely that in the next 'round' of the game the other player will also cheat. Indeed, over time states may be able to observe this happening by monitoring each others' behaviour. But if both continually cheat, each player faces the prospect of receiving (to use the numbers from Figure 4.2) –1 again and again into the future. This stands in comparison to the prospect of each receiving 5 from each round of play if both states cooperate. In this circumstance the pay-offs from cheating (–1 multiplied into the future) start to look much less attractive than those from cooperation (5 multiplied into the future). And each knows that even if they have a temptation to cheat in one round (and thus get a one-off payment of 8) they will then be 'punished' by the other player cheating in subsequent rounds. In these circumstances, it is possible that the game will change from one in which states have an incentive to cheat, to one in which states would individually (as well as collectively) be better off if they could find a way to cooperate. In short, the longer the game is played, the stronger are the incentives to cooperate.

You can see that the time dimension is crucial here. While there may be positive gains from cooperating to mitigate climate change, these may only be realised over a lengthy time period and at different rates for different countries. Furthermore, for states to cooperate they must be persuaded that the gains that will be realised in the future outweigh temptations to cheat in the short term.

In what follows, I assume that states will judge that they will be better off individually by cooperating. Indeed, as is known from a variety of collective action problems, there are many situations in which states can be better off both individually and collectively if they cooperate than if they do not. So even if states act self-interestedly, they may still gain from cooperation. Such situations, where the total net gains from cooperation (that is, the sum of all gains minus losses for all participants) are positive, are known as **positive-sum games**. It is worth noting here that while this may entail all players making gains, these

A **positive-sum game** is one where the total net gains – those of all participants added together – are positive.

gains may not be evenly distributed; some may gain more than others. Furthermore, an interaction is still a positive-sum game even if some gain and others lose, so long as the total gains outweigh the total losses. This may be depicted diagrammatically as in Figure 4.5.

Figure 4.5

Cooperation as a positive-sum game: a hypothetical interaction between the USA and China over climate change cooperation (Source: adapted from Gruber, 2000, p. 30)

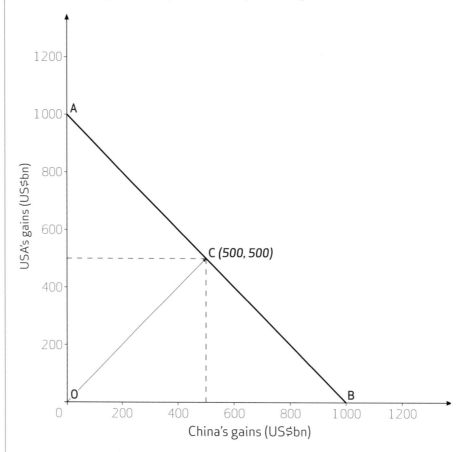

As with the Prisoners' Dilemma, this diagram represents a hypothetical interaction between the USA and China over agreement to cut CO_2 emissions. Here the vertical axis represents the potential net gains to the USA; the horizontal axis represents the potential net gains for China. I am simplifying things by assuming gains and losses can be represented by single monetary values (billions of US dollars). On the diagram point O represents the origin, namely the situation before the game begins. I assume that through cooperation the total potential gains for China and USA combined amount to US$1000 billion. So by cooperating – cutting CO_2 and mitigating global warming – positive gains may be realised. As with the Prisoners' Dilemma, the figures are for illustrative purposes only. The line AB on the diagram represents the range of possible divisions of these total gains: from the USA gaining all US$1000 billion and China receiving nothing (point A) to the USA receiving nothing and China US$1000 billion (point B).

The first thing to note is that even if net gains are realised only in the future, so long as those future gains are valued enough by today's states, then there is an incentive to cooperate. When the available gains are divided equally, each receive US$500 billion, putting the parties at point C. In order to realise these gains, the parties must come to a shared agreement on actions (what cooperation will entail) and mechanisms to ensure that each fulfils its obligations. Because states cannot ensure that treaty obligations are upheld agreement may never be reached, or states may only commit themselves to weak agreements. In weak agreements the costs and benefits of different courses of action are lower, although so too is the environmental effectiveness of the agreement. Stronger treaty design can help alleviate this situation. Treaties may stipulate actions to be undertaken, reporting requirements, and monitoring. In order to encourage participation and to ensure each abides by any negotiated agreement treaties may need to include 'carrots' (incentives to encourage cooperation, such as financial assistance) and 'sticks' (penalties for 'cheating') (Barrett, 2003). Indeed many treaties create mechanisms to ensure that parties fulfil their obligations; some, like the Montreal Protocol on ozone protection, even provide for trade sanctions.

The Kyoto Protocol has struggled to fashion a cooperative outcome partly because the joint gains from cooperation are not as clear cut as Figure 4.5 suggests, but also because it has devised only very weak mechanisms to reassure parties that all will implement the agreement (Barrett, 2003). Indeed, during the Kyoto negotiations there was a weakening of the monitoring requirements on the parties and a failure to agree sanctions against Annex 1 countries that failed to meet their targets. If a post-Kyoto agreement is to be effective in environmental terms it will need to meet the twin challenges of enticing participation and deterring cheating.

3.2 Side payments

The example used so far assumes that states have an incentive to cooperate. But the world is not only politically divided, it is also highly unequal. With climate change this is reflected in terms of the highly differentiated costs of action and inaction. Some states might not perceive that they have an incentive to undertake costly measures to mitigate climate change. Can incentives be devised to bring reluctant parties into an agreement?

I noted above that one can still have a positive-sum game, even if one side gains while the other loses, so long as the total net gains are positive. Is it possible to reach a cooperative agreement in this situation? In fact, in the negotiations for the Kyoto Protocol, while parties such as the EU were convinced that they would benefit from an agreement (the EU evaluated that future gains from greenhouse gas emissions reductions were potentially large and so was very keen on completing the Kyoto process), others such as Russia were less enthusiastic. As a legacy of the communist era, Russia had a technologically backward industrial sector that was highly reliant on inefficient use of fossil fuels for energy, so the short-term costs of cutting emissions were potentially high. In addition, some prognoses point to potential benefits (in the short term at least) to Russia from a warming climate; for instance, increasing outputs from agriculture and forestry. And yet following lengthy discussions with the EU, Russia was eventually persuaded to ratify the Kyoto Protocol. We can think through this problem using a stylised representation of the situation as given in Figure 4.6.

Figure 4.6

Side payments: a hypothetical interaction between the EU and Russia over climate change cooperation (Source: based on Sanchez, 2004)

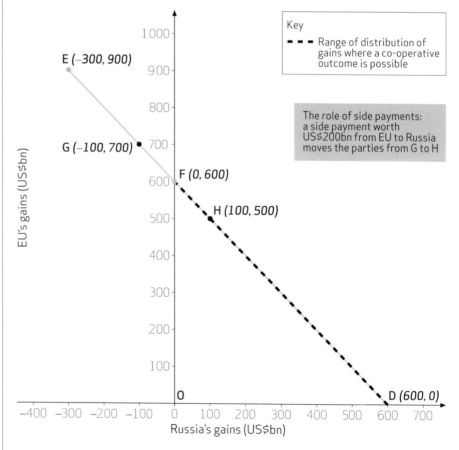

Here the range of possible outcomes is given by the line DE. You will notice that on this diagram the horizontal axis extends to the left, below zero, indicating the possibility of losses (negative gains) for Russia. Total possible joint gains are US$600 billion. However, let's assume that the agreement on the table would result in the EU gaining US$700 billion while Russia loses US$100 billion, given by point G.

Why is this still a positive-sum interaction? The answer is that positive total gains are available: 700–100 = 600. It's just that all gains go to the EU! What would Russia do? Clearly, no agreement is better than US$–100 billion so Russia would refuse to cooperate and the EU would lose all its potential gains. However, if the EU were to make a payment to Russia, it might persuade Russia to cooperate. In Figure 4.6 this would be depicted as a movement from the left hand side, where there is no scope for agreement, to the right hand side, where both may gain and agreement is possible. Of course, the EU will only offer a payment that is smaller than its expected total gains. So if the EU made a payment to Russia of US$200 billion, this would give the EU US$500 billion and Russia US$100 billion (point H). Such payments might take the form of trade or investment deals. Or they might take the form of technology transfer to address climate change. Such **side payments** – incentives or 'carrots' to achieve mutual gains – can be important in persuading reluctant parties to join international cooperative arrangements. However, the scale of side payments necessary to persuade reluctant parties like the USA, China and India to implement emissions reductions make the post-Kyoto era even more problematic.

A **side payment** is an arrangement in which one party offers an incentive to another in order to reach a cooperative agreement.

3.3 Power and threat points

Finally, let us assume that an agreement which delivers positive gains to both parties is possible. What then determines how the benefits of agreement are distributed between the parties? I have argued already that all parties have to gain something for both to participate. In the example above between the USA and China I simply assumed that benefits would be evenly shared (point C on Figure 4.5). In fact, it is often not so clear where on the line AB the division will occur. The key to this question, and what lies behind much international bargaining around treaty formation, is the power that different states have in negotiations. A fundamental aspect of states' negotiating strength is determined by their ability to walk away from an agreement. When deciding whether to walk away from an agreement states consider what they can achieve in the absence of cooperation.

In Figure 4.7 I give a hypothetical example to show how the ability of a state to walk away from an agreement has an impact on the balance of gains reached. In this scenario the USA, by enacting adaptation policies

Figure 4.7
Threat points: a
hypothetical
interaction between the
EU and the USA over
climate change
(Source: based on
Sanchez, 2004)

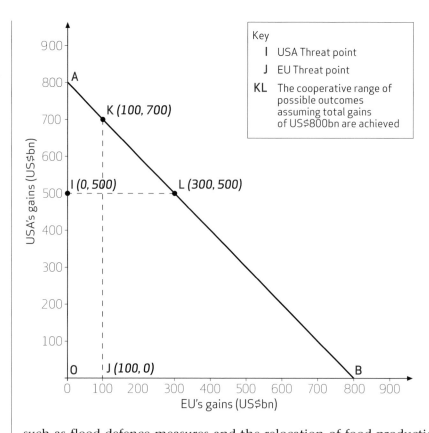

A **threat point** or
fallback position is how
a party to a negotiation
will fare if they walk away
from an agreement.

such as flood defence measures and the relocation of food production, could achieve gains of US$500 billion without cooperation to mitigate climate change (point I). The EU by contrast, which calculates that it will suffer more from climate change, could only gain US$100 billion by acting unilaterally (point J). So both the USA and the EU have what is called a **threat point** or **fallback position**: what a state can gain in the absence of cooperation. Threat points have a fundamental importance in negotiations and over who is in the stronger position. States with very strong threat points may gain a lot (or suffer the least) without cooperation. Such states are sometimes called 'veto states' because they can walk away from negotiations without suffering (Chasek et al., 2006).

Let us see how threat points help us to narrow the range of possible outcomes. The total available gains are US$800 billion. Assuming cooperation takes place, the parties will end up somewhere on line AB, which shows all the possible divisions of these gains. However, without cooperation the USA will be at point I and will not cooperate unless the division of gains on line AB give it more than the US$500 billion it can receive from acting alone. That is, it will only cooperate if the division of gains is at point L or higher, that is between points A and L. The EU will not agree to cooperate unless it receives more than the US$100 billion it can receive from acting alone, that is between points K and B. So cooperation will happen only if the division of gains lies between point K where the EU gains US$100 billion and the USA US$700 billion, and point L where the USA gains US$500 billion and the EU US$300 billion.

Therefore, the USA is in a much stronger bargaining position than the EU because it can gain more by acting alone than the EU. The USA thus has negotiating power which it can use to extract concessions from the EU. Although Figure 4.7 is hypothetical, in the actual negotiations leading up to Kyoto the USA's use of its threat point – to not sign an agreement – enabled it to negotiate lower commitments on greenhouse gas emissions reductions than those sought by, among others, the EU. The EU's calculation was that the benefits of not agreeing were lower than agreeing to a weaker deal, which is eventually what happened. So the USA had the stronger threat point.

Many factors lie behind a strong threat point. In the case of the USA, the high costs of mitigating climate change due to its profligate use of energy, and its ability, due to its immense wealth, to adapt to some of the negative effects of climate change, played a role in its ability to exert its power in negotiations. You will note that, as used here, the notion of power is akin to the idea of power as resources introduced in Chapter 1. The USA's power is, in part, based on its ability to mobilise resources to deal with climate change in the absence of cooperation. Others are not so fortunate, including the EU but even more so the low lying island states whose very existence is threatened by the exercise of such veto power. In climate change negotiations the need to persuade important and powerful emitters such as the USA, China, India and others not to walk away will remain a key constraint on possible outcomes.

3.4 The story so far

Let me sum up the arguments so far. The problem of cooperation over environmental issues – of achieving the supply of public goods that environmental cooperation offers – has a particularly difficult character at the international level. The political division of the world into sovereign states makes cooperation over global challenges like climate change difficult. Nevertheless, states have on many occasions found ways around these problems: they have negotiated agreements which deliver positive benefits to the parties; they have developed mechanisms to monitor agreements and to punish those who cheat; and they have sometimes been able to persuade reluctant parties to participate. With climate change, however, the difficulties of all of these issues mean that agreements such as the FCCC and Kyoto Protocol have been extremely limited in their effectiveness. Whether this reflects a persistent constraint to more effective policies or a short-term obstacle that can be overcome remains to be seen. Efforts to convince all parties that gains can be realised from cooperation are complicated by the uncertainties of the costs of action and inaction and the scale of the side payments which might be necessary to persuade reluctant parties to participate. In addition, the power of key states to walk away from agreement serves to limit what others can achieve. While not impossible, therefore, the collective action problem of climate change continues to pose real obstacles to international cooperation. However, the politics of climate change are fluid and in the next section I want to look at some of the changing factors which underlie negotiations at the international level.

4   Behind and beyond the games

My discussion so far has focused on interactions between states at a fairly abstract level in order to illuminate the problem of international cooperation on climate change and some of the challenges states face in reaching international agreements on the issue. However, the politics of climate change are not neatly confined to competing states; they permeate myriad interconnected levels of social life, from the international level down to national, community, household and even individual levels. In this section I want to explore some of the ways in which you can think about the interconnections between some of these different arenas. To do this I will focus on the interaction between the inter-state level and other levels of political action which, while not offering a comprehensive account, does capture some of the key ways in which climate change politics play out over different levels of political action. Figure 4.8 gives a summary of the processes I will discuss.

Figure 4.8

Linkages between intergovernmental and domestic/non-state political processes

A: *Formation of state preferences.* State preferences reflect the dominant influence of powerful social groups, mediated through forms of representation in the state (Moravcsik, 1997). In turn, domestic politcal constraints have a 'backwards influence' on what states will agree to internationally (see Barrett, 2003: p148).

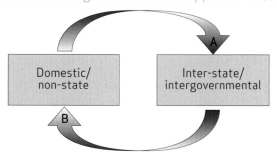

B: *Politics of ratification, implementation and agendas.* International agreements are transmitted back into domestic politics through processes of national level ratification and implementation in national and sub-national laws and regulations. Implementation has the potential to create collective action problems within countries. National level debates on international negotiations inform and shape domestic political agendas, debates, lobbying and campaigning. Knowledge generated through international processes such as the IPCC will help to shape actors' interests, as will national and local knowledge on the likely costs and impacts of climate change.

4.1 The politics of state preferences

The discussion here relates to arrow A in Figure 4.8. I shall start by unpicking the underlying notion used so far that states can be viewed as unitary actors which have known and relatively fixed definitions of their 'national interest'. In Sections 2 and 3 I presumed that states seek to maximise their interests defined in terms of economic gain. However, the idea of a unitary state pursuing a clear national interest may be challenged in two respects.

First, states may pursue very different aims. As was noted in Chapter 1, states are composed of different ministries and bureaucracies, each of which has different policy objectives, some of which may conflict with each other. Furthermore, environmental campaigners and other analysts argue that even if there are economic costs of action, the Earth and its ecosystems are too important for us to allow climate change to continue. And while there may not be much evidence so far that states are prepared to put 'the good of the environment' or even 'the common good of humanity' ahead of national economic interests, there is at least an arena of contestation as to what any particular government should be seeking to achieve internationally. Along the same lines, an alternative (and perhaps more likely) possibility is that states might put national security above other considerations. This is certainly a more traditional view of international relations and, indeed, issues of security have come to feature prominently in debates about climate change. Even if mitigation is economically costly, states may nonetheless agree to mitigation strategies if they address concerns about security. As David Victor puts it, the prospect of abrupt and catastrophic climate change is 'one of the few ways that risks of climate change could become evaluated in ways that are akin to traditional security threats, and nearly every society has shown that it is willing to spend something (often much) to avert even low-probability threats that could have large catastrophic consequences' (Victor, 2006, p. 94). Chapter 5 asks how our view of climate change might be reshaped by categorising it as a 'security threat'.

A second way in which you might question the notion of the national interest used so far is that even if monetary gains and losses are dominant in states' decision making, the sheer complexity of climate change, differing interests within states and differences between the winners and losers of any mitigation strategies mean that 'maximising economic gain' is not itself a simple notion. Here the unequal impacts of climate change and of mitigation draw attention to the complexities of interests involved and to the contested claims about whether mitigation is 'worth it' or not. As was argued in Chapter 3, this is not just a technical question of how to estimate the costs and benefits of different policies; it is also one in which different ethical judgements (for example, about the value to be placed on future gains), as well as different social interests (which policies benefit which groups), play a part. In both the debate over what general aim to pursue (economic gain, security or environmental sustainability) and the contests about defining what these aims entail, any simple notion of 'the national interest' starts to look a bit suspect.

These considerations can be put in a slightly more theoretical way. Andrew Moravcsik has argued that although the kind of analysis presented in Sections 2 and 3 is important, we also need to undertake a prior stage of analysis to arrive at an understanding of what determines **state preferences**, where preferences refer to what states seek to achieve at the international level (Moravcsik, 1997). States should be viewed, according to Moravcsik, not as synonymous with a society or a country, but as institutions of government over a society. Viewed this way, the international politics of climate change rests on the relationship of states to their society and the individuals, groups and ideas which compose it. In any society, according to Moravcsik, opposing interests and values mean that states can only ever reflect the preferences of a sub-set of the different competing interests rather than society as a whole. Furthermore, competition between these interests is often highly unequal due to the differential power of social groups and their access to the corridors of power. Unequal political competition is further shaped by the particular institutions through which interests are represented in government. A fuller picture of international politics therefore requires that we understand the competitive social interests which seek to influence different states' preferences, the exercise of social power, influence and representation, as well as the political and institutional processes which mediate how dominant interests may be represented in state policy.

As you saw in Chapter 2, the condemnation of US President George W. Bush's administration (2001–09) as being in thrall to oil interests, the funding of climate deniers by companies such as ExxonMobil, as well as the attempts by campaigners to expose such activities, are all instances of this kind of competitive political manoeuvring. The institutional structures of the US political system, such as electoral campaigns demanding vast sums of money and liberal laws permitting relatively open, albeit biased, debate and lobbying of Congress, all shape the ways such social interests are translated into US policy. Of course, not all states are liberal democracies and the variety of societal interests in different states, as well as the political systems which link those interests to state power, vary enormously. Yet even in highly repressive societies states 'represent' some selection of societal interests even if the mechanisms of representation are undemocratic. It is in the interaction of such uneven political forces across the world, and their transmission to the

---

State preferences are what states seek to achieve at the international level.

international level through state policy, which creates the patterns of interdependence around which states strategise and negotiate.

This broader social and political context within which states' policies are formed has another direct route into the intergovernmental negotiating arena. Scott Barrett has argued that not only do various political processes shape states' policies as they approach international negotiations, but the knowledge that any agreement would need to be ratified and implemented engages negotiators in 'backwards reasoning', limiting what they are likely to agree to (Barrett, 2003; Putnam, 1988). A state is unlikely to enter into an international agreement unless it believes that the agreement will be ratified domestically. Indeed, states often act strategically to emphasise such constraints. This was most clearly illustrated during the Kyoto negotiations in 1997 when, as you saw in Chapter 1, the US Senate passed, by 95 votes to nil, the Byrd–Hagel resolution stating that the Senate would not ratify any agreement on binding greenhouse gas emission cuts which did not include targets for developing countries, in particular China and India. The Byrd–Hagel resolution acted as a domestic political constraint on the Clinton administration. The US negotiators at Kyoto used the resolution to argue for lower emissions reduction targets for the USA (Barrett, 2003, p. 148).

Activity 4.5

In thinking through the factors which determine states' preferences, what do you think underlies US concerns about the absence of greenhouse gas emission reduction targets for large developing countries?

Part of the concern is that emissions reductions will harm US business, lead to lower economic growth and cost jobs. If large developing countries do not have to undertake emission cuts, businesses located in these countries may gain a competitive advantage over US business. Furthermore, some political and economic actors in the USA may fear that giving large and important countries like China such a competitive advantage may pose a risk to the country's security. Such views are articulated domestically by groups concerned by these arguments: companies in fossil fuel-dependent sectors; labour unions representing workers whose jobs may be threatened; and political parties who fear lost votes if economic growth is slowed. Against them are groups and individuals who evaluate the situation differently: companies who would benefit from increased investment in energy efficiency and new technology, and environmental groups who argue that the costs of climate change will eventually outweigh all the negatives of emissions reductions. And all of these, and others including representatives of foreign governments and interest groups based outside of the USA, seek to influence the US government's policy on climate change. In such ways are interest group competition and political conflicts transmitted through the agency of states into international politics.

4.2 Ratification, implementation and agenda formation

Issues of ratification and implementation draw our attention to the second set of processes, enmeshing the international and domestic political arenas as indicated by arrow B in Figure 4.8. There are two dimensions I would like to highlight: the political-legal impact of international agreements, and the broader agenda-setting effects of international negotiations.

In Section 3, I discussed the implementation of international agreements in a very general way, concentrating on whether states might deliberately seek to avoid implementing a treaty in order to free-ride. However, it is necessary to disaggregate national implementation a bit further. The signature of an international agreement is just the first step to improving environmental quality. For a treaty to come into force, it normally has to be ratified by a specified number of signatories and this process typically requires ratification by a state's legislature. The ratification process, which provides a formal link between domestic and international politics, varies enormously, depending on a particular state's political system. In the USA a two-thirds majority in the Senate is needed, a requirement which means that only international treaties that have genuine cross-party support are accepted. In comparison, in the UK, a simple majority in Parliament (normally controlled by the governing party) is needed. In more authoritarian systems, where the executive has greater control over legislative acts, ratification may be more straightforward. To enter into force, the Kyoto Protocol required ratification from 55 countries that together accounted for 55 per cent of the 1990 CO_2 emissions of the Annex 1 countries. Given the non-ratification of Kyoto by the USA and (until 2007) Australia, the final entry into force of Kyoto came to rely on Russia. As you have seen, considerable effort was expended, especially by the EU, to persuade Russia to ratify the treaty.

Nevertheless, once in force, the real test of a treaty's impact is in terms of implementation. In formal terms, a treaty may specify a range of actions that states should take to reach the agreed outcomes; both the FCCC and Kyoto Protocol did this. Such actions may involve states passing domestic laws, or changing domestic regulations, to give force to what has been agreed internationally. However, even if a government genuinely wishes to implement an agreement, a series of issues may cloud the process. The domestic constitution of different states affects their ability to give effect to international agreements. In the USA the balance of rights between the federal and state level constrains what an administration can do, as does the complex relationship between state and provincial levels of governance in China, for example. The institutional capacity of some states, particularly in the developing world, may mean that ratification and effective implementation are slow processes. Domestic opposition from those actors who may lose from international treaty obligations – energy-intensive industries for example – may obstruct effective implementation. Indeed, the prospect of this kind of opposition may lead governments to agree only to weak treaty obligations. In such circumstances the likelihood that international obligations will be translated into changed behaviour which has a real impact on environmental problems is significantly reduced. For example, the commitments given under the Kyoto Protocol by Annex I states led to the creation of an EU emissions trading system (ETS). However, the opposition from industry as well as within some European governments, meant that initially the impact of this mechanism was weak (Chapter 3).

In all these instances, the rather easy assumption I made in Section 2 – that because states have the authority to enforce changes in behaviour domestically, collective action problems can be solved – now needs to be qualified. States may deliberately avoid implementing treaty obligations; or they may wish to implement their obligations but fail to do so because they lack the capacity or resources; or because they face political opposition from key constituents not to implement the agreement. In addition, without effective government action, domestic actors may refuse to take action unless they know that others will do so too. So domestic level collective action problems may constrain the national level implementation of international treaty obligations.

The second, and broader, impact of international treaty negotiation that I want to raise is that interactions between states can shape the character of the political debate. One way this happens is by clarifying the fault lines in the debate. The divisions over targets and timetables in the negotiations for the FCCC and Kyoto had an enormous impact on the way non-state actors (campaigning groups, businesses, lobbyists and so on) both within states and internationally sought to influence the negotiations. The objections to targets and timetables, and the non-ratification by the USA of the Kyoto Protocol, sharpened political attention on the US administration's actions and in turn directed attention at political actors like the fossil fuel lobby who sought to influence government policy. In addition, international negotiations have become the locus of much political campaigning by non-state actors who direct attention at the negotiations themselves and the institutions within which they take place, as well as domestically, at the governments involved in the process (DeSombre, 2002, pp. 76–7). But actions at the intergovernmental level, most notably the activities of the Intergovernmental Panel on Climate Change (IPCC), have also reshaped different actors' understandings of the stakes of the political debate and how they frame their interests. Here the role of epistemic communities are particularly important in affecting not only states, but other political actors too (Chapter 2).

5   Conclusion

I began this chapter by suggesting that many international environmental problems have the form of collective action problems in which there is no overarching authority able to impose collectively rational solutions. The public good of climate stabilisation is a very large-scale, global example of this problem. In Section 3 I argued that if states look to the long term, they may see incentives to cooperate. In these circumstances, the prospects for solving collective action problems will be shaped by the ability to: formulate agreements on actions to be taken to mitigate climate change; pay side payments to reluctant parties; and offer incentives to states which have strong fallback positions. I argued that on all three accounts, while cooperation is possible, it nevertheless remains difficult to achieve. In Section 4 I suggested that one needs to broaden out the discussion, and explore the interconnections between state and non-state political actors at different locations.

There are three considerations with which I wish to conclude. The first is about the kind of analysis one might construct of climate change politics and the relationship between the different analytical tools I have introduced. One way of judging the analysis presented in Sections 2 and 3 is that the ideas introduced in Section 4 make models such as the Prisoners' Dilemma redundant. If states' interests are not known in advance, and are not fixed, then this kind of abstract model may seem rather removed from much 'real life' climate change politics. I would suggest that you need not go that far, but instead use these and other models with care, understanding their limitations as well as their explanatory strengths. Even with the caveats and embellishments introduced in Section 4, states do still enter international negotiations with generally clear ideas about what they want to achieve and what is acceptable and politically possible. In these circumstances the models presented in Sections 2 and 3 are still useful devices for understanding the patterns of interaction between states and for assessing the prospects for effective environmental cooperation.

Second, however, focusing on the dynamics which surround the formation of state preferences, and the politics of ratification and issue definition, helps to illuminate sources of change in the politics of climate change. One of the lessons of the analysis presented in Section 4 is that international climate change politics are not quite as static and fixed as they may at first sight appear. Changes to the politics that underlie state preferences can radically affect international politics and the potential for cooperative outcomes. This could be seen in a basic way through a change in US domestic politics: from the administration of Bill Clinton, which signed the Kyoto Protocol, to that of George W. Bush, which rejected it. In the future the political dynamics that underlie state preferences may shift as the knowledge about climate change develops and as political values change in response to this knowledge (*course theme 3*). City-level initiatives to reduce greenhouse gas emissions in the USA indicate some fluidity in the politics of climate change. New estimates about the effects of climate change, the development of new technologies with which it might be mitigated, new assessments of costs and benefits, and new ideas on how we should frame the problem, can all reshape the political fault lines at the international level and, therefore, the capacity of actors to tackle this highly challenging collective action problem.

Finally, the chapter has shown that the changing dynamics of this problem are shaped by power relations at a number of different locations. The prospects of cooperation between states, and the distribution of gains from cooperation, are fundamentally affected by the power of states, whether that is power to walk away from an agreement, or the power to create incentives for other states to join in. However, and as Section 4 has shown, the political positions states adopt – their very evaluation of the stakes in the climate change debate – are themselves a product of social power exercised by different actors across the world. For the most part my discussion has focused on power as the control and deployment of material resources. An understanding of power, I have suggested, is central to understanding international climate policy making. The preferences and bargaining positions of states are influenced by a range of powerful actors, and in international negotiations states will use their power to attempt to change the behaviour of other states (*course theme 2*).

In the next chapter you will engage with a different way of viewing international climate politics. The question that is explored is whether changes to how climate change is understood may revitalise international cooperation to address the problem.

Online Exercise 4

Now log on to the course website and complete Online Exercise 4: *Climate negotiations update.*

Video 2

Now watch Video 2: *Adapting to Climate change 2: the Thames Gateway, UK.*

References

Barrett, S. (2003) *Environment and Statecraft: The Strategy of Environmental Treaty-making*, Oxford, Oxford University Press.

Chasek, P. S., Downie, D. L. and Brown, J. W. (2006) *Global Environmental Politics* (4th edn), Boulder, CO, Westview Press.

DeSombre, E. (2002) *Global Environment and World Politics*, London and New York, Continuum.

Gruber, L. (2000) *Ruling the World: Power Politics and the Rise of Supranational Institutions*, Princeton, NJ, Princeton University Press.

Moravcsik, A. (1997) 'A liberal theory of international politics', *International Organization*, vol. 51, no. 4, pp. 513–53.

Ostrom, E. (1990) *Governing the Commons: The Evolution of Institutions of Collective Action*, Cambridge, Cambridge University Press.

People's Republic of China (2007) *China's National Climate Change Programme* [online], prepared under the auspices of National Development and Reform Commission, People's Republic of China, June, http://en.ndrc.gov.cn/newsrelease/P020070604561191006823.pdf (Accessed 6 July 2007).

Putnam, R. D. (1988) 'Diplomacy and domestic politics: the logic of two-level games', *International Organization*, vol. 42, no. 3, pp. 427–60.

Sanchez, R. (2004) 'Power among states: Mexico's membership of NAFTA' in Bromley, S., Mackintosh, M., Brown, W. and Wuyts, M. (eds) *Making the International: Economic Interdependence and Political Order*, London, Pluto Press in association with The Open University.

Victor, D. (2006) 'Toward effective international cooperation on climate change: numbers, interests and institutions', *Global Environmental Politics,* vol. 6, no. 3, pp. 90–103.

White House (2001) 'Press release: President Bush discusses global climate change' [online], 11 June, http://www.whitehouse.gov/news/releases/2001/06/20010611-2.html (Accessed 26 July 2007).

Chapter 5
Climate emergency: is securitisation the way forward?

Claudia Aradau

Contents

1	**Introduction**	**166**
	1.1 Learning outcomes	167
2	**Securitisation: what does it mean?**	**168**
	2.1 Climate change: a matter of security	168
	2.2 Security speech acts	171
	2.3 Security actors	174
	2.4 Security knowledge	178
3	**Securitisation: which meaning?**	**179**
	3.1 Climate change and the global community	179
	3.2 Going local? Climate change and human security	186
	3.3 Back to the state?	191
4	**Securitising climate change: assessing the advantages and disadvantages**	**193**
	4.1 The imperative of action	194
	4.2 The military: security actor for the environment?	196
	4.3 Security knowledge: preventing environmental conflicts?	198
5	**Conclusion: securitisation – success or failure?**	**200**
	References	**201**

1   Introduction

Take a look at the following headlines, which illustrate how the media reported an apparent change in the way climate change is portrayed:

> *Financial Times*: 'Global warming recast as security issue'
>
> (Harvey, 2007)
>
> *The New York Times*: 'Global warming called security threat'
>
> (Revkin and Williams, 2007)
>
> *The Guardian*: 'Climate change a bigger security threat than terrorism, says report'
>
> (Norton-Taylor, 2006)

These headlines suggest that something new has been happening in relation to how we understand climate change and the need to take action to tackle it. That something may be described as **securitisation**, by which I mean a process through which certain issues are framed as security threats to be tackled with the utmost urgency.

Securitisation is the process through which a particular problem is framed as a security threat.

The securitisation of climate change is not, however, an entirely unusual development in the international arena. In 2000, the UN Security Council considered the HIV/AIDS health epidemic as a matter of security. Once certain problems are reframed as security problems and are brought before security agencies such as the UN Security Council – or other regional security organisations such as the Organisation for Security and Cooperation in Europe, ministries in charge of security issues and defence or supra-national institutions such as the EU – then the approach to policy may be transformed. This chapter will help you understand what happens when climate change is framed as a security issue and what effects securitisation has for political action. To this purpose, it will examine securitisation as a political response that frames climate change as a security issue, and will consider whether it is a response that could overcome some of the constraints to more effective policy responses (*course questions 2 and 3*). The chapter will further consider whether the securitisation of climate change is a desirable option for future climate change policies (*course question 4*).

You might already be familiar with terms like 'food security' or 'energy security'. But what exactly does it mean to say that climate change is a security threat? Section 2 will unpack the process through which climate change has been securitised. What does it mean to securitise climate change? An appreciation of the process of securitisation will help you to understand how some threats are selected to be tackled immediately, while others are not.

Section 3 will show that different meanings can be attached to climate change as a security issue. Different people may mean different things when they talk about security. I shall consider two questions to clarify the meaning of climate change as a security threat: (1) what is the threat? and (2) who is threatened? You will see that both the meaning of the threat as well as understandings of who is threatened can vary significantly from one actor to another. When you think of food security, you might imagine people starving, but you might also conjure up images of war and conflict over the distribution of food, or of states unable to provide for their citizens, or images of environmental refugees who have been displaced due to food shortages. Depending on who is seen as threatened, climate change can be understood as a global, national or individual threat. Furthermore, the type of threat can vary over time and space, and may, for example, be manifested as armed conflict, lack of food, water, resource scarcity, or destruction of individual livelihoods (*course theme 5*).

In Section 4 I shall focus on actions that have been taken to tackle climate change as a security threat. In a conference on climate change in 2007, the then US Secretary of State, Condoleezza Rice, argued that 'nations must fight climate change as they do terrorism' (Rice, 2007). So has the process of securitising climate change been successful if a powerful actor, such as the US Secretary of State, agrees that climate change is something nations must fight? If so, are security measures desirable as policy options to tackle climate change?

1.1 Learning outcomes

This chapter should enable you to:

- become familiar with what is meant by the securitisation of climate change

- understand the role of speech acts, actors and knowledge in the securitisation of climate change

- discuss the advantages and disadvantages of securitising climate change

- evaluate the 'success' of the securitisation of climate change as a response to the threats that climate change poses

- use a variety of media to derive information about the securitisation of climate change.

2   Securitisation: what does it mean?

2.1   Climate change: a matter of security

Figure 5.1
The UN Security Council debate on climate change and security on 17 April 2007

On 17 April 2007, Margaret Beckett, at the time the UK foreign secretary, brought the question of climate change before the UN Security Council (Figure 5.1). In an address to the Council she said:

> Our responsibility in this Council is to maintain international peace and security, including preventing conflict. An unstable climate risks some of the drivers of conflict – such as migratory pressures and competition for resources – getting worse. The Stern Report speaks of a potential economic disruption on the scale of the two World Wars and the great depression. That alone will inevitably have an impact on all of our security – developed and developing countries alike.
>
> So today is about the world recognising that there is a security imperative, as well as economic, developmental and environmental ones, to tackling climate change. And for us to begin to build a shared understanding of the relationship between energy, climate and security.
>
> (Foreign and Commonwealth Office, 2007)

See Chapter 3 for a discussion of the Stern Review on the economics of climate change

Why did Margaret Beckett deliver her speech before the UN Security Council, and what does she mean by the 'security imperative'? According to the UN Charter, the UN Security Council is tasked with maintaining international peace and security. Why was an institution that has traditionally dealt with threats to peace discussing an international environmental issue? One of the dilemmas that previous chapters have addressed is how to spark action to tackle climate change. Chapter 4 argued that even if all scientific and economic uncertainties were to be eliminated state interests would remain a major constraint to collective action. But what if states were to see the problem of climate change as a problem of international security that affects them all? Would this make a difference to how climate change is handled as an international policy issue?

A few months after the UN Security Council meeting, the Norwegian Nobel Prize Committee awarded the Nobel Peace Prize jointly to Al Gore (Figure 5.2) and the Intergovernmental Panel on Climate Change (IPCC). Previous winners of the Nobel Peace Prize included people who have played an important role in the preservation of peace and the prevention of war. For example, in 1994, Yasser Arafat, Shimon Peres and Yitzhak Rabin were awarded the Nobel Peace Prize for their efforts to create peace in the Middle East. How is the role of Al Gore and the IPCC to be understood in this context?

Figure 5.2
Former US Vice-President Al Gore received the 2007 Nobel Peace Prize for his efforts to raise awareness about climate change

Margaret Beckett and Al Gore have not been alone in their efforts to argue about the dangers of climate change. The UK government's former chief scientist, Sir David King, has argued that climate change is a bigger threat than terrorism. Sir John Houghton, former co-chairman of the IPCC, has argued that climate change is a 'weapon of mass destruction' (Houghton, 2003). Why would these scientists, who usually describe climate change in terms of probable causes and effects, present climate change as a threat of such magnitude that it can be likened to terrorism?

To answer these questions, I shall define more precisely what is meant by the concept of securitisation. To this end, I consider three elements that define the process of securitisation:

- speech acts

- actors

- knowledge.

The UN Security Council debate example demonstrates that treating climate change as a security issue is the result of a political process through which climate change is presented as a threat by policy makers. This process involves particular speeches, utterances or images that frame climate change as a security threat. Have a look at how Al Gore's film on climate change, *An Inconvenient Truth*, was advertised:

> Humanity is sitting on a ticking time bomb. If the vast majority of the world's scientists are right, we have just ten years to avert a major catastrophe that could send our entire planet into a tail-spin of epic destruction involving extreme weather, floods, droughts, epidemics and killer heat waves beyond anything we have ever experienced.
>
> (Gore, 2006)

Activity 5.1

What particular words in this extract do you associate with a security threat?

To speak about security threats, policy makers use particular words, such as 'war', 'destruction', 'catastrophe' or 'emergency'. When answering Activity 5.1 you might have chosen 'ticking time bomb', 'major catastrophe', 'epic destruction', 'extreme weather' or 'killer heat waves'. These words are intended to convey a sense of the urgency with which we need to tackle climate change. However, are such words enough to persuade people that there is a security threat? What is it that makes most people believe the UN secretary general, heads of state or the UK government's chief scientist? Some actors can speak about security threats more convincingly than others. The public may believe them because of the knowledge and expert evidence they have about the problem at hand. I shall now consider in turn the three elements that define securitisation – speech acts, actors, knowledge – in order to unpack the process of securitising climate change.

2.2 Security speech acts

Securitisation refers to the political process through which certain issues are given priority on the political agenda by being framed as security issues. In the case of climate change it represents an attempt to place the issue on an international agenda which had been dominated for some time by the 'war on terror'. The term 'securitisation' was coined by Ole Waever in the mid 1990s and has become an accepted term in international studies, leading to the creation of the Copenhagen School of security studies, which places particular emphasis on the societal, political, economic and environmental aspects of security in addition to the traditional military one. According to Barry Buzan et al. (1998, p. 21) in the Copenhagen School's most often cited book, to securitise an issue is to present it as 'an existential threat to a designated object (traditionally, but not necessarily, the state, incorporating government, territory and society)'.

Traditionally, security has been understood as the security of the state. **National security** refers to the protection of a state from the military threats posed by other states or from internal civil war. The state is entrusted by its citizens to ensure their security and welfare, while protecting itself from external and internal threats. As you will see later in this chapter, this view of the state has historical roots that date back to seventeenth century political theories, in particular Thomas Hobbes. In this approach, the only way to ensure security is through the deployment of resources, such as military and economic power. **International security** refers to the security of states in the international system. Security as a policy objective leads to particular relations between states in the international system: states are potential adversaries and competitors.

During the Cold War, problems of national and international security were, in a sense, simple. An issue was considered a security threat if it involved military force. Stephen Walt saw security as linked to the 'study of *threat, use* and *control of military force*' (Walt, 1991, p. 211, emphasis in original). However, the end of the Cold War brought about concerns about new security threats. As the threat of nuclear war between the Cold War blocs disappeared, new threats such as ethnic conflict, migration, organised crime and terrorism became more prominent on the security agenda. Security scholars debated the relevance of these threats for the traditional security agenda, asking whether migration or the environment, for example, could pose a threat to national and international security. The Copenhagen School's contribution to this debate was to argue that the meaning of security is not given, but is the result of a social and political process of framing. Central to the

National security refers to the protection of the state from the military threats posed by other states or from civil war.

You may find it helpful here to return to the dicussion of power in Chapter 1 of this book

International security refers to the security of states in the international system.

Copenhagen School's approach is the role of speech acts in generating new understandings and interpretations of the concepts of security.

Let us now consider this idea of a speech act further. John Austin, the scholar who coined the term, referred to **speech acts** as specific types of statements which, while being uttered, did not simply describe reality but were also acting upon reality. Speech acts challenged the assumption that 'the business of a "statement" can only be to "describe" some state of affairs, or to "state some fact", which it must do either truly or falsely' (Austin, 1975 [1962], p. 1). Marrying, betting, bequeathing, christening, blessing, sacking, baptising, bidding, and so forth are not only speech acts; they are also social acts. Austin used the example of institutionalised utterances such as 'I pronounce you man and wife' to show how some utterances do not simply describe reality, but bring a particular reality, in this case marriage, into existence. These are instances in which a speaker is using language not just to describe, but actually to do something with considerable social significance. So speech acts are also deeds; they are not simply statements. When a head of state declares war this has profound consequences for what will happen within countries and in the international arena. As a consequence of such a speech act, armies may be mobilised, lives may be lost and actors such as the UN Security Council or North Atlantic Treaty Organization (NATO) may take measures to put an end to war and restore peace.

The speech act of declaring war, which is how national security has often been 'spoken', can be used to securitise other issues. For example, in the USA, President Lyndon Johnson declared a 'war on poverty' in the 1960s. You might also be familiar with declarations of wars on crime, cancer, drugs or, more recently, terror. The former UN Secretary General Kofi Annan 'declared war on AIDS' (BBC, 2001), while the South African government 'declared war on crime' (BBC, 1999).

> A **speech act** does not simply describe reality; it also changes what is being described.

Activity 5.2

Can you think of any other examples of important speech acts?

One example is when a judge utters the word 'Guilty', thereby transforming a defendant into a criminal. This is also a social deed in as much as it has intervened in reality, changing not only that person's social position but also the way in which society will deal with him or her. You might also want to think of what happens when somebody is labelled a 'terrorist'.

The idea of a speech act illustrates the process by which security is 'injected' into some issues. Think back to the example I gave earlier about HIV/AIDS. Securitisation presented HIV/AIDS as a security threat

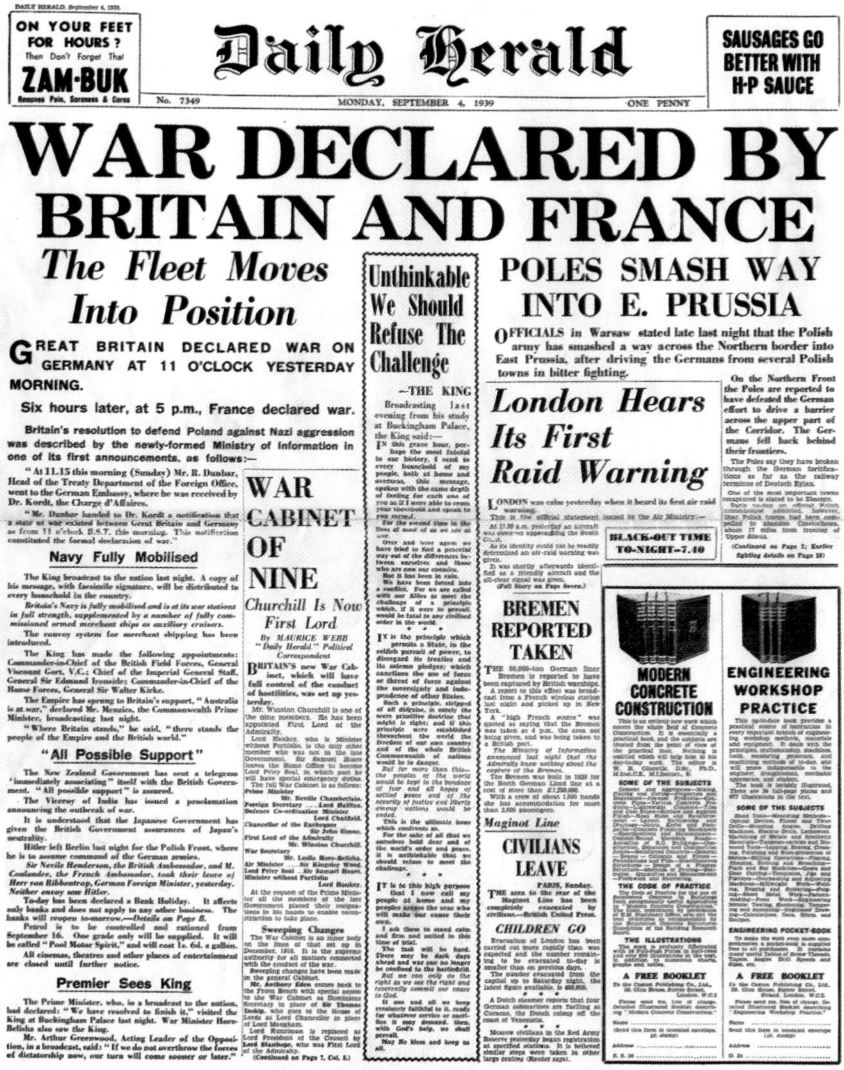
DAILY HERALD, September 4, 1939.

ON YOUR FEET FOR HOURS? Then Don't Forget That ZAM-BUK

Daily Herald

SAUSAGES GO BETTER WITH H-P SAUCE

No. 7349 MONDAY, SEPTEMBER 4, 1939 ONE PENNY

WAR DECLARED BY BRITAIN AND FRANCE

The Fleet Moves Into Position

GREAT BRITAIN DECLARED WAR ON GERMANY AT 11 O'CLOCK YESTERDAY MORNING.

Six hours later, at 5 p.m., France declared war.

Britain's resolution to defend Poland against Nazi aggression was described by the newly-formed Ministry of Information in one of its first announcements, as follows:—

Navy Fully Mobilised

"All Possible Support"

Premier Sees King

WAR CABINET OF NINE

Churchill Is Now First Lord

Unthinkable We Should Refuse The Challenge

—THE KING

POLES SMASH WAY INTO E. PRUSSIA

OFFICIALS in Warsaw stated late last night that the Polish army has smashed a way across the Northern border into East Prussia, after driving the Germans from several Polish towns in bitter fighting.

London Hears Its First Raid Warning

BLACK-OUT TIME TO-NIGHT—7.40

BREMEN REPORTED TAKEN

Maginot Line

CIVILIANS LEAVE

CHILDREN GO

MODERN CONCRETE CONSTRUCTION

ENGINEERING WORKSHOP PRACTICE

A FREE BOOKLET

Figure 5.3
The front page of the UK *Daily Herald*, 4 September 1939. The declaration of war is a speech act that makes war a reality

rather than a health or development issue. So for securitisation to happen, certain issues must be framed as a threat that requires an emergency response. This is the security speech act.

Through speech acts, security is **broadened** to encompass a series of issues (what is the threat?) and **deepened** to include other actors beyond the state (who is threatened?). For example, in the case of food or energy security, the speech act broadens security to include threats such as food scarcity and energy shortages. Speech acts may also deepen security to include, for example, individuals and communities alongside states. Through securitising speech acts, policy makers can achieve different forms of broadening and deepening. The meanings of security are, in this sense, the end result of a process of securitisation.

Broadening security is the adding of new issues to traditional threats to national security.

Deepening security is the adding of new actors to be secured beyond the state, such as individuals, local communities and regional populations.

Figure 5.4 shows how the concept of security can be plotted along two axes; broadening and deepening. The traditional notion of international security is represented by the ellipse at the intersection of the two axes. Within this ellipse security is limited to one actor, the state, and to traditional threats that constitute the core of security, such as war and military defence. Broadening and deepening expands the traditional notion of security:

- **Broadening**: The horizontal axis depicts 'What is the threat?' Broadening renders security a concept that no longer applies solely to traditional military threats, but one that encompasses new risks such as economic, food, health, environmental and community security.

- **Deepening**: The vertical axis depicts 'Who is threatened?' Deepening renders security a concept that no longer applies solely to the state, but one that encompasses other actors from the local level to the global. The array of actors that needs to be secured both transcends the state, such as regional populations and the idea of a global community, and extends to the sub-state level, including social groups and individuals.

I shall return to Figure 5.4 in the next section to unpack the ambiguous meanings that arise when climate change is framed as a security issue.

Activity 5.3

Can anybody utter a security speech act? You may wish to consider what might distinguish the speech act of a prime minister from that of an academic, an activist or a friend of yours.

When thinking about this question you may have considered the notion of authority. What is authority? I introduce you to this concept in the next section when considering the second element in the process of securitisation: actors.

2.3 Security actors

You have seen that the securitisation of climate change has been undertaken by different actors such as the UN secretary general, the UK foreign secretary and the UK's chief scientist. Securitisation can be successful, or it can fail, depending on who utters the speech act and what the audience thinks about the speech act. The success of securitisation depends, first, on the social position held by those who speak of security and, second, on whether the audience accepts these people and what they say as legitimate. The Copenhagen School suggests that a further element determining the success of securitisation

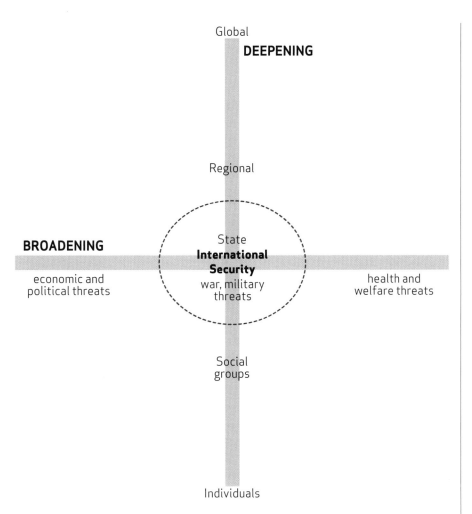

Global
DEEPENING

Regional

BROADENING

State
International Security
war, military threats

economic and political threats

health and welfare threats

Social groups

Individuals

Figure 5.4
Security can be plotted along two axes: 'broadening' and 'deepening'

is the 'extraordinary measures' advocated in response to a security threat. Successful securitisation needs to comprise the linguistic framing of an existential threat as well as emergency measures to deal with the threat (Aradau, 2004).

When Austin discussed speech acts he was aware of the possibility that an utterance could be unsuccessful. Think, for example, of what happens with 'I pronounce you man and wife' when there is no groom in sight. Or when I say 'I promise' when I do not intend to keep my promise. The speech acts that Austin considered were performed by authorised actors following specific procedures. If the speech act is performed by an unauthorised actor, then it will fail. If I say to my friends 'I pronounce you man and wife', most likely they will laugh and will not take me seriously. So if performative speech acts do not follow a conventional procedure or are not spoken by an authorised person in the circumstances specified in the procedure they will fail (Austin, 1975 [1962]).

Although in principle anybody can perform a speech act, we do not believe everybody who speaks about security problems. Some actors can speak about threats with authority, while others are not believed. The security scholar Michael Williams argues that speech acts are 'structured by the differential capacity of actors to make socially effective claims about threats, by the forms in which these claims can be made in order to be recognised and accepted as convincing by the relevant audience, and by the empirical factors or situations to which these actors can make reference' (Williams, 2003, p. 514). Successful speech acts need to be uttered from recognised institutional or social positions which give the speaker the authority to speak about security. Security speech acts can be successful or not depending on who speaks about the threat. We tend to trust experts and institutions – such as defence ministries, governments, the military and international security organisations – to speak about security threats. As Buzan et al. (1998, p. 32) have put it, the

> [c]onditions for a successful speech-act fall into two categories: (1) the internal, linguistic-grammatical – to follow the rules of the act (or, as Austin argues, accepted conventional procedures must exist, and the act has to be executed according to these procedures); and (2) the external, contextual and social to hold a position from which the act can be made ('The particular persons and circumstances in a given case must be appropriate for the invocation of the particular procedure invoked').

Thus in addition to using particular words and linguistic-grammatical formulations, the actors who can successfully securitise a social problem need to occupy particular institutional and social positions. Security speech acts need to identify a threat, account for its urgency, offer possible solutions for neutralising the threat or preventing conflict and establish a point of no return by which time action must be taken. And they need to be uttered by actors who hold social positions that allow them to speak 'with authority' about security problems, such as military experts and scholars specialising in security studies.

Activity 5.4

Make a note of how power as discourse was defined in Chapter 2. Does speaking 'with authority' fit the definition of power as discourse?

In the first two chapters of this book, you were introduced to two approaches to power: as resource and as discourse. In different ways both approaches emphasise that some actors are able to exercise power over other actors, who either have no power, or who have it to a lesser degree. Actors speaking 'with authority' can be influential in creating new discourses, such as securitisation, that others accept as valid and legitimate. Although authority is dependent upon institutional and social positions, it is also dependent on how we, the audience, relate to a particular speaker. Do we trust the speaker and what they say? The sociologist Max Weber defined **authority** as the belief in the legitimate exercise of power (Weber, 1947). We can still disagree with a prime minister or question the assessment of a military general based on our own knowledge and understanding of the situation, although we may also recognise that they have the authority to speak about security problems.

So a successful speech act does not depend only on the linguistic-grammatical rules of the act and the social and institutional positions of those who speak, but also on those to whom the speech act is directed. This audience or constituency may or may not accept the speech act as authoritative. The securitisation of climate change, although often uttered from positions of authority, for example by governments, the Pentagon and the UN, has not been accepted by all audiences worldwide. While many people are now concerned about climate change, many do not believe that climate change is a security problem, with some not accepting it as a problem at all.

Consequently, in one sense the success of a speech act depends upon its acceptance by the public. There is, however, a second sense in which speech acts need to be successful. Securitisation calls for extraordinary measures that need to be taken in order to neutralise the threat. To the Copenhagen School an **extraordinary measure** is a form of emergency action that needs to be taken to deal with existential threats. I shall return to the question of extraordinary measures in Section 4.

Now let us return to the UN Security Council. State representatives have the authority to speak about international security, although their speech acts are not necessarily accepted by other states. At the meeting in 2007 the representative of Pakistan argued, in the name of the Group of 77 Developing Countries (G77) and China, that climate change should be dealt with by the UN Economic and Social Council rather than by the Security Council. This position was based on the argument that climate change is primarily a development issue, rather than an 'actual threat to peace' (G77, 2007). The G77 also argued that the UN Security Council, whose membership is limited, was encroaching upon other UN agencies by discussing climate change and thereby compromising the voices of the UN's general membership. So the framing of climate change as a security issue was challenged, as were the institutional implications of this framing.

Authority is the belief in the legitimate exercise of power.

Extraordinary measures are a form of emergency action that is advocated by securitisation.

2.4 Security knowledge

Knowledge is the third element in the process of securitisation. The authority of actors and institutions is not enough for a successful speech act. The public normally trusts governments and policy makers to deal with security problems, although sometimes governments are distrusted or challenged. One example is the debates that preceded the Iraq war in the UK and at the UN Security Council. The evidence that UK Prime Minister Tony Blair presented in the UK and that was presented by US Secretary of State Colin Powell before the UN Security Council alleging that Iraq possessed weapons of mass destruction was shown to be at least dubious if not totally wrong. When policy makers speak about security threats, they can only be successful if the knowledge claimed about what the threat is and how it should be tackled is reliable. Authority can be lost if evidence that is presented to the public is shown to be false or misleading.

While authority can be lost when an audience realises that policy makers have presented misleading or false information, uncertainty remains an inescapable characteristic of knowledge. Climate scientists rely on probabilities to express uncertainty about the causes and effects of climate change. Can such uncertainty undermine successful securitisation? It might be argued that if we do not know for sure, then perhaps there is no urgency.

The concepts of knowledge and uncertainty were introduced in Chapter 2

The policy principle that is normally invoked in response to such an argument is the precautionary principle. In Chapter 1, David Humphreys introduced this principle, which offers a guideline for action when knowledge is uncertain, particularly where public harm is at stake. Humphreys argued that although the principle is clear, the practical details of its implementation are more problematic. Security policy avoids this dilemma as it has always been precautionary. Governments know that there always is uncertainty about a security threat, just as there are margins of uncertainty about climate change. Part of the rationale for securitising an issue is to assert that the consequences of not acting are so serious that governments must act. As a CIA character said in the film *The Bourne Ultimatum* 'We hope for the best and prepare for the worst' (2007). In security matters, states need to prepare for the worst. As Stefan Elbe has put it, security knowledge entails:

> making speculative predictions about future developments, necessitates prioritizing between competing claims with imperfect information, and, especially when it comes to wider social issues, requires deciding about whether an issue is best addressed under the heading of security rather than another competing framework.
>
> (Elbe, 2006, p. 125)

Security knowledge is concerned with neutralising threats or preventing conflicts, and does not concern itself with legal responsibility or uncertainty. So if scientific uncertainty would debilitate urgent political action, securitisation would seek to override such uncertainty with a call for immediate action, because the worst-case scenario is too threatening to be allowed to happen. Buzan et al. (1998) have argued that 'critical for the political agenda is not whether specific threats to the environment are real or speculative but whether their *presumed urgency* is a political issue' (p. 73, emphasis in original). In 2004 a report by Pentagon experts warned President George W. Bush that 'Climate Change Will Destroy Us', the implication being that urgent measures were needed to avert the worst-case scenario (Townsend and Harris, 2004).

> **Security knowledge** is the expertise that security agencies and scholars have in threat neutralisation and conflict prevention.

Online Exercise 5

Now log on to the course website and carry out Online Exercise 5: *Security speech acts*. When you have completed this exercise continue reading below.

3 Securitisation: which meaning?

You have seen that speech acts can modify the traditional notion of security by broadening it (by including other types of threats) and by deepening it (by including actors, besides the state, who are threatened). I shall now discuss the different meanings of security speech acts in relation to these two axes (Figure 5.4). I shall consider three entries on the deepening axis: global (Section 3.1), local (Section 3.2) and the state (Section 3.3). In so doing I consider how the broadening of security can be understood in relation to deepening. I argue that as actors attempt to deepen and broaden security, its meanings change depending on whether or not different audiences accept particular formulations of the threat of climate change.

3.1 Climate change and the global community

A global threat?

Activity 5.5

Look at the two images in Figure 5.5. Images similar to these were used by Greenpeace to draw attention to the consequences of climate change. Consider the following questions:

1   Who is threatened in these images?

2   Why do you think Greenpeace juxtaposed these two very different types of images?

Figure 5.5
Global warming:
weather of mass
destruction

Greenpeace used very similar images on its website when reporting the 2007 Security Council debate on climate change. Greenpeace compares a nuclear explosion to the erratic weather patterns that climate change will bring about in 'weather of mass destruction'. Just as a nuclear explosion may have global effects so too will climate change transcend the boundaries of the state. Greenpeace juxtaposed the two images to convey the threat of climate change, to represent its global reach and to suggest a moral equivalence between the destructive effects of nuclear war and those of climate change.

In the previous chapter you saw that climate change cannot be dealt with by any single state, but is a problem that requires collective agreements. Collective accord on climate change is only possible if the threat is understood as global. The 1992 UN Framework Convention on Climate Change (FCCC) presented climate change as a global problem and emphasised the need to 'prevent dangerous anthropogenic interference with the climate system' (UN, 1992, Article 2). In the representation of the threat of climate change presented by Greenpeace we will all be affected and therefore we all need to act to counter the threat of climate change. This may be seen as a speech act in which the global community is the relevant entry on the deepening axis (Figure 5.4). On this view the securitisation of climate change as a global threat surpasses the limited concerns of national and international security, which are focused on states and the military relations between them.

The German sociologist Ulrich Beck has argued that environmental risks are global in reach and potential effects and as a consequence we all live now in a global **risk society** (Beck, 1992, 1999). According to Beck, processes of industrialisation and accumulation in the West have given rise to catastrophic risks that threaten the survival of humanity. Ecological and nuclear risks completely change our societies, in as much as they threaten irreparable damage which cannot be predicted or insured against. It is the global aspect of risks such as climate change and the need for cooperation that gives them global relevance, beyond the boundaries of states:

A **risk society** is a society that is characterised by uncertainty and insecurity created by the ubiquity of environmental risks.

> The collapse of global financial markets or climatic change affect regions quite differently. But that doesn't change the principle that everyone is affected, and everyone can potentially be affected in a much worse manner. Thus, in a way, these problems endow each country with a common global interest, which means that, to a certain extent, we can already talk about the basis of a global community of fate.
>
> (Beck, 2002, p. 42)

If we are all in danger or at risk then it would appear that political actions must be taken as a matter of urgency. Securitisation is intended to create solidarity in the face of dangers or risks and to provide an injunction to act by presenting the problem at hand as urgent and potentially catastrophic if not dealt with immediately.

Although Beck argues that global risks could potentially affect everybody, both wealthy and poor – 'smog is democratic' (Beck, 1992, p. 36) – differences in effects have the potential to divide the global community; some people will be affected more than others. You have already seen that the risks of climate change are unequally distributed around the world. Even pollution, which at first sight might seem to affect everybody, is not equally distributed. Poor communities, which are more likely to live close to factories or waste disposal sites, will be disproportionately affected. With climate change some countries will suffer dire consequences, while others could even benefit in the short term (for example, Russia through the warming in Siberia). But in a risk society ultimately all are at risk over the long term.

The Fourth Assessment Report of the IPCC emphasised the unequal localisation of the risks that climate change poses both in developing states and in poorer communities. Poor communities, the report argues, 'can be especially vulnerable, in particular those concentrated in high-risk areas. They tend to have more limited adaptive capacities, and are more dependent on climate-sensitive resources such as local water and food supplies' (IPCC, 2007, p. 7). The report confirms that Africa is one of the most vulnerable continents to climate variability, while in the developing states of Asia climate change will impinge upon sustainable development, as it 'compounds the pressures on natural resources and the environment associated with rapid urbanisation, industrialisation, and economic development' (IPCC, 2007, p. 8).

A world of difference

Let us now consider the statement by UN Secretary General, Ban Ki-moon, to the UN Security Council debate of 2007:

> The adverse effects of changing weather patterns, such as floods and droughts, and related economic costs, including compensation for lost land, could risk polarizing society and marginalizing communities. This, in turn, could weaken the institutional capacity of the State to resolve conflict through peaceful and democratic means, to ensure social cohesion, and to safeguard human rights.

> Extreme weather events and natural disasters, such as floods and drought, increase the risk of humanitarian emergencies, and thus the risk of instability and dislocation.

> Migration driven by factors such as climate change could deepen tensions and conflicts, particularly in regions with large numbers of internally displaced persons and refugees.

> Scarce resources, especially water and food, could help transform peaceful competition into violence.

> Limited or threatened access to energy is already known to be a powerful driver of conflict. Our changing planet risks making it more so.

> (Ki-moon, 2007)

This statement serves to broaden the concept of security by enumerating the multiple threats posed by climate change. I now consider these threats in turn to see how broadening entails particular types of deepening.

First, floods and extreme weather events appear to be the most likely global effects of climate change. Many states, both rich and poor, have been affected by more serious flooding and weather events. You might remember Hurricane Katrina in the USA, which caused catastrophic damage to New Orleans. In 2007, Cyclone Cidr cyclone in Bangladesh led to the deaths of 3300 people, while 40,000 were injured. Such events can challenge the capacity of the state to deal with emergencies and create instability, although rich states are more likely to be able to mobilise resources to deal with such emergencies. What Ki-moon hints at is that poor states, which have more limited resources than rich ones, could be more severely affected as they may lack the capacity to solve societal conflicts in a peaceful way.

Population displacement induced by climate change may have important consequences for the stability of many destination states. Migration – particularly of large numbers of what are now described as climate or environmental refugees – is likely to place a strain on resources in destination countries and could lead to tensions among existing populations. The Geneva Convention relating to the status of refugees, which regulates the granting of asylum internationally, considers a **refugee** to be someone who is unable or unwilling to avail themselves of the protection of their country of nationality 'owing to well-founded fear of being persecuted for reasons of race, religion, nationality, membership of a particular social group or political opinion' (OHCHR, 1951, Article 1). By contrast, an **environmental refugee** is someone who is displaced due to environmental degradation. The term 'environmental refugee' has so far had no impact on international legislation concerning refugees, and environmental refugees enjoy no protection under the 1951 Geneva Convention. Even if the definition of refugees were to be expanded, environmental refugees would encounter practical problems that already face political refugees.

Many EU member states have been trying to reduce the number of refugees and migrants they receive. Indeed, in many European countries migration is securitised alongside terrorism and organised crime. Speech acts about migration present it as a potential threat to the identity of the nation, welfare, health and education services or even link it with potential terrorist attacks. The general policy is to deport illegal migrants and create very stringent conditions for granting asylum. Given the restrictive policies concerning migration and asylum in Europe and more generally in the North, it will be poorer states which are going to be more heavily affected by environmental and climate refugees. The case of environmental refugees, which will be further explored in Book 2, Chapter 1, underlines the importance of territorial borders in international politics.

The Secretary General's final points concern scarce resources and energy. As climate change will lead to increased desertification, certain states could be faced with food and water shortages. Similarly, questions of energy could be seen as a global problem as states could end up fighting over access to energy resources. Many scholars see the ongoing conflicts in the Middle East as driven by the US quest for new oil resources, while the EU is increasingly endorsing renewable energy as an attempt to minimise dependence on Russia for gas resources.

A **refugee** is someone who is outside their country of nationality owing to a well-founded fear of persecution for reasons of race, religion, nationality, membership of a particular social group or political opinion.

An **environmental refugee** is someone who is displaced due to environmental degradation and who does not enjoy protection under the 1951 Geneva Refugee Convention.

What I hope this brief discussion has illustrated is that Ki-moon's speech to the UN Security Council represents both a broadening and a deepening of climate change as a security issue. However, as the concept of security is expanded along these two axes more and more differences and inequalities are introduced into security discourse. Broadening security by introducing more issues as security threats presents policy makers with a dilemma: where should scarce resources be directed? As more actors are introduced the greater is the risk of conflict: whose interests should prevail? It can be argued that the combined effect of broadening and deepening is to undermine the securitisation of climate change as a global security threat.

Environmental conflict and the North/South dimension

Just as the effects of climate change will be experienced very differently by different states, so too will the securitisation of climate change be understood very differently. In the North, there is a tendency among some political leaders to frame the threat of climate change as one of potential war, conflict over resources and the destabilisation of countries in the South, leading to refugee flows from the South to the North. The 2003 European Security Strategy, for example, emphasised that '[c]ompetition for natural resources – notably water – which will be aggravated by global warming over the next decades is likely to create further turbulence and migratory movements in various regions' (European Commission, 2003). For many states in the developing world, however, the threat of climate change is one of survival.

The concerns, particularly in the North, with climate change and the threat of war and state destabilisation in the South have led to a substantial body of academic research that many policy makers rely upon. Some of the most famous analyses of the linkages between environmental degradation, resource scarcity and violent conflict have been undertaken by Thomas Homer-Dixon at the University of Toronto (1991, 1994, 2001). According to Homer-Dixon, people will fight to ensure access to a resource which is becoming scarce. The scarcer the resource, the more ferocious the fight. These conflicts are either caused by resource capture, when powerful groups secure access to a resource and deprive powerless groups access, or by ecological marginalisation, where the poor are driven to ecologically marginal areas. Homer-Dixon disputed earlier research suggesting that resource scarcity will cause war between states and argued that future conflicts will most likely be intra-state (within countries) rather than inter-state (between countries). He considered environmental conflicts to be societal and identity based, often following ethnic divisions.

Other researchers continue to support the hypothesis of inter-state conflict, particularly in the case of water and oil resources (Gleick, 1993; Postel and Wolf, 2001; Selby, 2005). Conflicts in the Middle East and the war in Iraq are sometimes interpreted as resource conflicts. However, intra-state conflict remains the major concern for most environmental research on climate change, security and conflict. A report published by the United Nations Environment Programme (UNEP) on the conflict in Darfur, Sudan argues that there are strong linkages between the environmental degradation caused by global warming, resource scarcity and violent conflict among ethnic groups. Environmental issues, the report argues, have contributed to the causes of conflict in Sudan, and they continue to do so. Sudan has the largest population of displaced persons in the world and suffers from desertification, devastating droughts and land degradation (Figure 5.6). Some of the country's environmental problems are the result of regional climate change and the southward shift of the boundary between desert and semi-desert (UNEP, 2007). In Book 2, Chapter 1, you will critically evaluate claims about how these problems are compounded by the impact of displaced populations who may cause security problems for the states which receive them, leading to further environmental degradation.

Figure 5.6
Abu Shouk in Northern Darfur, a settlement of displaced people in Sudan

Different states understand the threat of climate change differently. In low lying states like Bangladesh, the prospect of coastal flooding resulting from sea level rise threatens the survival of millions of people. For island states, the situation is even bleaker as they are threatened by territorial extinction. The Association of Small Island States (AOSIS), established in 1990 during the Second World Climate Conference in

Geneva, has played an important role in drawing attention to the consequences of climate change. It has argued, especially in negotiations under the auspices of the UN FCCC, that climate change is a matter of life and death for island countries (Stripple, 2002, p. 119). But other states, such as India and China, have been unwilling to accept climate change as a security problem, arguing that it should be seen as a problem of development. Meanwhile many states in the North see climate change as potentially leading to conflicts over resources, humanitarian emergencies and increased flows of environmental refugees.

I have already noted that during the UN Security Council debate of 2007 states were split over the question of securitising climate change. Unlike the earlier case of HIV/AIDS, when securitisation led to Security Council Resolution 1308 which emphasised that 'if unchecked, HIV/AIDS may pose a risk to security and stability', no consensus was reached in the case of climate change. There was no agreement that climate change should be framed as a security issue, no resolution was passed and there was no agreement to take further action.

Activity 5.6

Why do you think that the UK's attempts to securitise climate change at the UN Security Council were unsuccessful?

The attempt to securitise climate change was unsuccessful owing to different political understandings about the type of problem that climate change is and the effects it will entail for different states and populations. While in some parts of the world climate change can raise questions of survival, in the North climate change is framed as a security issue in as much as it raises the possibility of conflict over resources in the South and the potential increase in flows of environmental refugees, both within the South and to the North. In contrast, the G77 agreed with China that climate change is not a global security threat. The concern in the North with preventing environmental conflict is rather different from the concerns of those in the South who frame their priorities as economic development and, in some cases, survival. Political disagreements on the framing of climate change can therefore be explained in part as contention between states over environmental and developmental policy priorities (*course theme 4*).

3.2 Going local? Climate change and human security

Let us start here with three images that illustrate the risks of climate change faced by one country: Bangladesh (Figure 5.7).

Figure 5.7
In the summer of 2004 an area the size of Switzerland was flooded in Bangladesh

These images were used as part of an art exhibition on 'Climate Change and Security', organised at the initiative of the German Federal Foreign Ministry, which tried to make visible and place on the political agenda the effects of climate change on the security of individuals (Adelphi Research et al., 2007). These images speak of the plight of people in Bangladesh, a country where farmers regularly experience flooding that renders them vulnerable to serious food shortages. As a low lying coastal country Bangladesh has always been at high risk of flooding, especially during the monsoon season. However, with climate change, rising sea levels will increase the risks that the country and its people face. Flooding is also believed to have worsened over the past decades due to deforestation in Nepal.

These images clearly suggest that climate change is not solely a threat to an international community of states. It entails economic and social costs for communities and individual people. There are many different ways in which people can be threatened by the effects of climate change. John Barnett and Neil Adger have argued that we should focus on how the effects of climate change cause livelihood contraction and affect individuals (Barnett and Adger, 2005). By **livelihood contraction**, Barnett and Adger mean declining access to natural capital resulting from deforestation, desertification, natural disasters or population displacement.

Livelihood contraction is the declining access of individuals to natural resources due to environmental degradation and social factors.

Climate change may thus affect the security both of states and of individuals. What is the relationship between the state and individuals in political theory? The seventeenth century political theorist Thomas Hobbes argued that security is an individual right that states have undertaken to provide for their citizens. Individuals enter a covenant with the state in which they agree to obey the latter, while the state guarantees their protection against external and internal threats.

In this sense the idea of human security provides an ethical principle that offers a particular interpretation of security. This principle holds that security is a right for each and every individual. The origins of human security are usually associated with two UN documents: the *Agenda for Peace* of former UN Secretary General Boutros Boutros-Ghali (1992), and the 1994 report by the United Nations Development Programme (UNDP, 1994). *Agenda for Peace* argued that the post-Cold War world was shaped by threats to individuals rather than traditional inter-state wars. The UNDP report defined **human security** as 'safety from such chronic threats as hunger, disease and repression ... [and] protection from sudden and hurtful disruptions in the patterns of daily life – whether in homes, in jobs or in communities' (UNDP, 1994). The concept encompasses both physical security and more general notions of economic and social well-being. By introducing questions of social and

Human security is the principle that security is a right for every individual and a concept that embraces human life, dignity, welfare and freedom.

economic security, the concept of human security challenges the traditional understanding of security linked with war, conflict and destabilisation. As the UNDP report put it:

> Human security is a child who did not die, a disease that did not spread, a job that was not cut, an ethnic tension that did not explode in violence, a dissident who was not silenced. Human security is not a concern with weapons – it is a concern with human life and dignity.
>
> (UNDP, 1994, p. 22)

Let us now return to Figure 5.4. On the deepening axis we have individuals and on the broadening axis there are various categories of security threats: economic, food, health, environmental, personal, community and political security. The economist Amartya Sen has argued that in order to guarantee secure daily living, the concept of human security needs to incorporate social and economic provisions (such as 'economic safety nets' and guarantees of a basic education and health care) and also political participation, especially by the weak and the vulnerable, since their voice is often ignored (Sen, 2000). Sen's approach to human security has far-reaching implications that go beyond the protection of the individual: it requires political conditions for the participation of the vulnerable in decision making and the need to listen to the voices of the marginalised. In Sen's view, human security encompasses the freedom of 'doing' things, the 'real opportunity' to accomplish what we value (Sen, 1992, p. 31). This necessitates broad political, social and economic changes.

Unlike national security, which separates questions of security from questions of development, in Sen's view human security brings the two together. The threats of climate change cannot be considered separately from the threats that underdevelopment poses for the capabilities of people to accomplish what they value. However, neither the UNDP's definition of human security nor Sen's formulation have been successful in broadening security. Why have these particular speech acts been unsuccessful?

The main reason is that while the UNDP has the authority to speak about development issues globally, other actors such as national governments have primacy when it comes to security matters. Speech acts broadening security to 'human security' have been rejected as impracticable by many policy makers. The concept of human security includes so many issues under the label of security that policy makers would have to give priority to some security issues. So as a strategy to prioritise some issues over others the concept of human security has failed. The 1994 UNDP *Human Development Report* has not been widely used to inform policy making (HSC, 2005) (see Box 5.1). Moreover, in many countries after 9/11, especially the USA, development has been incorporated under security concerns, with aid resources to developing countries being refocused on those populations, regions and issues seen as relevant to US national security (Duffied and Waddell, 2006).

States like Canada and Japan in particular have used different speech acts to define human security. While Sen and the UNDP emphasise the link with development and attempt, in effect, to include economic and social issues on the broadening axis, governments in Canada and Japan have limited the scope of human security to 'violent threats to individuals' (HSC, 2005). According to Lloyd Axworthy, the Canadian foreign minister who spoke about the integration of human security in Canada's foreign policy, the UNDP criteria for human security pay insufficient attention to the threats to individuals of violent conflict (Burke, 2001, p. 219).

Box 5.1   Human security: development of a concept

- 1992 UN Secretary General Boutros Boutros-Ghali's *Agenda for Peace* (1992) suggests that the state should not be the central object of security.

- 1994 The UNDP *Human Development Report* declared that human security is not 'a concern with weapons – it is a concern with human life and dignity' (UNDP, 1994).

- 2001 The UN Commission on Human Security is established in response to the UN Secretary General's call for the millennium development goals to comprise both 'freedom from want' and 'freedom from fear'.

- 2001 The International Commission on Intervention and State Sovereignty (ICISS) in its report, *The Responsibility to Protect* (2001), argues that human security is complementary to national security.

- 2003 The final report of the Commission on Human Security by Sadako Ogata and Amartya Sen, *Human Security Now* (CHS, 2003), enlarges the definition of human security to encompass the protection of fundamental freedoms.

Security threats do not only raise questions about 'what the threat is' and 'who is threatened', but also imply that somebody will be given the task to ensure the protection of those in danger and to neutralise or eliminate the threat. You saw earlier how the Copenhagen School has argued that securitising a threat also calls for extraordinary measures to address the threat. Who should take these measures? According to

Hobbes the covenant between citizens and the state requires the latter to protect individuals both from external aggression and internal threats. For human security, too, the state remains the major actor that is entrusted with ensuring security. The 2005 *Human Security Report* (HSC, 2005) and the 2001 ICISS report on *The Responsibility to Protect* each argue that the state is instrumental in ensuring human security. The ICISS report argues that the sovereign state should be the guarantor of human security:

> In an interdependent world, in which security depends on a framework of stable sovereign entities, the existence of fragile states, failing states, states who through weakness or ill-will harbour those dangerous to others, or states that can only maintain internal order by means of gross human rights violations, can constitute a risk to people everywhere.
>
> (ICISS, 2001, para. 1.21)

Human security is ultimately dependent on the state and many who promote human security as a policy objective end up invoking the need for strong states. Given the history of the concept of security, I have argued that states are prone to understanding security threats in narrow terms, as war, conflict and destabilisation. I have suggested that reverting back to the state as the guarantor of security leaves little room for the broadening and deepening of the concept as envisaged by the UNDP. But why would that be a problem for tackling climate change? After all, we want states to act in the international arena. Might relying on the state lead to more effective climate policies? That is the question I pursue in the next section.

3.3 Back to the state?

So far I have analysed the securitisation of climate change as a global threat to states and as a localised one to communities and individuals. While human security speech acts attempt to deepen security to incorporate individuals and communities, and to broaden the range of threats beyond war and conflict, the state remains the central actor in the provision of security. I have suggested that policy makers often favour a limited version of human security that ultimately privileges the state and subordinates development to national security. This resonates with accepted understandings of security and chimes with established institutional practices for dealing with security threats. States know how to deal with violent threats and, as Hobbes made clear, have undertaken to protect their citizens from such threats. Hobbes argued that people submit to the authority of a sovereign state in order to escape the so-called **state of nature** in which there is no government or laws and life is nasty, brutish and short. The state of nature is a hypothetical situation in

The **state of nature** is a hypothetical condition of humanity where there is no government or laws and goals can be realised through violence.

which goals can be realised through violence, individuals are relatively equal (even the most powerful could be killed while sleeping), resources are limited and nothing forces individuals to cooperate. The sovereign state is the rational result of our 'need and desire for protection' and to move from a state of nature to a state of peace (Young, 2003, p. 224).

Hobbes' description of the state of nature is similar to how the international realm is understood. While individuals need the state in order to avoid the brutality of the state of nature, internationally states may contemplate the possibility of conflict and war. As Chapter 4 argued, the international political system can be characterised as one of *anarchy* as there is no collective means by which states can ensure that any agreements they make voluntarily are upheld. So both internally and externally the duty of the state is to protect its citizens by providing security. The sovereign has to 'do whatsoever he [*sic*] shall think necessary to be done, both beforehand, for the preserving of Peace and Security, by prevention of Discord at home and Hostility from abroad' (Hobbes, 1985 [1651], p. 233).

The other element characteristic of Hobbes' state of nature is that of resource scarcity. While for Hobbes resources are understood in the general sense of material goods, resource scarcity is one of the assumptions of policy makers about environment and conflict. Another assumption, as you saw in the previous chapter, is that of the self-interested individual. Hobbes argued that self-interested individuals will cooperate and transfer their rights to the state in order to gain security.

Hobbes might see the problem of climate change as resulting from an anarchical state of nature defined by resource scarcity and conflict. He would see the problem as a security threat and would suggest that the state must take measures to protect its citizens by providing security in the form of a stable climate. There are signs that some defence experts see climate change in Hobbesian terms. Note in the following newspaper extract how climate change is securitised as a national security threat:

> A secret report, suppressed by US defence chiefs and obtained by *The Observer*, warns that major European cities will be sunk beneath rising seas as Britain is plunged into a 'Siberian' climate by 2020. Nuclear conflict, mega-droughts, famine and widespread rioting will erupt across the world.
>
> The document predicts that abrupt climate change could bring the planet to the edge of anarchy as countries develop a nuclear threat to defend and secure dwindling food, water and energy supplies. The threat to global stability vastly eclipses that of terrorism, say the few experts privy to its contents.
>
> (Townsend and Harris, 2004)

In fact the report was neither suppressed nor secretive, as *The Observer* claims, but was made available online (Schwartz and Randall, 2003). The report presented the threats of climate change as a Hobbesian state of nature characterised by anarchy and instability in which the state must take action. In this sense the securitisation of climate change as an issue of global or human security reverts back to the state on the deepening axis. Although national security is broadened to include causes of conflict, the securitisation of climate change remains focused on questions of war and violence. The next section will consider the role of the main security actor within the state, the military, in dealing with climate change. It will also consider how the concept of time and the role of security knowledge can aid our understanding of environmental conflict.

4   Securitising climate change: assessing the advantages and disadvantages

As a strategy for dealing with climate change securitisation only makes sense if it leads to more effective policies. In this section I consider whether the securitisation of climate change is a strategy that policy makers and scholars should continue to pursue. In discussing the elements that constitute successful securitisation I return to a point that I developed earlier: that for securitisation to be effective 'extraordinary measures' must be taken in order to neutralise the threat.

In order to assess the advantages and disadvantages of securitising climate change I shall first discuss the question of time in relation to the vocabulary of urgency, catastrophe, survival and immediacy that is used in the security speech act. The extraordinary measures that need to be taken in response to the threat of climate change have a particular temporality of urgency or emergency. Second, I shall turn to the actor that is most privileged by national security discourse, namely the military, and look at how its role can be envisaged in relation to climate change. How suited are the military as an actor in the fight against climate change? Finally, I will look at the role that security knowledge plays in informing policy measures to tackle climate change. I shall argue that if policy makers privilege particular understandings of time, the role of the military and security knowledge, then the measures they take will be inadequate for tackling climate change.

4.1 The imperative of action

Time is an important consideration for climate change, as its effects will be manifested over a longer time span than is normally considered for policy making. In democratic countries the electoral cycle usually encompasses periods of four to seven years; this does not coincide with climate change, which will unfold over the long term. Moreover, the intergenerational element of climate change is a difficult consideration, particularly as there is uncertainty about the precise effects of climate change for future generations. These effects will vary according to the speed and scale of future temperature increases. A report by the German Advisory Council on Global Change speaks of a threshold of a 2 °C rise in the global mean temperature that would trigger 'abrupt climate change' (German Advisory Council on Global Change, 2007).

Activity 5.7

Look at the cartoon in Figure 5.8 by Tom Toles, a cartoonist for *The Washington Post*. What constraints to more effective climate policies are identified? How might securitisation change the problem of inaction that the cartoon depicts?

Figure 5.8
Climate emergency? A cartoon by Tom Toles for *The Washington Post*

The cartoon represents many of the constraints to more effective climate change policies that you have considered so far. These include debates on how certain knowledge of the problem should be before action is taken (point 1), the role of sceptics in delaying action (point 2), the costs of dealing with the problem (point 4) and discussion on who is responsible for implementing policy (point 8).

In terms of dealing with inaction, the intention of securitisation is that it will highlight the worst-case scenario of abrupt climate change so that discussions about time and future effects are suspended in favour of urgent action. A security speech act presents a threat as the supreme priority 'because if not handled now it will be too late, and we will not exist to remedy our failure' (Buzan, 1997, p. 14). By conveying a heightened sense of crisis and urgency, a security speech act tells us that we must urgently act to tackle the problem at hand in order to save ourselves. The Fourth Assessment Report of the IPCC also declared the impact of climate change to be 'abrupt and irreversible', therefore requiring immediate action by policy makers at the global level (Black, 2007).

The securitisation of climate change creates a sense of gravity, purpose, resolve and an imperative to action. If the threats that climate change poses are critical, if we are all affected in various ways, then immediate responses are needed. Securitisation is an attempt to impel policy makers to act to tackle climate change, because security is the language states understand (Eckersley, 2005). Security is the 'ultimate goal' of government policy makers whose legitimacy depends upon their capacity to protect their citizens by neutralising security threats.

The political scientist Daniel Deudney has argued that wars 'demand victory and a return to normality, producing a cycle of passivity and arousal that is not likely to make much of a contribution to establishing enduring patterns of environmentally sound behaviour' (Deudney, 2006, p. 246). Unlike most security threats that states have faced, achieving climate security will require sustained long-term commitment to action. Can the securitisation of climate change sustain such a long-term commitment towards action? Will members of the public tolerate a situation where other social and economic goals are subordinated to the quest for a stable climate? Such commitment, including the necessary allocation of financial resources that would ensue from prioritising climate change, might be particularly problematic when climate change competes for political attention with other national security threats. Counter-terrorism policies in particular risk shifting funds away from climate change. In the wake of Hurricane Katrina in the USA, which in 2005 destroyed parts of New Orleans, it became apparent that the Federal Emergency Management Agency had been underfunded and was

Book 2, Chapter 3 analyses Hurricane Katrina as a natural and social disaster unprepared to deal with such disasters. After 9/11 the Agency was incorporated in the Department of Homeland Security, with 75 per cent of funding being focused on fighting terrorism (*USA Today*, 2005). Speech acts of urgency and extraordinary measures can thus have unforeseen consequences for other social problems. Urgent action to address one threat can have disastrous consequences of inaction for others.

4.2 The military: security actor for the environment?

Another dimension of the securitisation of climate change concerns the actors involved in dealing with the threat. Although the broadening and deepening of security can lead to the involvement of civil society actors such as non-governmental organisations (NGOs), the military remain the traditional security actor entrusted by the state to tackle security threats. Elbe has argued in relation to HIV/AIDS, which has undergone a similar process of securitisation, that framing the problem as a security problem could have unwanted consequences in terms of the actors involved (Elbe, 2006). Such an emphasis, Elbe suggests, could exclude civil society and privilege the state and its security agencies.

My point here is that security speech acts do not only frame issues; they also mobilise specific institutions that are endowed with the authority to prevent conflicts, such as defence ministries, intelligence agencies, the military, the police and politicians. Although NGOs like Greenpeace or Friends of the Earth have embraced the representation of climate change as a security threat, paradoxically this can exclude them from further policy discussions on how the threat should be addressed. Although many NGOs have first-hand knowledge of how climate change is affecting people around the world and can speak with authority about their suffering, they do not speak with authority on security matters. NGOs can play an important role in humanitarian disaster relief, for example, but have less impact on how the role of security agencies is defined in relation to environmental threats.

Privileging the military could have unwanted environmental consequences. Wars have destructive environmental impacts, such as the deliberate destruction of the environment as a tactical manoeuvre, the use of hazardous substances, contamination of air and water resources and destruction of forests and crops (Elliott, 2004, p. 214). The world's militaries produce considerable air pollution and use as much petroleum as Japan, one of the world's largest economies. In many countries the military are also exempted from environmental regulation (Doolittle, 2003).

The feminist geographer Joni Seager has major reservations on the role of the military in environmental governance:

> Militaries are major environmental abusers. All militaries, everywhere, wreak environmental havoc – sometimes by accident, sometimes as 'collateral damage', and often as predetermined strategy. If every military-blighted site around the world were marked up on a map with red tacks, the earth would look as though it had a bad case of the measles.
>
> Militaries are privileged environmental vandals. Their daily operations are typically beyond the reach of civil law, and they are protected from public and governmental scrutiny, even in 'democracies'. When military bureaucrats are challenged or asked to explain themselves, they hide behind the 'national security' cloak of secrecy and silence – and it is military men themselves who get to define what 'national security' is. In countries that are in the grip of martial law, militaries have even more free and unhindered reign: with wide-ranging human rights abuses the norm under militarized regimes, environmental transgressions are often the least of the horrors for which critics try to hold militaries accountable, and thus even the fact that militaries are agents of major environmental degradation is often overlooked.
>
> Militaries are powerful environmental ravagers. The reach of militarized environmental destruction is global. The most powerful military contrivances, nuclear and chemical 'capability', push environmental capability to the limit – past the limits already for some of the radioactive, blighted wastelands created around the world by military testing, dumping, and adventurism.
>
> (Seager, 1999, p. 163)

Focusing on the state as the protector of its citizens shifts the emphasis from the military as a cause of environmental degradation to its role as an environmental protector. The military have claimed that they can play an important role in responding to the threats of climate change, both by making use of the technology available to them and by providing quick intervention in disaster situations. During Al Gore's vice presidency, the CIA permitted scientists to examine archives that might be useful in assessing environmental degradation (Matthew, 2000). The military also possess technology that could be useful for environmental assessment and monitoring. However, this would entail mobilisation of funds towards the military that could have damaging effects for social welfare and other areas of social life.

The role of the military as a privileged security actor addressing climate change is riven with contradictions. I would suggest that the military is an inappropriate actor to be given responsibility for protecting the environment. If the role of the military becomes dominant in environmental policies then the sort of policies it will favour are likely to be top–down and technology driven, and unlikely to be focused on the needs and livelihoods of communities. Militaries are not only implicated in the very processes of environmental destruction and degradation, but their knowledge about war and conflict is largely irrelevant to the measures that are needed to deal with climate change.

4.3 Security knowledge: preventing environmental conflicts?

The securitisation of climate change entails the mobilisation of the security knowledge of state institutions, particularly the military and intelligence, about war and conflict. Deudney has suggested that inter-state wars over resources are increasingly less likely as under the current world trading system states no longer experience resource dependency as a major threat to their economic and military power (Deudney, 2006, p. 236). However, while this may be true for states in the North, it is less applicable to the South. As you have seen earlier in this chapter, in the South climate change may lead to conflicts of scarcity, poverty and inter-ethnic violence.

According to Jon Barnett, however, studies of environmental and resource conflicts are 'almost entirely premised on the ethnocentric assumption that people in the South will resort to violence in times of resource scarcity ... There is a scripting of people from the South as barbaric, strongly implying that those in the North are more civilized' (Barnett, 2000, p. 274). Take for example the environmental conflicts analysed by Homer-Dixon (1991, 1994, 2001) in Section 3.1 above. You may recall that Homer-Dixon concluded that people will fight for scarce resources in what resembles a Hobbesian state of nature; the scarcer the resources, the more ferocious the fight. Homer-Dixon's research focused on resource scarcity in the Philippines, South Africa, Mexico, Rwanda, Pakistan and Gaza. Similarly, the German Advisory Council on Global Change has drawn a world map of 'hotspots', namely regions with the potential for environmental and natural resource conflict. As you can see in Figure 5.9, all these hotspots are located in the developing world,

Betsy Hartmann has challenged the idea that environmental scarcity will necessarily lead to a kind of 'localised ethnic and identity politics that causes social fragmentation and more opportunity for social groups to seize control of the state' (Hartmann, 2001, p. 56). To Hartmann oppositional forces can have a positive potential. Social conflict is not always bad. It need not necessarily be destabilising and can lead to more fair arrangements for resource management and more efficient patterns of resource use. Barnett arrives at a similar conclusion: while conflicts

Conflict constellations in selected hotspots

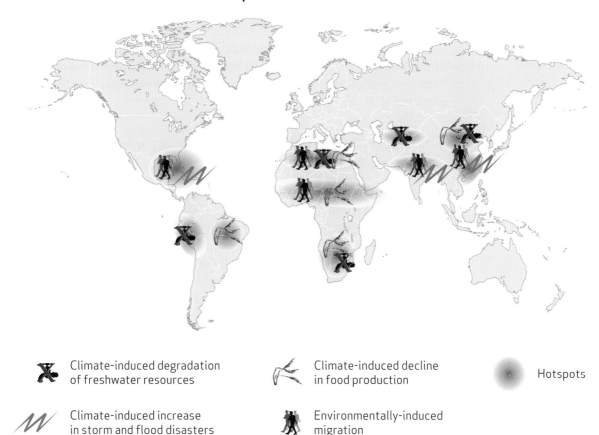

Climate-induced degradation of freshwater resources	Climate-induced decline in food production	Hotspots
Climate-induced increase in storm and flood disasters	Environmentally-induced migration	

can involve struggles between social groups in a society they do not necessarily lead to violence and may be peacefully resolved through political means (Barnett, 2001, p. 67). Conflict resolution may remedy existing social and political inequalities in access to and the distribution of natural resources.

The knowledge that is used in the studies of environmental conflicts and that is often taken up in security policy making divides the world into hotspots of conflicts and areas of normality. However, the causes of conflicts are not necessarily exclusively local and may include the legacy of colonialism and international economic relations in which Northern states are deeply implicated in the environmental problems in the South (Dalby, 2002).

Figure 5.9
Environmental conflict hotspots as mapped by the German Advisory Council on Global Change (2007)

5 Conclusion: securitisation – success or failure?

This chapter has shown how some security actors have attempted to move climate change up the political agenda by uttering security speech acts and mobilising security knowledge. This process of securitisation broadens the threats associated with climate change and deepens security as a concept by including actors beyond the state, such as regional populations and social groups.

Has the securitisation of climate change been successful? This chapter has offered a mixed answer. Many states in the North have embraced the securitisation of climate change. In the USA, the Clinton administration (1993–2001) had initially agreed to the broadening of national security to include environmental threats. Yet, despite its 'green' credentials, the Clinton administration disappointed many environmentalists through the limited progress it made on environmental issues. More recently, both in the USA and Europe, the military have been particularly successful in putting climate change on the security agenda. However, the securitisation of climate change has had only limited success. As not all speech acts have the same resonance or the same capacity to speak with authority, some actors have been more successful than others in defining what the securitisation of climate change means and how the problem is to be tackled. I have argued that attempts to securitise climate change as a global or human security threat ultimately revert back to the state as the provider of security and the source of peace against anarchy. As Hobbes envisioned in the seventeenth century, the state remains the major object of security, entrusted with protecting its citizens. I have also argued that security has been largely understood through the military lens of war, violent conflict and state destabilisation, and attempts to broaden security more radically or to deepen it beyond the state have been largely unsuccessful.

When examining the securitisation of climate change I have considered the notion of extraordinary measures. In claiming priority for climate change, security speech acts create a vicious circle of emergency that, I have suggested, is inadequate for dealing with climate change over the long term. Through securitisation, traditional security actors such as the military are privileged over other actors, such as non-state and local actors. Similarly, security knowledge about war, violent conflict and instability might be inadequate for understanding the complex social, political and economic conflicts that will unravel as climate change takes hold.

In unpacking the securitisation of climate change, the chapter has highlighted several elements that are relevant to the course themes:

■ The securitisation of climate change is intimately linked with political divisions and inequalities, between states and between the state and other actors (*course theme 2*).

■ Power depends upon the authority of those who make speech acts and on their relationship with those whom they seek to influence (*course theme 2*).

■ Actors contend over the meaning of climate change as a security issue and over the knowledge that is relevant for dealing with it (*course theme 3*).

■ Alongside spatial differences among states and regions in the world, the problem of time is an important consideration in the securitisation of climate change (*course theme 5*).

References

Adelphi Research, Adelphi Format and Weltformat. Design (2007) *Environment, Conflict and Cooperation* [online], German Foreign Ministry, http://www.ecc-exhibition.org/en/downloads.htm (Accessed 5 March 2008).

Aradau, C. (2004) 'Security and the democratic scene: desecuritization and emancipation', *Journal of International Relations and Development*, vol. 7, no. 4, pp. 388–413.

Austin, J. L. (1975 [1962]) *How To Do Things with Words* (2nd edn), Oxford, Oxford University Press.

Barnett, J. (2000) 'Destabilising the environment-conflict thesis', *Review of International Relations*, vol. 26, no. 2, pp. 271–88.

Barnett, J. (2001) *The Meaning of Environmental Security. Ecological Politics and Policy in the New Security Era*, London, Zed Books.

Barnett, J. and Adger, N. W. (2005) 'Security and climate change: towards an improved understanding', paper presented at the international workshop on Human Security and Climate Change, Asker, Norway, 20–21 June.

BBC (1999) *South Africa Declares War on Crime* [online], BBC News, http://news.bbc.co.uk/1/hi/world/africa/380125.stm (Accessed 8 January 2008).

BBC (2001) *Annan Declares War on AIDS* [online], BBC News, http://news.bbc.co.uk/1/hi/world/africa/1297474.stm (Accessed 8 January 2008).

Beck, U. (1992) *Risk Society. Towards a New Modernity* (trans. M. Ritter), London, Sage.

Beck, U. (1999) *World Risk Society*, Cambridge, Polity Press.

Beck, U. (2002) 'The terrorist threat: world risk society revisited', *Theory, Culture and Society*, vol. 19, no. 4, pp. 39–55.

Black, R. (2007) *UN Challenges States on Warming* [online], BBC News, http://news.bbc.co.uk/1/hi/sci/tech/7098902.stm (Accessed 3 December 2007).

Boutros-Ghali, Boutros (1992) 'An Agenda for Peace: Preventative diplomacy, peacemaking and peace-keeping', [online] http://www.un.org/docs/SG/agpeace.html (Accessed 25 June 2008).

Burke, A. (2001) 'Caught between national and human security: knowledge and power in post-crisis Asia', *Pacifica Review*, vol. 13, no. 3, pp. 215–39.

Buzan, B. (1997) 'Rethinking security after the Cold War', *Cooperation and Conflict*, vol. 32, no. 1, pp. 5–8.

Buzan, B., Waever, O. and de Wilde, J. (1998) *Security: A New Framework for Analysis*, Boulder, CO, Lynne Rienner.

Commission on Human Security (CHS) (2003) *Human Security Now* [online], http://www.humansecurity-chs.org/finalreport (Accessed 6 May 2008).

Dalby, S. (2002) *Environmental Security*, Minneapolis, University of Minnesota Press.

Deudney, D. (2006) 'Security' in Dobson, A. and Eckersley, R. (eds) *Political Theory and the Ecological Challenge*, Cambridge, Cambridge University Press.

Doolittle, S. (2003) 'Ten reasons why militarism is bad for the environment' [online], *Different Takes*, no. 22, http://popdev.hampshire.edu/projects/dt/pdfs/DifferenTakes_22.pdf (Accessed 3 December 2007).

Duffied, M. and Waddell, N. (2006) 'Securing humans in a dangerous world', *International Politics*, vol. 43, no. 1, pp. 1–23.

Eckersley, R. (2005) 'Climate change negotiations at the crossroads', *Global Change, Peace and Security*, vol. 17, no. 1, pp. 7–10.

Elbe, S. (2006) 'Should HIV/AIDS be securitized? The ethical dilemmas of linking HIV/AIDS and security', *International Studies Quarterly*, vol. 50, no. 1.

Elliott, L. (2004) *The Global Politics of the Environment* (2nd edn), Basingstoke, Palgrave Macmillan.

European Commission (2003) *European Security Strategy. A Secure Europe in a Better World* [online], http://ue.eu.int/uedocs/cmsUpload/78367.pdf (Accessed 20 March 2006).

Foreign and Commonwealth Office (2007) 'Margaret Beckett at UN Security Council climate change debate' [online], http://www.fco.gov.uk/servlet/Front?pagename=OpenMarket/Xcelerate/ShowPage&c=Page&cid=1007029391629&a=KArticle&aid=1176454354972 (Accessed 11 March 2008).

G77 (2007) 'G77 says Security Council debate on climate change violation of charter', *Journal of the Group of 77*, vol. 19, no. 1 [online], http://www.g77.org/nc/journal/printarticle.php?artno=05&id=0704 (Accessed 5 March 2008).

German Advisory Council on Global Change (2007) *World in Transition. Climate Change as a Security Risk. Summary for Policy Makers* [online], http://www.wbgu.de (Accessed 3 December 2007).

Gleick, P. H. (1993) 'Water and conflict: fresh water resources and international security, *International Security*, vol. 18, no. 1, pp. 79–112.

Gore, A. (2006) *An Inconvenient Truth. About the Film* [online], http://www.climatecrisis.net/aboutthefilm (Accessed 23 October 2007).

Greenpeace (2007) 'Weather of mass destruction' [online], 16 April, http://www.greenpeace.org/international/news/wmd-weather-041607 (Accessed 11 March 2008).

Hartmann, B. (2001) 'Will the circle be unbroken? A critique of the project on environment, population and security' in Peluso, N. L. and Watts, M. (eds) *Violent Environments*, Ithaca, NY, Cornell University Press.

Harvey, F. (2007) 'Global warming recast as a security issue' [online], *Financial Times*, 12 October, http://www.ft.com (Accessed 7 May 2008).

Hobbes, T. (1985 [1651]) *Leviathan*, London, Penguin.

Homer-Dixon, T. (1991) 'On the threshold: environmental changes as causes of acute conflict', *International Security*, vol. 16, no. 2, pp. 76–116.

Homer-Dixon, T. (1994) 'Environmental scarcities and violent conflict: evidence from cases', *International Security*, vol. 19, no. 1, pp. 5–40.

Homer-Dixon, T. (2001) *Environment, Scarcity and Violence*, Princeton, NJ, Princeton University Press.

Houghton, J. (2003) 'Global warming is now a weapon of mass destruction' [online], *The Guardian*, http://politics.guardian.co.uk/green/comment/0,9236,1007302,00.html (Accessed 5 March 2008).

Human Security Centre (HSC) (2005) *Human Security Report. War and Peace in the 21st Century* [online], Vancouver, University of British Columbia, http://www.humansecurityreport.info/content/view/25/60 (Accessed 15 November 2007).

Intergovernmental Panel on Climate Change (IPCC) (2007) *Climate Change 2007: Impacts, Adaptation and Vulnerability. Summary for Policy Makers* [online], IPCC, http://www.ipcc.ch/SPM13apr07.pdf (Accessed 18 July 2007).

International Commission on Intervention and State Sovereignty (ICISS) (2001) *The Responsibility to Protect. Report of the International Commission on Intervention and State Sovereignty* [online], Ottawa, International Development Research Centre, http://www.iciss.ca/pdf/Commission-Report.pdf (Accessed 5 July 2007).

Ki-moon, B. (2007) 'Secretary-General's statement at open Security Council debate on energy, security and climate' [online], http://www.un.org/apps/sg/sgstats.asp?nid=2524 (Accessed 20 July 2007).

Matthew, R. A. (2000) 'The environment as a national security issue', *Journal of Policy History*, vol. 12, no. 1, pp. 101–22.

Norton-Taylor, R. (2006) 'Climate change a bigger security threat than terrorism, says report', *The Guardian* [online], 12 June, http://www.guardian.co.uk/politics/2006/jun/12/uk.environment (Accessed 7 May 2008).

Office of the High Commissioner for Human Rights (OHCHR) (1951) *Convention Relating to the Status of Refugees* [online], http://www.unhchr.ch/html/menu3/b/o_c_ref.htm (Accessed 6 May 2008).

Postel, S. and Wolf, A. (2001) 'Dehydrating conflict', *Foreign Policy*, no. 126, pp. 60–67.

Revkin, A. C. and Williams, T. (2007) 'Global warming called security threat' [online], *New York Times*, 15 April, http://www.nytimes.com/2007/04/15/us/15warm.html (Accessed 5 March 2008).

Rice, C. (2007) 'Nations must fight climate change like terrorism, Rice says' [online], CNN, http://www.cnn.com/2007/POLITICS/09/27/rice.climate.conference (Accessed 23 October 2007).

Schwartz, P. and Randall, D. (2003) *An Abrupt Climate Change Scenario and Its Implications for United States National Security* [online], Global Business Network, http://www.gbn.com (Accessed 20 May 2007).

Seager, J. (1999) 'Patriarchal vandalism. Militaries and the environment' in Silliman, J. and King, Y. (eds) *Feminism, Population and the Environment*, London, Zed Books pp. 163–88.

Selby, J. (2005) 'Oil and water: the contrasting anatomies of resource conflicts', *Government and Opposition*, vol. 40, no. 2, pp. 200–24.

Sen, A. (1992) *Inequality Reexamined*, Cambridge, MA, Harvard University Press.

Sen, A. (2000) 'Why human security?', paper presented at the International Symposium on Human Security, Tokyo, 28 July.

Stripple, J. (2002) 'Climate change as a security issue' in Page, E. and Redclift, M. (eds) *Human Security and the Environment*, Cheltenham, Edward Elgar.

Townsend, M. and Harris, P. (2004) 'Now the Pentagon tells Bush: climate change will destroy us' [online], *The Observer*, 22 February, http://www.guardian.co.uk/climatechange/story/0,12374,1153530,00.html (Accessed 23 March 2006).

United Nations (UN) (1992) *United Nations Framework Convention on Climate Change* [online], UN, http://unfcc.int/essential_background/convention/background/items/2853.php (Accessed 3 December 2007).

United Nations Development Programme (UNDP) (1994) 'New Dimensions of Human Security' in UNDP, *Human Development Report* [online], New York, NY and Oxford, Oxford University Press, http://hdr.undp.org/reports/global/1994/en (Accessed 20 July 2007).

United Nations Environment Programme (UNEP) (2007) *Sudan. Post-Conflict Environmental Assessment. Synthesis Report* [online], UNEP, Nairobi, http://www.unep.org/sudan (Accessed 20 July 2007).

USA Today (2005) 'Exposed by Katrina, FEMA's flaws were years in the making' [online], http://www.usatoday.com/news/opinion/editorials/2005-09-07-our-view_x.htm (Accessed 3 December 2007).

Walt, S. (1991) 'The renaissance of security studies', *International Studies Quarterly*, vol. 35, no. 2, pp. 211–39.

Weber, M. (1947) *The Theory of Social and Economic Organization*, New York, NY, Free Press.

Williams, M. C. (2003) 'Words, images, enemies: securitization and international politic', *International Studies Quarterly*, vol. 47, no. 4, pp. 511–31.

Young, I. M. (2003) 'Feminist reactions to the contemporary security regime', *Hypatia*, vol. 18, no. 1, pp. 223–31.

Chapter 6

Energy and climate change: sustainable options, political choices and ethical considerations

Andrew Blowers

Contents

1	**Introduction**	**208**
	1.1 Learning outcomes	209
2	**Energy options and environmental impacts**	**209**
	2.1 Fossil fuel power: the heart of the problem	211
	2.2 Ways of tackling the problem	218
	2.3 Renewable energy: constraints and possibilities	220
	2.4 Is there a solution?	225
3	**Energy and sustainability**	**227**
	3.1 Nuclear energy: discourses and development	227
	3.2 Energy and ecological modernisation	230
	3.3 Nuclear energy, power and democracy	234
4	**Ethics and energy**	**238**
	4.1 Uneven development over space	238
	4.2 Intragenerational equity	240
	4.3 Intergenerational equity	244
5	**Conclusion: ethics and the energy debate**	**249**
	References	**250**

1   Introduction

> From heating and lighting to transport, industry and communications, energy is fundamental to almost everything we do. We expect it to be available whenever we want it, to be affordable, safe and environmentally sustainable.
>
> (Department of Trade and Industry, 2003, p. 6)

This statement sums up the intrinsic, if taken for granted, role that energy plays in modern industrialised societies. Of course, there are many parts of the world where energy is not so easily available, affordable or safe. I shall come to the problems of unevenness in energy supply and demand later in this chapter. For the moment let us focus on the key role that energy plays in transforming the relationship between nature and society (*course theme 1*). Throughout human civilisation there has been evidence of environmental degradation through deforestation, overgrazing or exploitation of resources (Diamond, 2005). But, on the whole, the impact of human actions was limited over both space and time (*course theme 5*). Resources, for the most part, were barely depleted and pollution and degradation were localised. Then came the transformation which has been labelled the 'Industrial Revolution', a transformation in ideas, in social development as well as technology. As Clarence Glacken (1967) put it: 'With the eighteenth century there ends ... an epoch in the history of man's relationship to nature. What follows is of an entirely different order, influenced by the theory of evolution, specialisation in the attainment of knowledge, acceleration in the transformations of nature' (p. 707). It was the process of industrialisation that brought about the conversion of fossil fuels into power, heat and light, thereby releasing within a mere 250 years carbon that had lain dormant underground for millions of years. Within a (geologically speaking) tiny time span the volume of greenhouse gases in the atmosphere increased from a level of an equivalent of 280 parts of carbon dioxide (CO_2) per million (280 ppm) before the Industrial Revolution to 379 ppm in the early twenty-first century (IPCC, 2007) and, if the same trends continue, it will reach about 550 ppm by the middle of the century. Such a level, as we have already seen in Chapter 1, would, at least in some regions, have catastrophic impacts on both human and non-human life.

Society appears to have reached a critical point. Fossil fuels, the energy of modernisation, which constitute about 70 per cent of global energy output, now threaten the survival of life on Earth as we know it. The key to survival lies in conserving energy and switching to carbon free or, at least, low carbon sources. This chapter focuses first on whether the necessary changes *can* be achieved within a continuing context of industrial development and economic growth (broadly a 'business as usual' approach). It soon becomes apparent that it is not simply a technical question. There are, in terms of *course theme 2*, political divisions, inequalities and distributions of power that may both promote and constrain change. They provoke the question of what *should* be done, whether climate change requires a more radical transformation in the way energy is used and distributed. This normative question impels us to think about some of the ethical issues that influence the way we think about and choose between alternative energy strategies. It is a question that concerns inequalities in the availability and consumption of energy between places. And it is a question that forces us to consider the implications of our actions not merely for ourselves but for the generations to follow. Energy policy requires us to think about the kind of world we are creating through decisions taken now which will have implications for society and environment in the generations to come.

1.1 Learning outcomes

This chapter should enable you to:

■ recognise the environmental implications of alternative forms of energy production

■ understand the technical and political constraints on the development of alternative energy strategies (*course question 3*)

■ reflect on the contemporary discourse of ecological modernisation and its relationship to sustainable development

■ consider the relationship between new forms of governance and new forms of democratic decision making

■ explore the uneven development of alternative energy strategies over time and space and the ethical issues of intragenerational and intergenerational equity that arise.

2 Energy options and environmental impacts

It would be impossible within the space of a chapter to cover all the aspects of energy so I shall not provide a detailed evaluation of the technical aspects but instead will consider how technical along with political considerations shape the debates about energy policy in particular and environmental policy in general. I shall further limit my attention to electricity supply, which accounts for around two-fifths of global carbon emissions from energy production and 37 per cent of those in the UK. A continuous supply of electricity has become critical to everyday living in most (though not all) societies. In James Lovelock's words, 'it is an essential requisite for civilisation' (2006, p. 88). Electricity is a flexible form of energy used for power supply (industrial, domestic, transport), lighting and space heating. It can offer insights into a wide range of debates on energy and environment. So, this chapter takes energy, particularly electricity, as the subject for exploring some of the political and ethical issues that face society in the search for a sustainable future.

It must be remembered that electricity is only a secondary form of energy, converted from primary sources to supply power to drive machines and to provide lighting and heating. Primary energy supply comes mainly from the fossil fuels of oil, gas and coal, as shown in Figure 6.1a, which are used to produce heat, power and fuel for the transport, domestic, industrial and service sectors (Figure 6.1b). It is these fossil fuels that are responsible for the vast bulk of carbon output (Figure 6.1c).

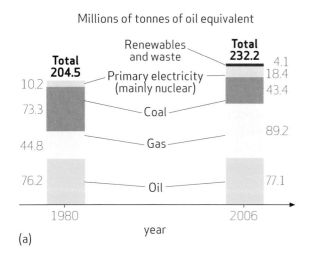

(a)

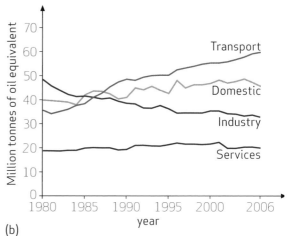

(b)

Figure 6.1a
UK energy consumption by primary sources, 1980 to 2006

Figure 6.1b
UK energy consumption by sector, 1980 to 2006

Figure 6.1c
UK carbon dioxide emissions by sector

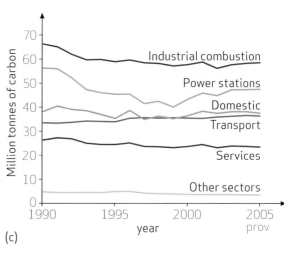

(c)

Initially, I shall focus on one industrialised country, the UK, to identify some of the policy debates surrounding energy production. I am using the UK to provide a specific illustration of broader policy discussions that take place in an international context. In terms of sheer scale the rapid development of electricity production in China, India, Brazil and other rapidly developing economies may seem to make 'the debate on a small northern European island look increasingly irrelevant' (*The Guardian*, 2007, p. 32). Yet the debate on solutions in the UK is similar to that occurring across the world. The UK, where the Industrial Revolution began, faces issues of energy supply and security which are experienced elsewhere and illustrates the problems as well as the possibilities of reducing global carbon output. The UK offers a way of exploring the question 'What *can* be done for the future and what *should* be done?' (*course question* 4). I shall begin by looking at the technical and political constraints of different options for a low carbon economy.

2.1 Fossil fuel power – the heart of the problem

Dominating the flat and featureless low lying lands of the River Ouse in East Yorkshire are three coal-fired power stations, Ferrybridge, Eggborough and Drax (Figure 6.2). Situated a little south-east of Selby, Drax is the largest coal-fired power station in the UK. Its six generators with a total installed capacity of 4000 megawatts (MW) produce around 7 per cent of the country's total electricity. Its massive cooling towers with their long plumes of relatively harmless steam can be seen from miles away, as can the web of high transmission power lines connecting the station to the grid. However, emissions of sulphur dioxide (SO_2), nitrogen oxides (NO_X) and, more especially, the more than 20 million tonnes of CO_2 poured out per year are invisible. To put this into perspective, the carbon output of Drax alone is equivalent to the emissions from a quarter of the cars or a third of the homes in the UK. The CO_2 output from Drax and other fossil fuel (coal and gas) power stations in the UK in 2006 accounted for three-quarters of the nearly 43 million tonnes of carbon (MtC) emissions from electricity generation, out of a total of 149 MtC (around 2 per cent of the global total) that the UK produces each year. Energy supply from fossil fuels has become a key issue in the climate change debate and a focus for protests such as the one at Drax in 2006 (Figure 6.3). The example of Drax provides a context for us to identify the central importance of energy production for the problem of climate change.

In the middle of the last century coal accounted for as much as 90 per cent of the UK's electricity production. Its contribution has gradually declined in the wake of competition from gas, nuclear and other sources, industrial disputes and the environmental damage caused

Figure 6.2a
Drax power station

(a)

Figure 6.2b
Location map of Drax
power station

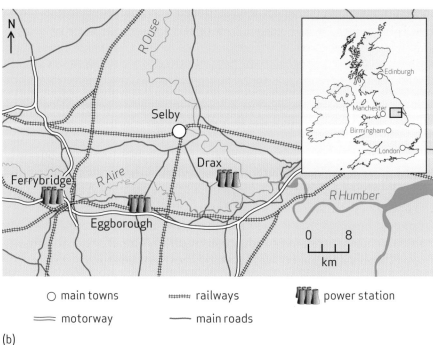

(b)

especially by SO_2 emissions that produce acid rain. Despite this, at the
beginning of this century, coal still provided about 15 per cent of total
energy in 2000 (Cabinet Office, 2002) and about a third of the UK's
electricity. Although older, less efficient coal-fired plants are being
retired they will be replaced, in part at least, by new coal-fired plants,

Figure 6.3
Protesters at Drax, 2006

for example on the Thames estuary. Coal is a relatively secure fuel, produced both domestically and in many other countries, and there are plentiful, accessible and widespread reserves estimated to last for around 200 years. Coal is supplied from a variety of sources, which helps to make it a competitive form of energy in the liberalised electricity market.

The biggest problem facing coal is its environmental impact. Coal mining exploits a non-renewable resource, exhausting the most accessible and highest quality reserves first. As the scale of production increases there is a widening environmental impact as it is hauled to markets. There is also the environmental degradation created by mining, particularly opencast mining (Figure 6.4). This has almost entirely replaced deep mining in the UK. But it is the atmospheric pollution from coal burning that is the most extensive and serious environmental issue. In the early phase of industrialisation the impact of coal burning fires, furnaces and boilers was localised, but very destructive to environment and human health (Figure 6.5). In the latter half of the last century smokeless fuels and central heating systems, combined with the Clean Air Act (1956) and subsequent legislation, vastly improved air quality in British cities. However, the development of large power plants with tall stacks created a major international problem, with wind borne transfers of acid pollution that caused acid rain, damaging forests, lakes and rivers as well as human health as far away as Scandinavia. The installation of flue gas desulphurisation equipment has reduced emissions of SO_2 in large plants such as Drax by 90 per cent (although marginally increasing CO_2). However, coal – by far the most polluting energy technology – and other fossil fuels also create a much wider impact, global in scale.

Figure 6.4

Environmental degradation resulting from opencast lignite mining in the eastern German village of Heuersdorf

Worldwide, coal accounts for 40 per cent of electricity production, which is increasing rapidly, notably in the industrialising and carbon-intensive economies of the Far East and south Asia. Although statistics change rapidly and can be unreliable, the figures for China are arresting.

Figure 6.5
Air pollution in the
1950s

In 2007 China's energy consumption was rising at about 7 per cent per year from about 10 per cent of the world total at the beginning of the century to over 14 per cent by 2025. But its consumption per head in 2007 was eleven times lower than the USA. The country is heavily dependent on coal for more than two-thirds of its primary energy consumption and consumes nearly two-fifths of world supply. In 2006 China was said to be constructing 550 coal-fired power stations, the equivalent of one or two every week. China's population and coal dependence combined with a very rapid economic growth have made it the world's largest emitter of CO_2 by the end of the first decade of this century. Figure 6.6 shows world carbon emissions in 2005.

World total
28,190 million tonnes of CO_2
28% growth in world
carbon emissions,
1995–2005

All figures shown on the map are expressed as
million tonnes of carbon dioxide emmitted

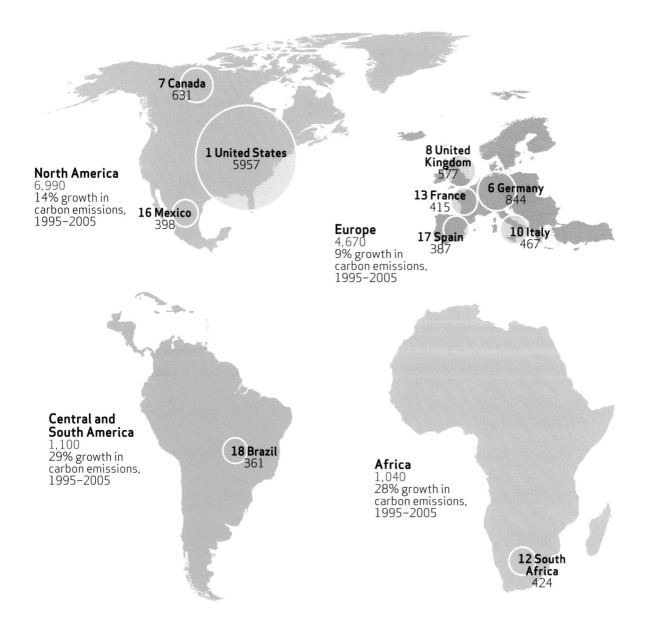

7 Canada
631

1 United States
5957

North America
6,990
14% growth in
carbon emissions,
1995–2005

16 Mexico
398

**8 United
Kingdom**
577

13 France
415

6 Germany
844

Europe
4,670
9% growth in
carbon emissions,
1995–2005

17 Spain
387

10 Italy
467

**Central and
South America**
1,100
29% growth in
carbon emissions,
1995–2005

18 Brazil
361

Africa
1,040
28% growth in
carbon emissions,
1995–2005

**12 South
Africa**
424

Figure 6.6
World carbon emissions in 2005 by region highlighting the twenty highest producing countries

Eurasia
2,580
4% growth in
carbon emissions,
1995–2005

3 Russia
1696

20 Ukraine
343

Middle East
1,450
62% growth in
carbon emissions,
1995–2005

9 South Korea
500

2 China
5323

4 Japan
1230

11 Iran
451

5 India
1166

**14 Saudi
Arabia**
412

Asia and Oceania
10,360
58% growth in
carbon emissions,
1995–2005

19 Indonesia
359

15 Australia
407

The world remains massively dependent on fossil fuels to meet its energy demands. Fossil fuels are at the heart of the climate change debate, which has several dimensions. Some of these focus on the *supply* of energy. Of major concern is the future security of supply of fossil fuels; for example, the possible threat to the supply of gas arising from the geographical concentration of gas reserves; or the fuel shortages likely to occur as the point is passed when oil reserves diminish relative to oil production ('peak oil'). Other debates focus on issues of *demand,* for example whether it is possible to reduce the demand for car and air travel, or the prospects for improving energy efficiency and conservation, and the possibilities for constraining domestic and commercial demand. These are important in terms of carbon output and climate change; indeed, demand management is widely regarded as an essential component of carbon reduction policy. Nonetheless, political attention has focused mainly on reducing carbon output from energy supply (Figure 6.6). Here, I shall concentrate on what has, perhaps, become politically the most vigorous debate, namely the debate about the potential for reducing CO_2 from the production of electricity and in particular the roles of alternative low carbon technologies in providing a response to climate change.

So the issue is, can we solve the problem of carbon emissions technically, by reducing energy supply?

2.2 Ways of tackling the problem

Technically, there appear to be four basic ways of tackling the problem of CO_2 emissions from coal.

1. *Reduce the CO_2 emissions by improved coal utilisation and carbon abatement technologies.* Carbon output may be reduced by improving coal burning efficiency (using more advanced boilers, improved gasifiers and turbines), by carbon abatement technology, and by co-firing with biomass. But, the development of so-called 'clean coal' hinges on the concept of carbon capture and storage (CCS) whereby carbon is sequestered, that is captured, transported and stored underground in the voids left by mining and oil exploitation, notably under the North Sea and also in deep saline aquifers (see Chapter 1). In principle, there is sufficient suitable geological capacity to accommodate more carbon than is likely to be produced by fossil fuel plants during the whole of this century. A basic question is whether CCS on the scale required is technically achievable. Beyond that is the question of whether sufficient incentives and regulations can be put in place to make CCS a practical and achievable way of decarbonising fossil fuel energy production. There is also the risk that stored carbon might escape into the atmosphere at some point in the future.

2. *Ensure greater efficiency in the distribution and consumption of electricity.* This may be achieved in a variety of ways, collectively sometimes called 'distributed energy'. This refers to technologies that supply localised distribution networks rather than taking energy from the national transmission network. Examples are small-scale plant supplying a local community, combined heat and power systems and other technologies that generate energy near where it is consumed. This may achieve greater efficiency in consumption (though not necessarily in production). For example, combined heat and power and district heating systems ensure that much of the heat from generating electricity is not wasted (see Figure 6.7).

Figure 6.7
District heating system transmission pipeline being installed at Kongens Nytorv in Copenhagen

3. *Switch fuels to reduce carbon emissions* by replacing coal with natural gas, which produces 97 tonnes of carbon per gigawatt hour (+C/9WH) compared with coal's 243tC/GWH (SDC, 2006, p. 6). In fact, this is what is occurring. Natural gas, first from the North Sea and subsequently brought in from Norway, Russia and other countries, has become the leading source of electricity supply in the UK

(38 per cent electricity generation in 2002 and rising to possibly as much as two-thirds by 2020) and throughout much of Europe (Figure 6.8). Gas raises other issues, notably of security of supply since it is increasingly imported and the sources are much more limited than for coal. However, in common with coal, gas provides a relatively cheap source of power but still at a cost of emitting carbon into the atmosphere.

4. *Switch to other low carbon sources.* The methods described so far focus on what can be done to reduce carbon output from fossil fuels. The fourth method is to switch to other low carbon sources, namely renewables or nuclear energy (which produces only about 4.4tC/GWH). By focusing on **renewables** (section 2.3 below) and nuclear, we can consider the technical possibilities and also identify and explore the social constraints that determine the political feasibility of alternative forms of electricity production.

Before we continue, see if you can tackle the activity below.

Activity 6.1

Think about what the terms 'renewable', 'low carbon' and 'carbon neutral' mean. How would you define them? Consider your answers as you read the next section.

2.3 Renewable energy – constraints and possibilities

In this section I shall concentrate mainly on wind power which, in the UK and many other countries, is the most rapidly developing of the renewable sources of electricity supply (Figures 6.9 and 6.10). Wind energy, like other renewables, is a low carbon technology. Indeed, although energy (most of it, at present, from fossil fuel electricity) is necessary for the construction of the turbines and initial capital costs are high, once operating, wind power is largely both cost and carbon free. Furthermore, it is a relatively safe technology (though offshore wind farms may pose some risks to shipping), it is secure (widely available within the UK and many other countries and largely immune to terrorist threats) and it creates no waste until decommissioning.

Wind power is in the vanguard of a group of developing renewable technologies which together have been set a government target to supply a fifth of the UK's electricity by 2020. Wind energy is renewable; in other words, unlike fossil fuels, wind is a resource that is not depleted once used. In common with tides, waves, rivers and solar energy, wind is a natural resource that can be used in an inexhaustible manner. These

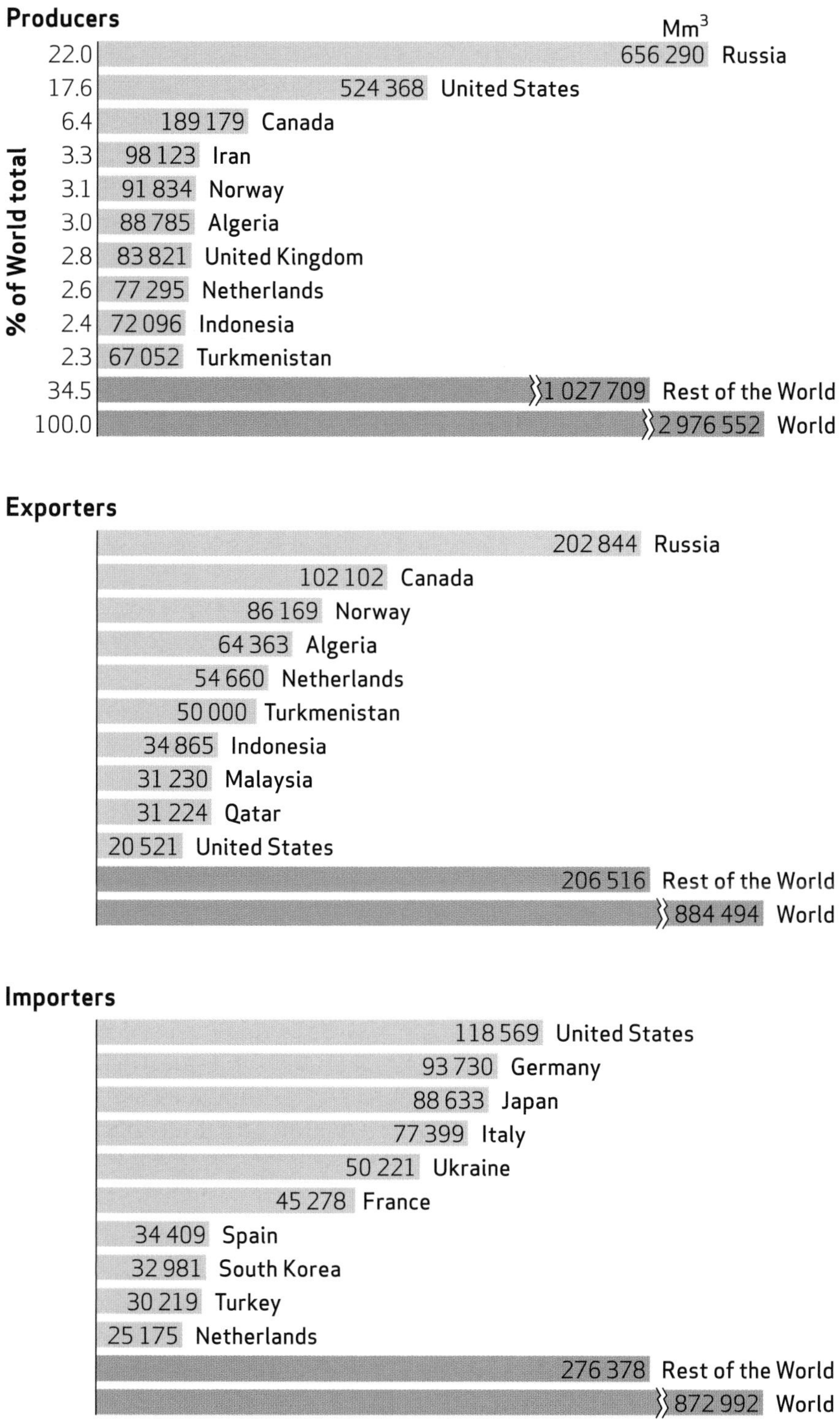

Producers

Mm³

% of World total		
22.0	656 290	Russia
17.6	524 368	United States
6.4	189 179	Canada
3.3	98 123	Iran
3.1	91 834	Norway
3.0	88 785	Algeria
2.8	83 821	United Kingdom
2.6	77 295	Netherlands
2.4	72 096	Indonesia
2.3	67 052	Turkmenistan
34.5	1 027 709	Rest of the World
100.0	2 976 552	World

Exporters

202 844	Russia
102 102	Canada
86 169	Norway
64 363	Algeria
54 660	Netherlands
50 000	Turkmenistan
34 865	Indonesia
31 230	Malaysia
31 224	Qatar
20 521	United States
206 516	Rest of the World
884 494	World

Importers

118 569	United States
93 730	Germany
88 633	Japan
77 399	Italy
50 221	Ukraine
45 278	France
34 409	Spain
32 981	South Korea
30 219	Turkey
25 175	Netherlands
276 378	Rest of the World
872 992	World

Figure 6.8

World producers, exporters and importers of natural gas in 2006 (in millions of cubic metres)

Figure 6.9

Examples of wind farms in the UK. Offshore in Whitstable, north Kent; onshore at Black Law, southern Lanarkshire, Scotland; offshore in Liverpool Bay, north Wirral

Figure 6.10

Global wind capacity, 1990–2007

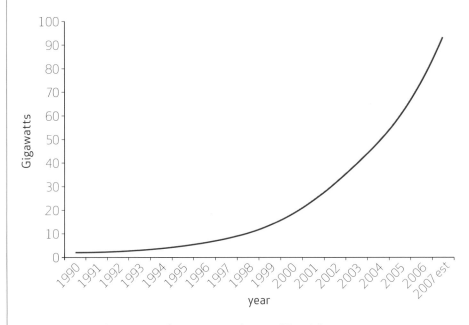

resources vary in terms of constancy (some, like tides, are pretty constant while others – wind, waves, solar and rivers – are variable), availability (varies according to climate, access to coastline) and capacity (for example, rivers have limited capacity, onshore wind is more limited than offshore, solar energy is universal). Other so-called renewable resources such as biomass while not strictly speaking inexhaustible can be replenished once used.

Wind energy does have a number of drawbacks. One is economic. Competition within energy markets is dependent on many variables including subsidies, the capital cost of entering the market, the availability of transport and transmission and so on. Wind energy is not competitive in price with fossil fuels and, consequently, is supported, in the UK, by the Renewables Obligation. Essentially, this obliges suppliers to provide an increasing proportion of their electricity from sustainable sources, for which they receive a Renewables Obligation Certificate or otherwise pay a penalty (the buy-out price). Like carbon trading (see Chapter 3) it is an example of using market mechanisms (incentives, penalties) to reduce carbon output. The Renewables Obligation has supported established technologies such as onshore wind and can be used flexibly to overcome the development and technology risks with offshore wind, biomass and newer technologies. As the scale of renewables development increases it is expected that the cost of delivered energy from renewables will eventually reduce to levels competitive with fossil fuel technologies.

A second problem affecting wind energy in particular is intermittency of supply since wind is not constantly available. (There is sufficient wind in the UK to produce some electricity for about 70 per cent of the year, although a typical wind turbine only generates to about 30 per cent of its capacity.) So long as the level of wind generated energy in the total electricity output is low, intermittency is not a problem since the power system has backup designed to cope with variations in supply and demand. However, once wind goes beyond about 20 per cent of total electricity output there would be a need for more backup capacity to maintain stable supplies. Since this backup would come mainly from fossil fuelled plants there would be some associated carbon emissions but, given that backup would only be needed occasionally, the extra emissions would be small compared with the emissions avoided by using wind power. Moreover, some renewables (wave and tidal) could be used to reduce intermittency while others (hydro and biomass) could supply emission-free backup. Perhaps more importantly, there are also problems in connecting some renewables to the national grid, especially for those schemes that are in remote locations far from the centres of greatest demand.

Wind energy is also controversial and projects have met with opposition in many proposed locations, leading to a failure to achieve planning consent. Examples of controversial proposals include a major scheme near Penrith in Cumbria and a scheme for 500MW on the Isle of Lewis in the Outer Hebrides. Objections to such schemes are mainly on grounds of visual impact, noise and effects on wildlife, especially bird migration. The resistance of local communities is a major reason why wind farms are being developed offshore where they are less visually intrusive and further away from potential protesters. But, here the effects on shipping and birds and the need for landward grid connections may provoke opposition.

Once wind farms are established local opposition tends to decline. Overall, wind energy is a popular option with over two-thirds of the population consistently in favour (with some polls registering as many as three-quarters). How much of the potential of wind energy can be realised will depend on various constraints, in particular technical (for example, grid connection), political (for example, planning permissions) and economic (for example, the competitiveness of wind against alternative sources) constraints. But, in the UK and in other countries, wind will account for an increasing proportion of capacity and output of electricity in the energy mix. The potential and problems of some other renewables are presented in Box 6.1.

Box 6.1   Some renewable technologies

Wind energy is the most developed renewable technology at present, but other possibilities are beginning to emerge. Among these are tidal and wave power, barrages across estuaries, biomass and solar (photovoltaics). Taken together it has been estimated that renewables potentially could supply between a half and two-thirds of projected supply of 400–500 terawatt hours (TWh) of electricity in the UK by 2050 in the following proportions: wind offshore (18–23 per cent), wind onshore (8–11 per cent), wave/tidal (12–14 per cent), biomass (9–11 per cent), solar (6–8 per cent) (DTI/Carbon Trust, 2004).

Some of these sources present environmental problems. For example, a barrage across the Severn estuary would theoretically be able to provide 8.6GW and save 5MtC per year but would threaten marine ecosystems. The growing of biomass for biofuels offers a carbon neutral renewable resource in that carbon emitted from combustion is balanced by the new growth of plant material to produce more biofuels. This affects the carbon cycle, in other words the flows of carbon throughout the biosphere and atmosphere, although it is, in principle, carbon neutral as there is no net increase in the carbon in the atmosphere (although this theoretical equilibrium is difficult to achieve within one place and within a short time-frame). Biofuels converted from biomass to power motorised transport may have unintended but devastating consequences. The planting of sugar cane, palm oil and other crops may cause biodiversity loss, soil erosion and nutrient leaching. Carbon released through burning forests and peat and to provide the energy required to harvest, transport and process the crops can undermine the emissions saved in using the fuel. Furthermore, land used to grow biofuels (maize, wheat, etc.) may mean less land available for growing crops, often in the poorest countries.

Renewables, then, are not without problems, notably the cost of development and the need for government support, especially in the early stages of development. They are also liable to arouse local opposition and concerns about damage to amenity and ecosystems. Biofuels, especially, create environmental (Figure 6.11) and social inequalities. They can have a disproportionately destructive impact on poorer societies where they are grown as commercial crops.

(a)

(b)

(c)

Figure 6.11a

Clearing land for biofuels can lead to environmental degradation such as this example of deforestation for a palm oil plantation in Malaysia

Figure 6.11b

A Palm oil plantation entrance sign in Subang Jaya, Malaysia. Palm oil is a major biofuel crop in developing countries

Figure 6.11c

Large acreages are devoted to maize production for biofuels such as these grain silos in a corn field in Manitoba, Canada

Biofuels aside, in terms of carbon output, renewables are by far the most environmentally benign form of energy, and, except in those communities where they arouse local opposition, they are an uncontroversial and popular option and likely to increase their share in the energy mix. While this may be true of the UK, and also of Europe and North America generally, elsewhere the pressures of rapid economic growth or lack of investment will tend to restrain the contribution of renewables.

2.4 Is there a solution?

Having considered the problem of fossil fuel energy and the prospects of renewables we may pause and consider whether we have any answer to the first part of *course question 4*: what *can* be done for the future? This is a question about both technical and political feasibility and, not surprisingly, there are different views. Let's look at two diverging views about the technical prospects for a low carbon solution. The more optimistic views suggests that, 'Humanity can solve the carbon and climate problem in the first half of this century simply by scaling up what we already know how to do' (Pacala and Socolow, 2004, p. 968). To stabilise the atmospheric concentration of CO_2 at around 500 ppm of greenhouse gases would require holding emissions at the present global level of 7 billion tonnes of carbon per year. This could be achieved through a combination of methods. The first is improved energy efficiency and conservation, including more efficient buildings and power plants, greater fuel efficiency and lower use of transport. A second approach is decarbonising energy through a shift from coal to natural gas, CCS, nuclear energy and renewables (the approach that has been covered so far in this chapter). Third, there is the prospect of better biological storage in natural sinks through conservation and development of forests and reducing the loss of carbon through improved agricultural soils management. This optimistic assessment seems heroic but plausible if only technical considerations apply.

By contrast, Fells et al. (2005) provide a technical assessment of the potential to reduce emissions in the UK by 60 per cent by 2050 (the target proposed by the Royal Commission on Environmental Pollution in 2000). Again, the technologies are arranged in three, though quite different, groups. There are those immediately available, including energy conservation and efficiency, some renewables and nuclear energy. Then there are those technologies which are within reach but require major investment or subsidy such as passive, safe nuclear reactors, carbon sequestration and tidal barrages notably across the Severn estuary. Third, there are those that are 'within sight but not yet within easy reach' (p. 28) which include hydrogen fuelled transport, photovoltaic cells deployed on a large scale and fast breeder and fusion reactors. Taking the first two groups, where necessary backed by government support and subsidy, Fells et al. concluded a 25 per cent reduction in carbon output by 2025 was a possibility. Beyond that, diminishing returns and the inexorable rise in transport emissions made 'the long-term future less optimistic. The chances of achieving the 60 per cent figure must be very slender indeed' (p. 32).

In terms of 'What can be done for the future?' it seems that technology provides some hope, if not the imminent prospect of success. We also saw in Chapter 3 that carbon trading offers, at least in theory, the prospect of a policy mechanism that uses market principles to achieve specified reductions in carbon output. It is conceivable that progressive reductions in targets combined with developments in technology could avert some, but probably not all, of the impacts of climate change. So the most optimistic position is that technically and in terms of policy mechanisms the solution appears to be there. But it is obviously not just a matter of technology nor policy alone; it is also a social question. The question of whether it can be done involves societal understanding and willingness to change.

Activity 6.2

Look back over the previous sections and summarise the technical constraints facing low carbon technologies. As you read on, note down what the political constraints might be.

3 Energy and sustainability

In so far as renewables offer one possible solution to climate change they also appear to provide an obvious answer to the question, what *should* be done? But even here, as we have seen, with some technologies there may be undesirable environmental and social consequences. These become more evident when we consider another low carbon technology, nuclear energy, which is often proposed as part of the solution. However, the nuclear option is deeply controversial and raises a range of social and political issues which enable us to explore some key debates on *course themes 2, 3* and *4*: inequalities and distributions of power; contention over values and knowledge; and the relationship between sustainability and development.

3.1 Nuclear energy – discourses and development

Nuclear energy is a well established technology. Today it accounts for around 16 per cent of global electricity supply. There are some 440 reactors located in more than 30 countries with particular concentrations in North America and Europe, where most power plants were developed in the latter part of the last century, and in Asia (India, China, Japan and South Korea), where expansion has recently occurred (Figure 6.12). Nuclear energy originated with the development of reactors for producing uranium and plutonium for atomic bombs in the Second World War and its association with awesome destructive power and widespread and long-lived contamination has always been its central problem. However, the fortunes of nuclear energy have shifted over the years in response to what I shall describe as changing discourses. In the early years there was a *discourse of trust in technology* in which nuclear energy, 'the peaceful atom', was promoted as a safe, economic ('too cheap to meter') and environmentally benign source promising unlimited energy. This was a time of deferential trust in expertise, of closed and secretive institutions and of high expectations from technological solutions. The dangers were discounted or undisclosed, for example the risks to workers and the local population arising from contamination from the reactor fire at Windscale (now Sellafield) in 1957.

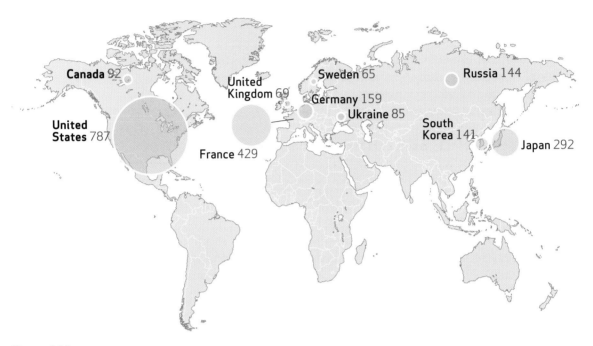

Figure 6.12
World nuclear power in 2008 in the ten highest producing countries (in billion Kilowatt hours of electricity)

Nuclear electricity generation 2006		
Country	Billion kilowatt hours	Percentage of total electricity
USA	787.2	19
France	428.7	78
Japan	291.5	30
Germany	158.7	32
Russia	144.3	16
South Korea	141.2	39
Canada	92.4	16
Ukraine	84.8	48
UK	69.2	18
Sweden	65.1	48
World	**2658**	**16**

By the 1970s the discourse had entirely shifted to a *discourse of danger* characterised by mistrust of experts, concerns about impacts on health and environment and fears about accidents and the military implications. This discourse was encouraged by the revelation of spectacular accidents (Windscale in 1957, Three Mile Island, USA, in 1979 and culminating in Chernobyl in the Ukraine in 1986), fears of the proliferation of nuclear weapons during the Cold War and changing social attitudes. These were manifested in challenges to government and the nuclear establishment from environmental and peace movements, protests and demonstrations in many countries, notably against nuclear weapons deployment and the construction of power plants, reprocessing facilities and radioactive waste repositories. Opposition to nuclear, combined with its commercial uncompetitiveness, halted its expansion and several countries either stopped further development (for example, Sweden and, later, Germany) or abandoned it altogether (Denmark, Ireland, Italy).

Eventually, towards the end of the last century, this turbulent period subsided as a *discourse of consensus and cooperation* emerged. With the nuclear industry seemingly in retreat and suffering some reverses, the Cold War over and accidents fading in memory, there was in many Western countries an opportunity to bring together the nuclear industry and its opponents in the search for solutions to the seemingly intractable problems of long-term radioactive waste management. There was a spirit of greater openness and dialogue, an emphasis on the need for public involvement in decision making. However, this period of relative tranquillity has been undermined by a developing discourse which places climate change as the overwhelming problem and for which nuclear is, for some, part of the solution. With the prospect of a 'nuclear renaissance' old antagonisms have been resurrected and old fears concerning proliferation (exacerbated by terrorism), accidents and radioactive waste have resurfaced in several countries.

The UK's reappraisal of the case for nuclear energy illustrates these arguments and reflects the recent discursive shift and connected changing power relations in the conflict over energy policy. In the early years of the twenty-first century, with North Sea oil and gas declining, attention turned towards the future energy mix for the UK. An important factor was the imminent retirement of around a third of the electricity generating capacity, consisting of ageing high carbon fossil fuel plants and most of the nuclear power stations, leaving only 7 per cent of electricity from nuclear by 2020. Although the 'energy gap' will be filled substantially from gas, thereby saving carbon output relative to coal, the government has argued that nuclear's contribution to carbon saving of between 7.95–19.9MtC (range 5–12 per cent) of the total UK emissions in 2004 would be lost unless the plants were replaced (DTI, 2007). It is in this context that the debate about nuclear energy has revived.

Both the discursive shift towards nuclear and the transition to a more favourable, but by no means enthusiastic, reconsideration of the nuclear option, can be traced in opinion polls which, at the beginning of the century, showed a declining opposition and a growing but still minority opinion in favour (Figure 6.13). In the UK this shift may also be seen in successive energy reviews and White Papers. The 2002 *Energy Review* (Cabinet Office, 2002) suggested there were 'good grounds for taking a positive stance to keeping the nuclear option open' (p. 124) and the subsequent White Paper endorsed this while regarding the nuclear option as 'unattractive' at that time (DTI, 2003). Within the space of three years, following a public consultation (DTI, 2006a), the government was arguing in a further review that 'nuclear has a role to play' (DTI, 2006b, p. 113) and in a subsequent White Paper pronounced that it was in the public interest to take a decision in favour of allowing the nuclear option (DTI, 2007). It was claimed that, within so short a space of time, circumstances had sufficiently changed to cause a reappraisal. Certainly, it seems, policy discourse had shifted sufficiently to embolden those who favoured nuclear energy and to encourage the government to announce in a White Paper, in early 2008, that it favoured nuclear energy and was inviting energy companies to bring forward plans to build new nuclear stations 'and that the Government should take active steps to facilitate this' (BERR, 2008, p. 7).

Online Exercise 6

Log on to the course website and go to Online Exercise 6: *The nuclear energy debate*.

3.2 Energy and ecological modernisation

As the debate presented in the online activity shows, the case for nuclear energy, in the UK and other countries, rests primarily on its contribution to energy security and environmental sustainability. Proponents argue that the economics of nuclear energy are increasingly favourable and the problem of radioactive waste can be solved. Nuclear is seen as a necessary part of the energy mix, alongside clean coal, renewables and energy efficiency. However, these arguments are challenged by opponents of nuclear energy, who argue that nuclear will only make a minor contribution at best to cutting greenhouse gases, and then not for at least a decade. Further, nuclear represents a focus on large-scale, technologically-driven solutions to environmental problems. If it is developed, it 'could lock the UK into an inflexible, centralised electricity generating system for the next fifty years' (SDC, 2006, p. 20).

Q. *Are you totally in favour, fairly in favour, fairly opposed or totally opposed to energy produced by nuclear power stations?*

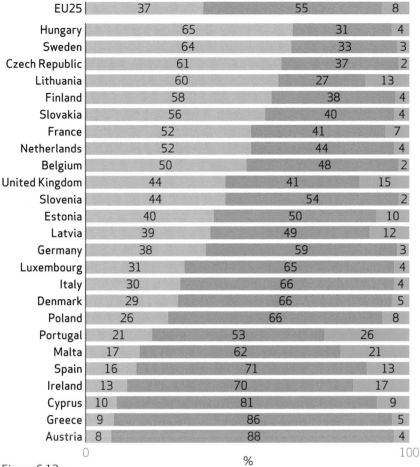

Figure 6.13a

Q. *To what extent would you support or oppose the building of new nuclear power stations in Britain? (2001)*

Q. *To what extent would you support or oppose the building of new nuclear power stations in Britain **to replace** those are being phased out over the next few years? (2002 onwards)*

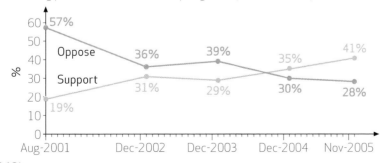

Figure 6.13b

Figure 6.13a
Poll findings on nuclear energy (Source: Eurobarometer, June, 2005)

Figure 6.13b
Poll findings on nuclear energy (Source: MORI, November, 2005)

In some respects the debate over nuclear energy may be seen as a diversion. Critics say it could divert funds 'away from more sustainable technologies that will be needed regardless, hampering other long-term efforts to move to a low carbon economy with diverse energy sources' (SDC, 2006, p. 19). More importantly, it may divert attention away from the need for wider social change in the effort to combat climate change. As the UK Sustainable Development Commission (SDC) puts it, 'We are concerned that a new nuclear programme would give out the wrong signal to consumers, encouraging the impression that the challenge of climate change can be tackled by a large-scale technology fix' (SDC, 2006, p. 20). Adopting a nuclear strategy is one way of supporting the idea of business as usual, a relatively painless, if controversial, way of adapting to environmental change. In this sense the debates over nuclear energy, and over energy more generally, can be seen in the wider context of the contemporary discourse of **ecological modernisation.**

Ecological modernisation describes the contemporary technical and political approaches to environmental conservation.

Ecological modernisation has emerged as a way of describing environmental policy making in both the state and commercial sectors in advanced industrial societies, particularly those in western Europe (see, for example, Hajer, 1995; Mol, 1995; Weale, 1992). It provides both an explanation for society's responses to problems of resource depletion and pollution and presents a normative position on how environmental problems should be tackled. Under ecological modernisation, environmental conservation can be achieved, indeed may be promoted, through economic growth. As Maarten Hajer (1995) has put it, 'Ecological modernisation does not call for any structural change but is, in this respect, basically a modernist and technocratic approach to the environment that suggests that there is a techno-institutional fix for the present problems' (p. 32).

Developments in energy policy provide a good illustration of ecological modernisation. The energy sector, once state controlled in many countries, is now largely privatised (or at least at arm's length from state control) and big transnational corporations have built up investment portfolios often containing a mix of fossil, renewable and sometimes nuclear energy systems. These changes in the economic sphere are reflected in changes in the political sphere, producing forms of production and governance that are the characteristic features of ecological modernisation. These features are:

1 *The process of production.* Ecological modernisation emphasises the application of technology to reduce pollution, conserve resources and achieve green and efficient forms of production, what Mol calls the 'ecologisation of production'. The development of CCS or the use of nuclear energy is consistent with ecological modernisation as are

large-scale renewable projects or distributed power systems designed to avoid the waste of heat and power.

2 *State/market relationships*. Ecological modernisation is consistent with the principles of neoliberalism, in which industry is self-regulating within a framework of environmental standards and policies that are set by agencies of the state, or international organisations such as the EU. This is compatible with new forms of governance that have emerged more generally with the state adopting a facilitating or enabling role often in partnership with the private sector. It amounts to a kind of 'marketisation' of the state's role in governance.

3 *Incorporation of civil society*. Ecological modernisation argues for the opening up of collaborative relationships between state, business and groups in civil society, notably environmental movements. There is an emphasis on what has been called 'cooperative environmental governance' (Glasbergen, 1998), applying negotiative, collaborative and cooperative forms of decision making in which civil society plays an important role. While this provides some participation for environmental movements, they, in turn, help to legitimate the process of ecological modernisation.

The nuclear industry reflects these characteristics of ecological modernisation. It claims to be a form of production that contributes to lowering carbon output. It fits into a liberalised market where investment comes from the private sector. The state's role is facilitative, providing a regulatory framework and, in the case of the UK, a planning regime for infrastructural developments which emphasises national needs above local concerns. As for civil society, nuclear policy has become more open to consultation and limited participation in decision making by stakeholders. In all these ways nuclear illustrates the application of ecological modernisation in energy policy making. Nonetheless, the state's role is still significant. Given its safety and security risks, the nuclear industry continues to be heavily regulated by state bodies and responsibility for managing reprocessing, some power stations and radioactive waste has been devolved to a quango, the Nuclear Decommissioning Authority (NDA), which, in turn, employs contractors from the private sector.

Activity 6.3

Think back to the definitions of sustainable development discussed in Chapters 1 and 3 and consider these questions:

1 Why does ecological modernisation reflect a 'weak' interpretation of sustainable development?

2   In what ways is ecological modernisation different from sustainable development?

Some ideas are given in the next paragraph.

Ecological modernisation appears to represent a 'weak' interpretation of sustainable development as elaborated by the World Commission on Environment and Development (WCED, 1987). Chaired by former Norwegian Prime Minister Gro Harlem Brundtland the emphases of the WCED on cooperative forms of development, on the compatibility of development (in effect, economic growth) and sustainability, and on coordinated action and participation are similar to the characteristic features of ecological modernisation. Weak sustainability allows for the substitution between various types of capital (natural capital and capital produced by human effort) and accepts a dwindling of natural resources if compensated for by other types of capital. In contrast, a strong interpretation of sustainable development is sceptical of technological and managerial approaches, and argues that natural resources can only be used if they are later replenished. The 'strong' interpretation of sustainable development is conceptually similar to ecocentrism (Chapter 1) and it forms the basis of ecological economics (Chapter 3).

Both ecological modernisation and sustainable development are essentially anthropocentric, concerned mainly with human health and welfare, now and in the future. However, there are important distinctions to be made. Sustainable development is a much broader concept. Dryzek (1997) calls it 'the dominant global discourse of ecological concern' (p. 123). Whereas ecological modernisation focuses on economic and technological dimensions, sustainable development has a broader, social purpose. Ecological modernisation has its origins and primary concern in the 'ecologisation' of industrial production in mainly western European countries; sustainable development is concerned with environmental conservation in the context of North–South relationships and issues of poverty, inequality and social justice within the present and between generations. I shall return to the question of environmental justice and social inequality in the final section of this chapter. For the moment I wish to keep the focus on ecological modernisation and energy policy to consider the implications for governance and democracy.

3.3 Nuclear energy, power and democracy

Ecological modernisation may be seen as the expression of a form of governance in the environmental sphere of policy that is, at once, both highly centralised and decentralised. The concentrated power of large corporations has been matched by greater central control by government. At the same time the state's role has become more decentralised as governments increasingly rely on other organisations, quangos, and partnerships in which both public and private sectors participate. The increasing role of the private sector has been, to some degree, mitigated by a feature already noted: the incorporation of elements of civil society through participation of stakeholders, voluntary bodies, community interests and NGOs in policy making.

The effect on power relationships and on the process of democracy is significant. The withdrawal or devolution of functions once run by central or local government has been called the 'hollowing out of the state' (Rhodes, 1996). On the face of it considerable power has been transferred to the private sector. However, the transfer of functions does not, of itself, weaken the state's overall capacity to govern, provided the state retains its regulatory, financial and legal functions. The development of new institutional arrangements, notably public/private partnerships, ensures continued state participation in decision making. But what has occurred appears to be a growing 'democratic deficit', a decline of representative institutions, a shift of decision-making power to non-elected institutions. In short, the influence of citizens on policy expressed through the exercise of the vote (**representative democracy**) is considered to be in decline. Governmental decision making thereby becomes less open and accountability less transparent.

Conversely, it may be argued that stakeholders' and citizens' power can be exercised in many other ways – through membership of organisations, through consumer action, through shareholding, through protest – as well as through representative forms of democracy. Cooperative or participative forms of governance have the virtue of incorporating a diversity of interests, often including elected representatives, able to apply wide-ranging expertise to complex environmental issues (Meadowcroft, 1998). There are signs, too, of shifts in power relations, complex and subtle, as new forms of democratic participation emerge. Again, the nuclear industry offers an illustration.

As the nuclear discourse shifted towards cooperation and consensus it was recognised that a new approach to policy making was needed, one that could inspire public support and confidence. Accordingly there was a commitment to greater openness and transparency in decision making and to public participation. There was stress on 'engagement' with stakeholders and the public. The method of engagement was to be through deliberative processes which seek to understand people's values and viewpoints to identify, where possible, 'common judgements on common interests founded on reasons and argument' (O'Neill, 2001, p. 491). The basic idea is to encourage dialogue among small groups of stakeholders or citizens, where necessary informed by experts. Ideally,

Representative democracy is a system of government whereby people elect representatives to a legislature in free, secret ballot elections. Examples at the national level include the British House of Commons and the Indian Lok Sabha. There are also representative forms of government at the local level.

the process is democratic in the sense that it is inclusive and unconstrained, offering all participants the opportunity to engage on an equal basis. But it is not democratic in terms of popular control. Deliberative forums do not take decisions but they do provide a basis for informed political judgements and decisions taken through representative processes. By enabling expression of values it may be possible for deliberation to provide a basis for decisions that are both publicly acceptable and politically implementable; at the very least deliberative processes should enable conflicts to be made explicit and the areas of potential agreement to be identified. Deliberative forms of democratic participation (**deliberative democracy**) are, therefore, not a substitute for, but a complement to, representative democracy.

Deliberative democracy describes processes of public and stakeholder participation that enable knowledge, values and ideas to be discussed openly in order to provide a basis for more informed political decisions.

It has been suggested that 'deliberative democracy has established itself as a new orthodoxy within contemporary democratic theory' (Smith, 2005, p. 53). In practice, it is a relatively new process, one that has been limited in application. Deliberative democracy has begun to be applied to decision making in areas where the issues are complex and uncertain, notably long-term, environmental issues such as energy policy, radioactive waste and climate change. Robert Goodin (2003) considers that 'the environmental area has led all other issue areas in democratic innovations' (p. 164).

Scientific knowledge may be constrained by inherent uncertainties of data and methods, especially when dealing with complex problems involving prediction into the far future. Thus, experts cannot provide all the answers and the status of expert knowledge is subject to challenge. Deliberative processes are a way of bringing together different knowledge streams, scientific and social as well as lay persons' knowledge based on experience and values. Deliberation can widen the basis for building consensus and achieving legitimacy for policies. It can help to shift power relations away from the dominance of expertise and towards the interests of stakeholders and citizens, giving them an important, perhaps even decisive, influence on decisions. Deliberative processes have their limitations depending on such factors as: how representative the participants are; how open and unconstrained the process is; and how far the outcomes are taken into account.

Radioactive waste management provides the most extensive application of deliberative techniques so far adopted in the UK. The Committee on Radioactive Waste Management (CoRWM) claimed that the process 'offers a far more informed basis for political decisions on the management of radioactive waste than has existed previously' (CoRWM, 2006, p. 6). While engagements with citizens and stakeholders reflected the diversity of viewpoints in society they also helped to support the overall judgements and recommendations of the committee. The Public and Stakeholder Engagement (PSE) process used a variety of methods (round-table discussions, citizens' panels, open meetings, a national stakeholder forum, schools project, a discussion guide for small groups) designed to involve participants in a continuing contribution to key decisions (Figure 6.14). The PSE process was just one input to the recommendations, which also took into account ethical considerations, overseas experience and expert knowledge. All these, together with the PSE, were integrated in a set of recommendations which emphasised the need for continuing engagement in a long-term, staged process of decision making leading eventually to deep disposal of wastes at a location selected through the willing participation of a host community in partnership with the waste management body. This, it will be noted, is a very far cry from the imposed solutions of the past.

Figure 6.14
Deliberate democracy in action: CoRWM's National Stakeholder Forum

In this section I have focused mainly on the changing social and political context of environmental policy making, referring in particular to nuclear energy. Contemporary debates about the role of nuclear in energy policy take place within a prevailing discourse of ecological modernisation. These debates reflect broader political changes that have occurred, with an emphasis on the market and cooperative forms of governance involving parts of civil society. Within the nuclear sector there have been signs of a potential shift in power relations enabling greater openness and public participation, but so far this has been largely restricted to policy making for managing the UK's existing long-lived radioactive wastes, not policy making on new power stations. Public engagement on the wider issues of energy policy has also been limited. It is, as yet, unclear how pervasive and influential deliberative democracy may become. However, it does at least open up the prospect for greater awareness and mutual understanding of conflicts between interests and the values that inform them. It is conceivable that deliberative approaches applied to energy strategy as a whole may expose to a wider public the limitations of the business as usual assumptions on which ecological modernisation is based. This could open up the prospect for changes in understanding, attitudes and behaviour that will be necessary if carbon emissions are to be curbed and reduced.

As we have seen, the removal of technical and political constraints on low carbon energy strategies requires changes at the societal level, changes of awareness, understanding and the willingness to make changes in the way we live. However, within a politically divided and unequal world the impacts of energy policies on different places and upon future generations will be uneven (*course theme 2*). Progress towards a sustainable energy strategy requires an awareness of differences across time and space (*course theme 5*) and raises questions about citizenship and responsibility (*course theme 6*). These considerations bring into focus some of the ethical issues surrounding energy strategies to which I now turn.

4   Ethics and energy

Ethics are sets of principles or standards concerned with behaviour and well-being.

Ethics are sets of principles or standards concerned with behaviour and well-being. They act as a guide to what is acceptable or unacceptable, what we should do, what is right or wrong, good or bad. There is a distinction between 'ethical issues – about what ought to be the case – and empirical issues about what is/will/might be the case' (Rawles, 2006, p. 26). The distinction is recognised in our course question for this chapter: what can be done for the future and what *should* be done? Here I am going to focus on the second, ethical, part of the question.

4.1 Uneven development over space

Activity 6.4

Consider this statement: 'The impacts of environmental degradation are always socially and spatially differentiated. They may end up affecting the global environment, but first they damage small parts of it' (Low and Gleeson, 1998, p. 19).

Can you think of ways in which the development of energy might impact unevenly both globally and locally?

I think that there are two kinds of uneven impact, social and environmental. First, there is unevenness in energy production and consumption. Inequalities might be a better description since unevenness has both a social as well as a geographical context. Such inequalities exist between North and South, between countries, between social groups and between places within countries. The contrast in energy production and consumption between the richest and poorest countries is quite startling. In the poorest countries electricity may not be available to some of the population at all. Even within the rich countries, inequalities are stark; for instance, at the beginning of this century within the UK there were over 3 million households in fuel poverty (defined as spending more than 10 per cent of household income on fuel). It should be clear that inequalities may impose a moral constraint on cutbacks in energy which impact disproportionately on the poor.

Second, there is the unevenness of environmental impact. This has two dimensions. The first is the uneven impact caused by the transfer of pollution. As we have seen the Nordic countries were affected by acid rain from UK power stations, and the 'Black Triangle' on the borders of Germany, Poland and the Czech Republic has suffered from transboundary pollution flows across central Europe. Nuclear accidents, too, may have transboundary impacts, as Chernobyl demonstrates. At a global level the impacts caused by CO_2 on global warming are also uneven. The case of global changes in water distribution is illustrative. Some parts of the world (very often the poorest) will experience inundation through, for example, increased rainfall and melting ice caps, while others are likely to suffer increased drought (Chapter 1). The second dimension is the impacts caused by the uneven distribution of energy production. For instance, coal-fired power stations cause local pollution, wind farms are thought by many to be unsightly and noisy while nuclear power stations or reprocessing works present risks of damage to health and environment from possible release of radioactivity. Local regions or communities hosting these activities bear a disproportionate burden on behalf of society as a whole.

The broader inequalities at the global and international level are considered at several points in this course. Here, I intend to concentrate on unevenness, or rather inequalities, at the local community level and use, once again, nuclear energy as my example. Nuclear energy is, to some extent, representative of many of the other hazardous and polluting technologies that are generally classed as locally unwanted land uses (LULUs): chemical plants, power stations, waste disposal facilities, incinerators or certain major infrastructure projects like airports, motorways and port developments.

There is a tendency for the communities in which LULUs are situated to be peripheral in geographical, economic, political, social and environmental terms. Geographically, these communities tend to be remote or at least relatively inaccessible to metropolitan centres. They are economically marginal, often dominated by a single activity. Politically they are often powerless since decisions affecting them are taken by companies or authorities located elsewhere. At the social level these communities may exhibit a culture of acceptance, defensiveness and hostility to external influence. And, almost by definition, they suffer environmental degradation by virtue of the activities they are hosting. West Cumbria, where Sellafield is located, is a good illustration of the characteristics of peripheral communities (Figure 6.15).

The peripheral nature of these communities is reproduced and reinforced by what may be termed a process of **peripheralisation** (Blowers and Leroy, 1994). This is an expression of power relations. On the one hand there is the power of communities able to mobilise resources to organise and protest against the siting of LULUs in new 'greenfield' locations. On the other there is the dependent status of peripheral communities for whom loss of the economic activity might have devastating consequences. This push and pull of peripheralisation is, in effect, a process of social inequality. While peripheral communities are not necessarily poor (indeed those working in the nuclear industry, for example, are relatively well paid) they are unequal, in the sense that they are subordinate to powerful forces elsewhere.

Peripheralisation describes a process of inequality whereby communities suffer environmental risk or degradation as a result of becoming geographically, economically and politically marginalised.

4.2 Intragenerational equity

The principle of intragenerational equity is introduced in Chapter 1

In terms of what should be done, peripheral communities illustrate a problem of *intragenerational equity* (Chapter 1). Here, I am concerned with the ethical principle that actions should not impose an unfair or undue burden on individuals or groups within the present generation. This principle becomes important in the context of decisions about siting LULUs such as radioactive waste facilities. In the past, siting decisions were taken centrally and often in secret and had little regard for ethical questions. With the emerging emphasis on such motions as openness, consent, trust and participation, ethical considerations have become increasingly important in environmental decision making.

A major question facing countries with nuclear energy is what to do with the long-lived high and intermediate level radioactive waste and spent fuel and where to put it (Figure 6.16 illustrates the locations, volumes and radioactivity of these wastes in the UK). I will come back to the first part of the question in a moment. The 'where' question involves applying ethical criteria to the problem of siting long-term interim

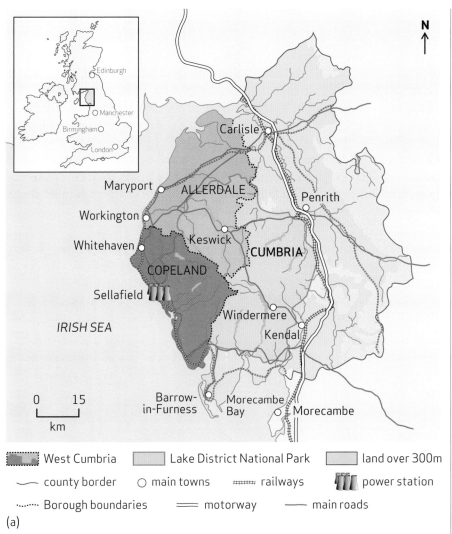

Figure 6.15a
Map of West Cumbria:
a peripheral region

West Cumbria   Lake District National Park   land over 300m
— county border   ○ main towns   railways   power station
Borough boundaries   motorway   main roads

(a)

(b)

Figure 6.15b
A peripheral
community: the
Sellafield nuclear
complex was built in a
remote area on the
coast of Cumbria

storage facilities or a deep geological repository. Among the criteria set out by Anna Vari (2006) are, first, *well-being*, the utilitarian principle which, if applied, would achieve greatest benefit to the greatest number and, therefore, would site facilities where they affect fewest people. The principle of *justice* comprises a group of criteria which aims at a fair distribution among people and communities. This might be achieved by *parity* (distributing facilities as widely as possible), *proportionality* (relating the benefit to the burden), *responsibility* (leaving waste where it already is) or *vulnerability* (avoiding communities which already host facilities). A final criterion is *dignity*, the need to achieve acceptability from those communities that may be affected.

Activity 6.5

Taking these six criteria – well-being, parity, proportionality, responsibility, vulnerability and dignity – think about which may be either impractical or contradictory as a guide to siting a radioactive waste facility. When you have considered this see how your answer relates to mine below.

I suggest that parity is an impractical criterion since it implies a number of facilities whereas, in practical terms of cost and feasibility, the wastes could be accommodated in one or two facilities. Two other criteria are contradictory. Responsibility suggests siting a facility where wastes already exist whereas vulnerability argues that such locations which already bear a burden should be avoided.

We are left with well-being, proportionality and dignity. The principle of well-being, affecting fewest people, could be satisfied in terms of a peripheral location. This might also be a pragmatic solution. But, the other two criteria require further consideration for a successful siting process. In terms of proportionality, the burden of risk, cost and work that is imposed on a community which hosts a radioactive waste facility might require compensatory benefit. It would be unethical to offer compensation as an inducement since this might target vulnerable communities. Any compensation paid should be a matter for negotiation and provided as recognition of a responsibility undertaken on behalf of society as a whole. Compensation is a broad concept extending beyond financial and other community benefits. It can embrace policies which contribute to the community's sense of identity, development and positive self-image. These concepts may be realised in a variety of ways through economic development, through greater control over the community's affairs and through an ability to define and realise its own vision for its future.

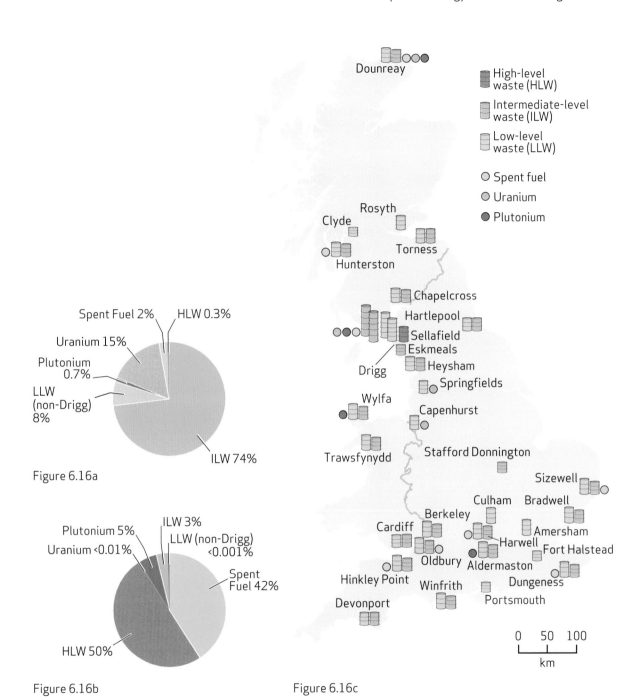

Figure 6.16a

Figure 6.16b

Figure 6.16c

Please note the low level waste referred to in Figures 6.16a and 6.16b is that which cannot be managed at Drigg in Cumbria where a national repository receives the bulk of low level waste for disposal.

Figure 6.16a
The UK radioactive waste inventory by volume (Source: CoRWM, 2006)

Figure 6.16b
The UK radioactive waste inventory by radioactivity (Source: CoRWM, 2006)

Figure 6.16c
Location of radioactive wastes in the UK. Volumes are indicative only (Source: CoRWM, 2006)

In addition, the principle of dignity must also be satisfied. This can be achieved in two ways. One is through ensuring the process of siting is voluntary, in other words it is conditional upon a community's willingness to host a facility. The other is through participation in decision making. The new approaches to deliberative democracy, linking participative to representative democracy outlined earlier, may be essential to achieve the public acceptability necessary to ensure a successful implementation of radioactive waste management policy. Such an approach involving the participation of citizens and stakeholders has been adopted, in principle, by the UK and is practised in other countries such as Canada, Belgium and Sweden.

4.3 Intergenerational equity

The principle of intergenerational equity is introduced in Chapter 1

While intragenerational equity is mainly concerned with the spatial distribution of activities, *intergenerational equity* is concerned with the impacts of activities over time. At the opening of this chapter I pointed to the relatively limited spatial and temporal impact of human actions on the environment before the Industrial Revolution. Today the situation has been totally transformed as scientific discovery and technological development have unleashed impacts of global spread extending into the far future (*course theme 5*). The present generation now has the capacity to deplete natural resources and to create pollution that is passed down the generations with potentially disastrous effects. For example, tropical forests may be cut down, oil reserves used up or vast areas laid waste through pollution and degradation. Some impacts may last into the far future for unimaginably long periods. Radioactive waste is an obvious example. Some of the most dangerous radionuclides in high-level radioactive wastes have half-lives extending over hundreds of thousands, even millions, of years.

We have reached a situation where, in conditions of uncertainty about what may happen in future, our power exceeds our knowledge and our capacity to do harm extends our responsibility far into the future. As Hans Jonas (1984 [1979]) puts it, 'the discrepancy between the tremendous time-reach of our actions and the much shorter reach of our foresight concerning their outcome is almost bound to grow bigger as we go on with "big technology"' (p. 118). It is helpful here to make a distinction between two different timescales. One may be called *geoscientific time*, that is the very long timescales extending to millions of years over which the Earth evolves. In terms of future evolution scientific uncertainty increases over time. Yet in terms of radioactive wastes, predictions must be made about the safety of engineered and geological barriers in containment systems and whether they are sufficiently robust over immensely long time periods. Conversely, *sociocultural time* covers the timescale of human perceptions and concern, one or two generations, a hundred years at most. The main concerns for the near future are the stability and survival of social institutions. In terms of radioactive waste management the emphasis tends to be on whether safety and security can be maintained in the relatively short term.

Consideration of the timescales of impacts opens up a range of ethical questions concerning issues of intergenerational equity. In particular it raises the question of *responsibility*, especially the responsibility of the present for the future (*course theme 6*). It is the sheer power of the present generation to create pervasive environmental degradation in the future that brings the issue of responsibility to the centre of ethical concerns. There are several aspects of responsibility to be considered here. I shall now deal with each in turn in the form of a question and a prompt. You might like to frame your own answer to each question before reading on, using the prompts as a guide.

Why should we be responsible to the future? (prompt: sustainable development)

In so far as the future does not yet exist and never need exist why should we feel obligations towards it? Ultimately this is a question about existence itself. There is no theoretical answer to this question; it becomes a requirement, a categorical imperative that we have a duty to ensure there is a future and a duty to ensure a worthwhile quality of life. It is on this belief that the idea of sustainability, a future presence, ultimately rests. It is our 'duty to preserve this physical world in such a state that the condition for that presence remains intact' (Jonas, 1984 [1979] p. 10). Put into the terms of radioactive wastes, the sustainability principle becomes interpreted by the International Atomic Energy Agency (IAEA) thus: 'Radioactive waste shall be managed in such a way that predicted impacts on the health of future generations will not be greater than relevant levels of impact that are acceptable today' (IAEA, 1995, Principle 4). Or, in an echo of the Brundtland Report's definition of sustainable development, society should be protected 'in such a way that the needs and aspirations of the present generation are met without compromising the ability of the future generation to meet their needs and aspirations' (IAEA, 1997, Article 1).

How can we take the future into account? (prompt: precautionary approach)

Beyond a generation or so the future has no voice, it has no vote. The further ahead we look the more difficult it becomes to imagine what the future might be like, whether it will exist at all in forms recognisable today. The best that we can do is to invoke the *precautionary principle*

(Chapter 1). This has been defined in various ways of which the following is an example: 'When an activity raises threats to the environment or human health, precautionary measures should be taken, even if some cause-and-effect relationships are not fully established scientifically' (Hileman, cited in Sandin, 1999, p. 891). As I shall show in a moment, the precautionary principle, which is intended to promote environmental policy responses in the face of uncertainty, becomes difficult to interpret in practice, precisely because of uncertainty.

How does increasing uncertainty affect our responsibility for the future? (prompt: maintain or remove responsibility?)

The long timescales involved are the key factor. Over time the ability of science to predict risk, and of economics to provide against risk, will diminish. Although we cannot know what the future will be like, that does not absolve us of all responsibility for it. As Barbara Adam argues, 'the *unknown* and *unknowable* future of our making is inescapably in the realm of morals and values and irrefutably our responsibility' (2006, p. 12). However, some would argue that obligations to the future cannot continue unchanged for all time. 'On sufficiently long time scales, any statement at all about the impacts of current actions and about obligations of current societies towards the future eventually become meaningless' (NEA/OECD, 2006, p. 21). While responsibility in some form in conditions of uncertainty may be recognised, discharging that responsibility requires an answer to the following two ethical questions.

How far into the future does our responsibility extend? (prompt: for ever, for as long as possible)

One view is that responsibility never ceases; 'responsibility has to extend to the limit of impact of our actions' (Adam, 2006, p. 14). There should be no cut-off point. Such a position, applied to radioactive waste, implies that we need to consider what means there are to compensate future generations for the harm radioactive wastes may cause and to ensure they are informed of the danger. Another view, which mixes the pragmatic with the ethical, is to say that we should do all that we can while recognising our capacity to affect the future must diminish over time. It is this that makes the precautionary principle difficult to apply 'since significant degrees of uncertainty will apply to any set of available options for dealing with radioactive waste over the indefinite future' (Craggs, 2006, p. 68). This second view also reflects a greater concern for the more immediate future (in sociocultural time) over which we have greater influence and interest. It suggests that, at a certain point, we must necessarily let the future take care of itself. You may observe an ethical similarity between this view and the concept of discounting, which you encountered in Chapter 3. While the first view emphasises a continuing responsibility, the second recognises a diminishing one. These contrasting views influence the way the next question is answered.

What are the ethical principles that should inform our concerns about the future? (prompt: justice, liberty)

The ethical issue here is whether we should do all that we can now to avoid placing a burden (of cost, work or risk) on the future, or leave the future the freedom to make its own choices. There is here a conflict between the principle of justice (those who benefit should bear the burden) and the principle of liberty (providing the flexibility for future choice). Of course, they are not necessarily incompatible. Which principle is favoured will depend on the issue in question, on whether it is possible to delay a decision and if, in so doing, the burden imposed would be intolerable. Ethical judgements are not the only consideration: technical practicalities, scientific knowledge and political possibilities also play a part in reaching decisions. The eventual choice will result from an interaction of values, knowledge and power (*course themes 2 and 3*).

When should we exercise our responsibility to the future? (prompt: take action now or leave it till later)

From what we have seen so far in this course, in terms of climate change the ethical position seems reasonably clear. The principle of justice is paramount. There is an urgency for action now to avert disaster later. We need to reduce the levels of CO_2 being discharged into the atmosphere. There should be no ethical dispute about the general principle of applying CCS, developing renewables, energy conservation, reducing vehicle and air miles, and so on. These seem necessary measures to ensure a future existence, our prime responsibility to the future. There may well be ethical questions about where and when to apply such policies and over the fairness of the outcomes. There will certainly be pragmatic questions of cost, technology and priority to consider. But, expressed in terms of ethical principles, where the benefits of taking action now actually remove burdens from the future then environmental justice urges action now.

However, in the case of some energy sources such as biofuels or nuclear energy, the situation is not so clear-cut. In the case of nuclear energy the benefit of low carbon energy comes at the cost of creating a different environmental problem: the management of long-lived radioactive waste. There are choices to be made in how to manage the waste. The essential choice is between storing the wastes indefinitely and burying them deep underground. As you have seen, radioactive waste management has been a major issue of conflict, especially during the period when the discourse of danger was dominant. Proposals for deep repositories were opposed at Sellafield, at Gorleben (Germany), and at Yucca Mountain (USA) among other places. But, as the discourse of cooperation developed, deep geological disposal has become the favoured approach in most countries, supported by a consensus emanating from what is effectively an epistemic community of scientists (Chapter 2) and gathering acceptability from public and community groups in, for example, Finland, Sweden, Belgium and France.

Deep disposal is a 'do it now' approach based on the justice principle. The present generation has the benefits of nuclear electricity and we should not bequeath the burden of waste on future generations who may be unwilling or lack the capacity to provide for its safe management. This ethical justification is supported by other reasons. Deep disposal is intended to provide a final solution using engineered and geological barriers underground to keep the wastes isolated from the accessible environment. It therefore places no reliance on continuing institutional control or societal stability and it also protects the immediate future in terms of safety and security and the dangers of proliferation. The scientific consensus considers that:

> from an ethical standpoint, including long-term safety considerations, our responsibilities to future generations are better discharged by a strategy of final disposal than by reliance on stores which require surveillance, bequeath long-term responsibilities of care, and may in due course be neglected by future societies whose structural stability should not be presumed.
>
> (NEA/OECD, 2006, p. 8)

Storage is the only other feasible option and supports the principle of liberty, leaving future generations free to take decisions. This approach is predicated on: insufficient confidence and trust in the science of disposal; a concern to keep the problem visible and to maintain access to a potential resource; the possibility of better options being developed in future; and the avoidance of high costs. Ethically, the emphasis is on responsibility to the far future. Storage reflects the view that responsibility persists indefinitely and that the possibility of leakage into the accessible environment in the far future requires us to maintain vigilance. 'What possible justification could there be for an arbitrary cut-off point after which the burden is externalised to others who had no say in the matter?' (Adam, 2006, p. 14).

A compromise position is the concept of phased geological disposal whereby access to the wastes in a repository would be maintained for up to, say, 300 years. This retrievability option appears to satisfy principles of both justice, in that the costs fall mainly on the present, and liberty, in keeping the options open for longer. However, keeping open a repository may compromise near-term safety and impose some burden of cost, risk and effort on the future. In any case, siting, designing, constructing and operating a repository is likely to span a hundred years or so before closure, which might be regarded as providing sufficient flexibility.

5 Conclusion: ethics and the energy debate

I have introduced some of the ethical questions concerning intra- and intergenerational equity using the example of radioactive waste. The answers were addressed to the issue of legacy wastes, those wastes already existing or inevitably arising. When we turn to the issue of wastes arising from new nuclear plants the ethical issues are somewhat different. Depending on the volumes and timescales involved, new wastes might affect the design, size and number of facilities required. The future volumes of existing and committed wastes are known, those of new build uncertain. Consequently, 'it is one thing to ask a community or a region of the country to consider becoming the destination of a relatively specifiable quantity of radioactive waste. It is quite another to propose that a site will continue to receive waste of indefinite quantities into an indefinite future' (Craggs, 2006, p. 66).

The ethics of new build wastes connect us back to the wider debate on nuclear energy. Why is nuclear energy an ethical issue? One answer is that its impacts are uneven and unbounded both in time and space, whether from routine or accidental releases of radioactivity now or in the far future from waste repositories. Moreover, nuclear energy is associated both in the public mind and in practical ways with nuclear weapons, with nuclear proliferation and with possible terrorist attacks. In short, nuclear energy is an ethical issue because of the dangers it poses to human and non-human life.

However, the dangers of nuclear energy have to be set against its potential benefits in contributing to energy security and a low carbon electricity supply. As we have seen the case for new nuclear build is premised on avoiding higher emissions from fossil fuel plants, on contributing to energy security and supporting economic growth, and on its potential cost effectiveness compared to alternative forms of low carbon generation. In 2007 the UK government took the view that 'the balance of ethical considerations does not require ruling out the option of new nuclear power' (DTI, 2007, p. 200). Nevertheless, it may be argued that nuclear raises far more ethical problems than most of the renewable sources of energy discussed earlier in the chapter.

This wider ethical debate touches on energy policy writ large. Ethical considerations affect every aspect of energy and, indeed, all other environmental issues. They are relevant to the choice between energy options, to the distributional impacts between countries, communities and generations and to the fundamental issue of sustainable development. Ethical considerations, whether implicit or explicit, are an input into policy making taken alongside the technical/scientific and political considerations. However, whereas technical and political issues tend to be considered within the limits of ecological modernisation, ethical questions can probe and penetrate some of the fundamental issues of human existence, future responsibility and environmental sustainability. In terms of *course question 4*, ecological modernisation is essentially a pragmatic response to the challenge of what *can* be done. But asking what *should* be done raises ethical questions that may lead us to challenge and possibly break the confines of the contemporary discourse of ecological modernisation.

Audio 2

Now listen to Audio 2: *Sustainable solutions for transport.*

References

Adam, B. (2006) 'Reflections on our responsibility to and for the future' in Blowers, A. (ed.) *Ethics and Decision Making for Radioactive Waste*, a Committee on Radioactive Waste Management (CoRWM) Report, London, CoRWM.

Department for Business, Enterprise and Regulatory Reform (BERR) (2008) *Meeting the Energy Challenge, A White Paper on Nuclear Power*, CM7296, London, The Stationery Offfice.

Blowers, A. and Leroy, P. (1994) 'Power, politics and environmental inequality: a theoretical and empirical analysis of the process of "peripheralisation"', *Environmental Politics*, vol. 3, no. 2, summer, pp. 197–228.

Cabinet Office (2002) *The Energy Review*, A Performance and Innovation Unit Report, London, Cabinet Office.

Committee on Radioactive Waste Management (CoRWM) (2006) *Managing Our Radioactive Waste Safely: CoRWM's Recommendations to Government*, Report by Committee on Radioactive Waste Management, London, CoRWM.

Craggs, W. (2006) 'Reflections on the workshop' in Blowers, A. (ed.) *Ethics and Decision Making for Radioactive Waste*, Committee on Radioactive Waste Management (CoRWM) Report, London, CoRWM.

Department of Trade and Industry (DTI) (2003) *Our Energy Future, Creating a Low Carbon Economy*, CM5761, London, The Stationery Office.

Department of Trade and Industry (DTI) (2006a) *Securing Clean, Affordable Energy for the Long-term: Energy Review Consultation Document*, London, DTI.

Department of Trade and Industry (DTI) (2006b) *The Energy Challenge Energy Review: A Report*, London, DTI.

Department of Trade and Industry (DTI) (2007) *Meeting the Energy Challenge. A White Paper on Energy*, CM7124, London, The Stationery Office.

Department of Trade and Industry (DTI)/Carbon Trust (2004), *Renewables Innovation Review*, URN No: 04/2327, London, BERR.

Diamond, J. (2005) *Collapse: How Societies Choose to Fail or Survive*, London, Penguin Books.

Dryzek, J. (1997) *The Politics of the Earth*, Oxford, Oxford University Press.

Fells, A., Fells, I. and Horlock, J. (2005) 'Cutting greenhouse gas emissions – a pragmatic view', *The Chemical Engineer*, July, pp. 28–32.

Glacken, C. (1967) *Traces on the Rhodian Shore*, Berkeley, CA, University of California Press.

Glasbergen, P. (1998) 'The question of environmental governance' in Glasbergen, P. (ed.) *Co-operative Environmental Governance*, Dordrecht, Kluwer Academic Press.

Goodin, R. (2003) *Reflective Democracy*, Oxford, Oxford University Press.

Guardian, the (2007) 'The burning issue', Weekend Supplement, 14 April.

Hajer, M. (1995) *The Politics of Environmental Discourse*, Oxford, Oxford University Press.

Intergovernmental Panel on Climate Change (IPCC) (2007) *Climate Change 2007: The Physical Science Basis – Summary for Policymakers*, Paris, IPCC.

International Atomic Energy Agency (IAEA) (1995) *The Principles of Radioactive Waste Management*, Safety Series no. 111-F, Vienna, IAEA.

International Atomic Energy Agency (IAEA) (1997) *Joint Convention on the Safety of Spent Fuel Management and on the Safety of Radioactive Waste Management*, Information Circular INF/546, Vienna, IAEA.

Jonas, H. (1984[1979]) *The Imperative of Responsibility*, Chicago, IL, University of Chicago Press.

Lovelock, J. (2006) *The Revenge of Gaia*, London, Penguin.

Low, N. and Gleeson, B. (1998) *Justice, Society and Nature*, London, Routledge.

Meadowcroft, J. (1998) 'Co-operative management regimes: a way forward?' in Glasbergen, P. (ed.) *Co-operative Environmental Governance*, Dordrecht, Kluwer Academic Press.

Mol, A. (1995) *The Refinement of Production*, Utrecht, van Arkel.

Nuclear Energy Agency (NEA) and Organisation for Economic Cooperation and Development (OECD) (2006) *The Environmental and Ethical Basis of Geological Disposal*, Paris, NEA/OECD.

O'Neill, J. (2001) 'Representing people, representing nature, representing the world', *Environment and Planning*, vol. 19, pp. 483–500.

Pacala, S. and Socolow, R. (2004) 'Stabilization wedges: solving the climate problem for the next 50 years with current technologies', *Science*, vol. 305, 13 August, pp. 968–72.

Rawles, K. (2006) 'Key issues' in Blowers, A. (ed.) *Ethics and Decision Making for Radioactive Waste*, Committee on Radioactive Waste Management (CoRWM) Report, London, CoRWM.

Rhodes, R. (1996) 'The new governance: governing without government', *Political Studies*, vol. 44, no. 3, pp. 652–67.

Royal Commission on Environmental Pollution (2000) *Energy – The Changing Climate*, 22nd report, CM4749, London, The Stationery Office.

Sandin, P. (1999) 'Dimensions of the precautionary principle', *Human and Ecological Risk Assessment*, vol. 5, no. 5, pp. 889–907.

Scientific American (2006) *Energy's Future Beyond Carbon*, Special Issue, September.

Smith, G. (2005) *Deliberate Democracy and the Environment*, London, Routledge.

Sustainable Development Commission (SDC) (2006) *The Role of Nuclear Power in a Low Carbon Economy*, SDC Position Paper, London, SDC.

Vari, A. (2006) 'Radioactive waste management – ethical considerations' in Blowers, A. (ed.) *Ethics and Decision Making for Radioactive Waste*, Committee on Radioactive Waste Management (CoRWM) Report, London, CoRWM.

Weale, A. (1992) *The New Politics of Pollution*, Manchester, Manchester University Press.

World Commission on Environment and Development (WCED) (1987) *Our Common Future*, Oxford, Oxford University Press.

World Nuclear Association (WNA) (undated) *The New Economics of Nuclear Power*, London, WNA.

Conclusion: summing up and looking ahead

Andrew Blowers and David Humphreys

The accelerating pace and potential consequences of climate change have now been clearly identified, seemingly marking a transforming moment in the relationship between the natural and social worlds (*course theme 1*). Although some scientists and political leaders remain in denial, there is a general realisation of the causes and consequences of climate change (*course question 1*). Industrialisation and resource-intensive economic growth have driven fossil fuel consumption by industry, transport, agriculture and the energy sector, leading to rising atmospheric concentrations of carbon dioxide (CO_2). It is increasingly accepted that if nothing is done, the pressures on the Earth's resources of land, water and atmosphere will result in the long-term deteriorations in ecosystems and human well-being, possibly threatening survival.

This book has explored some of the political responses to climate change (*course question 2*). Solutions include reducing carbon output through energy efficiency, carbon capture and storage (CCS) and renewable energy sources. The main international policy responses are voluntary emissions reductions from industrialised countries and the use of market mechanisms such as carbon trading. But despite the urgency of the problem, the efforts to implement solutions are, it would appear, proving too little, and possibly too late. In both an environmental and a political sense, at the turn of the century the Earth appeared, as the course title suggests, 'in crisis'.

To explain this we need to examine the constraints to more effective policy responses (*course question 3*). Although the rise in global temperatures is accepted by all but a few scientists, there are some residual problems of scientific uncertainty (Chapter 2). The pace of the increase is unclear, as are the differential impacts of climate change between regions and over time (*course theme 5*). These uncertainties help explain the lack of a coherent and viable global response. There is also uncertainty over the costs of taking action now and the impacts such action might have on economic growth (Chapter 3). Effective action might result in inconveniences and sacrifices that people are unwilling to accept. Another constraint is the collective action problem, which helps explain why some policy makers acting on behalf of national governments are unwilling to reach agreements which might promote the common good (Chapter 4).

This book offers some explanations for the contemporary approach to international policy making for climate change. In so doing it reveals some underlying concepts which both deepen and extend our understanding of the constraints on policy making and which point to some answers to the question of what can and should be done (*course question 4*). Inequality is a fundamental concept that has recurred throughout the analysis in the six chapters of this book. We have identified three dimensions of inequality which both integrate much of the thinking that informs Book 1 as well as providing a conceptual basis for some of the analysis in Books 2 and 3. These three dimensions are power, participation and equity. We now consider them in turn.

Inequalities of power

Much of this book has focused on inequalities and distributions of power (*course theme 2*). We have drawn a basic distinction between power as resources and power as discourse (Chapters 1 and 2). The powerful may exercise power by mobilising resources and deploying them through persuasion, negotiation or, on occasion, force. Powerful states can secure their objectives by withholding resources or by the threat of disengagement from collective policy making. More positively, powerful states can use their power to promote international cooperation by offering side payments to induce others to cooperate, as the European Union (EU) did to secure Russian ratification of the Kyoto Protocol (Chapter 4). Powerful states and business enterprises know that without their investment or cooperation effective policies cannot be made. By its unwillingness to participate, one very powerful state, the USA, seriously undermined the Kyoto Protocol (Chapter 2).

By contrast, there are those who remain relatively powerless, unable to resist or prevent the negative externalities imposed on them by the actions of the powerful. It is likely that the weakest states will suffer the impacts of climate change earlier and more intensely. Low lying countries such as Bangladesh and the Pacific Ocean islands are vulnerable to sea level rise, and in sub-Saharan Africa the effects of climate-induced drought are likely to be harsh (Chapter 1). In these places inequality of power manifests itself in the inability of communities to adapt effectively to the impacts of climate change and in their dependence on the powerful to inaugurate policies that will mitigate greenhouse gas emissions. Often there is a tendency to inaction, because action is perceived as ineffective. But the weakest states may not be entirely powerless. Some of the most important carbon sinks are found in tropical forest countries. Poorer countries often have considerable resources of biomass and solar energy on which mitigation depends. So the less powerful countries may be able to exert increasing leverage on international policy. The same may also apply to less powerful communities within countries. Using the illustration of nuclear energy, Chapter 6 showed how apparently powerless, peripheral communities can achieve power through hosting activities that are unwanted elsewhere. The principle that economic activities should not impose burdens on communities without compensation may in the future be applied to climate change as the role of weaker states in providing solutions is increasingly recognised.

The second definition of power we have used is power as discourse. A discourse is a set of linked understandings and ideas that structure how people think about, interpret and understand the world. In this book there are several examples of how discourses develop, settle and are succeeded, and of how they are used to justify the interests of particular actors and policies. Almost all climate scientists subscribe to the Intergovernmental Panel on Climate Change (IPCC) discourse, which holds that anthropogenic climate change is taking place and that its consequences will be serious. However, although scientifically discredited, the discourse of denial retains significant political influence (Chapter 2). Some actors have attempted to reframe climate change as a security issue in order to advance it up the international political agenda as an issue that requires an urgent, high-level response. But security discourse may reinforce tensions and conflicts rather than provide a renewed basis for cooperation (Chapter 5). Over a period of half a century nuclear energy passed through three discourses, with a fourth strongly emerging at the present time (Chapter 6). There are also more ecocentric discourses which emphasise the consequences of human action for environments as a whole (Chapters 1 and 6).

The role of discourses is also relevant to the relationship between sustainability and development (*course theme 4*). Neoliberalism, which is the dominant political and policy discourse of our time, favours certain types of environmental policies, such as market-led instruments, voluntary arrangements and public–private partnerships, favouring only light intervention and regulation by the state. In terms of international climate policy, neoliberalism is manifested in market-based approaches like carbon trading rather than interventionist strategies of command and control (Chapter 3). In most industrialised societies environmental policy making takes the form of 'ecological modernisation' (Chapter 6). With its emphasis on the primacy of the market within an enabling framework set by the state, ecological modernisation fits well within a neoliberal perspective.

Ecological modernisation emphasises technological solutions to environmental problems, such as CCS, and low carbon energy technologies, such as renewables, nuclear and wind (Chapters 1 and 6).

Ecological modernisation takes an anthropocentric position, viewing the environment not for its intrinsic value but instrumentally as a means for providing resources and support for human well-being. This encourages a 'weak' interpretation of sustainable development, supporting human demands through the conservation or, if necessary, the substitution of resources. It tends to regard 'development' as synonymous with economic growth. The emphasis on markets and technological solutions encourages a business as usual approach which stops short of the fundamental changes that may be required to tackle climate change. The alternative, 'strong', definition of sustainable development focuses on sustainability as the satisfaction of needs and the protection of environments for their own sake. The policy perspective here is derived from the ideas of ecological economics, with its emphasis on the physical limits to economic growth (Chapter 3).

Neoliberal approaches to economics and politics constrain the possibilities for sustainable development so that it is, perhaps, all too easy to take a pessimistic view of the future. But we should not conclude that the dominant discourse of neoliberalism is unchanging and everlasting. We have only to look back to the era of the welfare state in the UK or of centrally planned economies in the former Soviet Union to recognise different policy approaches reflecting quite different discourses. As the implications of climate change and other environmental problems seep more deeply into individual and collective consciousness, so it is likely, even inevitable, that new policy discourses will emerge, at first competing with and later supplanting those which seem all-pervasive today. In this process different power relations will develop which may, we must hope, be reflected in policy making that reflects a strong, common commitment to long-term sustainability.

Inequality of participation

Inequality of participation has not been a prominent issue in Book 1, which has focused particularly on relationships between states. Nevertheless, the inequality in participation in policy making underlies much of the analysis; some people, groups and states have greater access to policy making than others. Power is demonstrated by the ability to influence policies. More powerful states have a greater capacity to make their presence felt in international negotiations than less powerful states (Chapters 1, 2 and 4). Business corporations routinely seek, and are often granted, privileged access to government. Often this influence is exercised covertly, out of the public gaze. There is a symbiotic relationship between government and business based on mutual understanding, a relationship cryptically described by Charles Lindblom long ago in reference to air pollution: 'Yet ordinarily as new conditions or problems arise – for example, public demands for restriction on air pollution – businessmen know that government officials will understand their wishes – in this case their unwillingness or incapacity to bear without help the costs of stopping industrial discharges into the air' (Lindblom, 1977, p. 184). Business influence helped to shape the discourse of denial (Chapter 2) and is evident in mitigation and energy policies (Chapters 3 and 6).

Other groups may participate in policy making in various ways. Among them are environmental non-governmental organisations (NGOs), a bewildering variety of groups of different size, objectives and methods. Although they do not figure in Book 1 they are important actors in environmental policy and feature later in the course. Examples range from small-scale, local community groups to international NGOs such as Friends of the Earth and the World Wide Fund for Nature (WWF). Some of these groups may be seen as 'mainstream'; they exert influence through collaborative relationships with government and business. There are also more radical NGOs, pursuing their aims through both conventional means and direct action. The proclaimed role of many NGOs is to change environmental policy making by shifting established discourses such as neoliberalism as well as to increase participation. The arguments of NGOs for greater social equality and urgent responses to environmental degradation appear to play to a sympathetic but so far, it would seem, largely unheeding audience.

Increasing participation also requires some commitment to more open and transparent policy making. In authoritarian regimes participation is limited, often confined to protest that is ignored or suppressed. In democratic states participation varies according to the devolution of power to lower tiers of government and is limited to representative government exercised through the vote, with citizens' influence over policy tending to be indirect and general. There is a danger that policy making will fall into the hands of elites (executives in government, business and the civil service) who are largely unaccountable to the general public.

Wider participation brings a greater span of knowledge and values to the policy process (*course theme 3*). There has been some effort to deepen and broaden democratic processes through engaging stakeholders and citizens in deliberation on policy. This is yielding a new form of participation, *deliberative democracy*, in which stakeholders and citizen groups may help to shape and inform policy making and implementation. The role of deliberative processes in radioactive waste management policy and its potential for climate policy was discussed in Chapter 6. Deliberative democracy is in its infancy but could help to reinvigorate and restore confidence in the democratic process. There is, at least, the hope that participation will confer a greater sense of responsibility and citizenship on those who participate (*course theme 6*). Over the longer term greater participation may lead to greater empowerment of citizens and a shift in the prevailing power relations which constrain effective environmental policy making.

Intergenerational equity

Another dimension of inequality is time. Participation in policy making is confined to present generations; clearly it is impossible to involve those who have yet to be born. Yet the effects of today's policies may be felt far into the future. Intergenerational equity concerns fairness between generations, including the present one. According to current predictions, severe impacts of climate change will start to occur over the next one or two generations (Chapter 1). The actions of the present have implications for our children, grandchildren and for generations to come. The decisions we take now may require some sacrifices for no immediate benefit to the present generation, but will avoid future environmental costs and degradation. A relatively small cost now may reap considerable benefits later.

The question of what is a fair distribution of resources between present and future generations is not simply an economic one; it is also a philosophical and ethical one. Ethics provide a guide to what we should do. Environmental ethics are concerned about how we ought to act in contexts that have significant implications for human and non-human lives, now and in the future. However, ethics do not always point to clear and unambiguous policies (Chapters 1 and 3). One view is that future well-being should be valued in the same way as the present. This is the nub of the Brundtland definition of sustainable development as 'development that meets the needs of the present without compromising the ability of future generations to meet their own needs' (WCED, 1987, p. 43). But another view is that there should be limits on the obligations of the present generation to those who have yet to be born. The ultimate expression of this view is that the future should take care of itself.

Ethics were considered in the context of radioactive waste, which has timescales that persist into the far future (Chapter 6). The ethical dilemma is made explicit in the question: Why should we be responsible for the future? To this existential question we may respond in ethical terms: because it is right to do so. And to the related question – How far into the future does our responsibility extend? – the absolutist view is that responsibility never ends. But environmental policy is not driven solely by ethical principles; it is also informed by feasibility. A pragmatic view would argue that the further ahead we look, the greater is the uncertainty about the effects of our actions. Here the practical is intertwined with the ethical in seeking answers to the question 'What can be done for the future, and what should be done?' (*course question 4*).

This book has provided a flavour of some of the overarching concepts that recur throughout the course. Our focus has been on climate change, although the ideas developed throughout this book are relevant for the environmental problems and policies analysed in Books 2 and 3. One of the central messages of this book, and of the course, is that while the constraints on effective international policies need to be recognised and engaged with, there are nonetheless significant grounds for optimism. In the case of climate change there is a strong scientific consensus on causes and consequences and an increasingly energetic and integrated response on the part of politicians acting within an international framework. This may stem partly from the increased leverage of the less powerful countries and also from the understanding that we all live on the same Earth. The powerful are, ultimately, unable to escape the consequences of environmental degradation. The common understanding of a shared responsibility may, in the end, prove the way forward to a more sustainable form of development. In the final analysis the responsibility to take action is one that, as citizens, we all share.

References

Lindblom, C. E. (1977) *Politics and Markets: The World's Political-Economic Systems*, New York, Basic Books.

World Commission on Environment and Development (WCED) (1987) *Our Common Future*, Oxford, Oxford University Press.

Acknowledgements

Grateful acknowledgement is made to the following sources:

Cover

Copyright © 2006 SASI Group (University of Sheffield) and Mark Newman (University of Michigan) www.worldmapper.org

Figures

Figure 1.1: MODIS images courtesy of NASA's Terra satellite, supplied by Ted Scambos, National Snow and Ice Data Center, University of Colorado, Boulder; Figure 1.2: Reproduced with permission from *The Atlas of Climate Change,* by Kirstin Dow and Thomas E Downing copyright © Myriad Editions/www.MyriadEditions.com; Figure 1.2 Arapaho Lake: Copyright © W.T.Pfeffer, INSTAAR, University of Colorado; Figure 1.2 Glacial lakes, Bhutan: Copyright © Nasa http://visibleearth.nasa.gov; Figure 1.4: Brown, P. (2006) *Global Warming: The Last Chance*, Guardian Books; Figure 1.6: *The Independent on Sunday*, 5 November 2006. Copyright © The Independent; Figure 1.7: Copyright © John lvester/Alamy; Figure 1.8: Copyright © Michael & Patricia Fogden/Minden Pictures/FLPA; Figure 1.9: By kind permission of Christain Aid; Figure 1.12: Courtesy of the Energy Saving Trust, Copyright © David Modell; Figure 1.13: Monbiot, C. (2006) *How to stop the planet burning*, Allen Lane; Figure 1.14: Copyright © Fran Orford; Figure 2.1 top: The Guardian, 3 February 2007. Copyright © Guardian News & Media Limited 2007; Figure 2.1 bottom: The Independent, 3 February 2007. Copyright © The Independent; Figure 2.2: Copyright © Fran Orford; Figure 2.3: Copyright © Keystone/Getty Images; Figure 2.4: Copyright © Roger Wesson; Figure 2.5: Andresen, S. (2000) Science and Politics in International Environmental regimes: Between integrity and involvement, Manchester University Press; Figure 2.6: Copyright © Jonathan Ernst/Reuters; Figure 2.7: Copyright © Seppo Leinonen 2005; Figure 2.8: Copyright © Steve Greenberg; Figure 3.1: Stern, N. (2006) The Stern Report, Executive Summary: The Economic of Climate Change, HM Treasury. Crown copyright material is reproduced under Class Licence Number C01W0000065 with the permission of the Controller of HMSO and the Queen's Printer for Scotland; Figure 3.2(a): Copyright © Alastair Grant/AP/PA Photos; Figure 3.2(b): Copyright © Cambridge University Press; Figure 3.3: Copyright © Novastock/Stock Connection/Rex Features; Figure 3.5 left: Copyright © Martin Gerten/epa/Corbis; Figure 3.5 right: Copyright © Reuters/Corbis; Figure 3.6: Copyright © Jenny E Ross/Corbis; Figure 3.7: Copyright © Christie's Images/Corbis; Figure 3.10: Copyright ©

Mark Boulton/Alamy; Figure 3.11: Copyright © Evo Publications Ltd; Figure 3.12: EU Action Against Climate Change, European Commission. http://ec.europa.eu/environment/climat/pdf/emission_trading3_en.pdf; Figure 4.1: Copyright © Katsumi Kasahara/AP/PA Photos; Figure 4.3 left: Copyright © Bob Sacha/Corbis; Figure 4.3 right: Copyright © Art Kowalsky/Alamy; Figure 4.4: Barrett, S. (2003) Environment and Statecraft: The Strategy of Environmental Treaty-making, Oxford University Press. Copyright © Scott Barrett 2003; Figure 5.1: Copyright © Richard Drew/AP/PA Photos; Figure 5.2: Copyright © John McConnico/AP/PA Photos; Figure 5.3: Courtesy of John Frost Newspapers; Figure 5.5 left: Copyright © Popperfoto/Getty Images; Figure 5.5 right: Copyright © Greenpeace/Daniel Beltra; Figure 5.6: Copyright © Alfred de Montesquiou/AP/PA photos; Figure 5.7 top: Copyright © G M B Akash/Panos Pictures; Figure 5.7 centre and bottom: Copyright © Dr Alejandro Cravioto/ICDDRB; Figure 5.9: German Advisory Council on Global Change (2007) 'World in Transition: Climate Change as a Security Risk', German Advisory Council on Global Change (WBGU), reprinted with permission; Figure 6.2(a): Copyright © John Giles/PA Wire; Figure 6.3: Copyright © Owen Humphreys/PA Archive/PA Photos; Figure 6.4: Copyright © REUTERS/Arnd Wiegmann; Figure 6.5: Copyright © Bettmann/Corbis; Figure 6.7: Courtesy of Logstor A/S, Denmark; Figure 6.9 left: Copyright © David Bebber/AP; Figure 6.9 centre: Copyright © David Cheskin/PA; Figure 6.9 right: Copyright © Colin McPherson/Corbis; Figure 6.11a: Copyright © Erik Schaffer; Eoscene/Corbis; Figure 6.11b: Copyright © Shepard Sherbell/Corbis Saba; Figure 6.11c: Copyright © Corbis; Figure 6.14: courtesy of the Committee on Radioactive Waste Management; Figure 6.15b: Copyright © Collier Photos Bob/ Corbis Sygma.

Every effort has been made to locate all copyright-owners, but if any have been overlooked the publishers will make the necessary arrangements at the first opportunity.

Index

acid rain
  and fossil fuels 212, 213
  and global dimming 39
  and market failure 98, 103
actors
  and agenda formation 161–2
  and climate security 170, 174–7, 193, 196–8
  framing climate change policies 30–1
  power of 163
Adam, Barbara 246
adaptation policies 31, 32, 33, 38, 79
Africa
  carbon output (2005) 216
  and contraction and convergence schemes 53
  declining crop yields 109
  drought in 27, 28, 254
  risk of climate variability 181
agency–structure debate 44–5
agenda formation 156, 160–2
Agenda for Peace 188, 190
agent-relative ethics, and future generations 115
AIDS, as a security issue 166, 172–3, 186, 196
Alaska, glacial change 16
albedo 19, 20, 23, 24, 69
Allison, Graham 38
Alps, glacial change 17
altitudinal migration 27
amphibians, as indicator species 27
analytical framework (of DU311) 7–8, 53–4
anarchy
  and the international state system 146–7
  and the state of nature 192–3
  A Inconvenient Truth 170
Annan, Kofi 172
Antarctica
  glacial change 16
  ice shelf melting 14, 15, 18, 19, 23, 26
anthropogenic climate change, see climate change, global warming
AOSIS (Association of Small Island States) 31, 185–6

Arafat, Yasser 169
Arctic ice cap 14, 26
Aristotle 115
Asia
  carbon output (2005) 217
  climate change and sustainable development 182
  and contraction and convergence 53
  nuclear power plants 227
asteroids, and climate change 18
Austin, John 172, 175
Australia, and the Kyoto Protocol 136, 160
authority 177
Axworthy, Lloyd 190

Bali Communiqué 84
Bangladesh 32, 182, 185, 186–8, 254
Barnett, J. 198–9
Barrett, S. 159
baseline and credit approach, to carbon trading 125–6
Beck, Ulrich 181
Beckerman, W. 115
Beckett, Margaret 168, 169
bias (in scientific research) 70
biodiversity, loss of 27, 111, 224
biofuels 224, 225
biomass 222, 223, 224, 254
biosphere, and CCS (carbon dioxide capture and storage) 40
Blair, Tony 100, 178
Bocking, Stephen 69
boundary organisations 71
The Bourne Ultimatum 178
Boutros-Ghali, Boutros 188, 190
Boykoff, Jules and Maxwell 89–90
Brazil 77, 136, 211
British Antarctic Survey 14
broadening axis of security 173–4, 175, 179, 189, 190, 196, 200

Broome, John 114, 115

Brown, Gordon 100

Brundtland Commission, *see* World Commission on Environment and Development

bureaucratic politics model 38

Bush administration (United States) 31, 82, 84–8, 124, 145, 158–9, 178, 179

Buzan, Barry 171, 176, 179

Byrd-Hagel resolution 33, 34, 85, 159

Canada 190
  glacial change 16

cap and trade system, of carbon emissions trading 124–7

capital, and economic growth 128

capture and storage (CCS) 40, 41, 42, 80, 218, 232, 247, 253

carbon 21, 224, 225, 253
  social cost of 98, 100–16, 130
  world carbon output (2005) 216–17

carbon cycle 224

carbon dioxide (CO_2) 19, 20–1, 22
  and photosynthesis 21, 22
  see also emissions reductions

carbon footprints 52

carbon monoxide 122

carbon pricing 117

carbon sinks 21, 69, 79

carbon taxes 38, 117, 119–21, 146

carbon trading 99, 117, 122–7, 130, 255, *see* also emissions trading
  baseline and credit approach to 125–6
  and the EU emissions trading system (ETS) 124–7
  and international collaboration 126–7
  and the Kyoto Protocol 124, 125
  and neoliberalism 122–3
  and the Renewables Obligation 223

cars, reducing emissions from 116, 121–2

CCS, *see* carbon dioxide capture and storage

CDM (Clean Development Mechanism) projects 36, 48–9, 51

Central America, carbon output (2005) 216

CFCs (chlorofluorocarbons) 19, 21

China
  and carbon trading 124
  and climate security 177, 186
  electricity production 211, 214–15
  and emissions reductions 33, 136
  and international climate policy
    implementation of treaties 161
    positive-sum games 150–1
    the Prisoners' Dilemma game 140–2, 144, 145
    side-payments 153
    threat points 155
  and the IPCC 76
  and the Kyoto Protocol 145, 159
  National Climate Change Plan (2007) 145
  nuclear power plants 227
  and state sovereignty 147

citizenship
  and participation in policy making 258
  and sustainable energy strategies 238

civil society
  and deliberative democracy 237
  and ecological modernisation 233

classical liberalism
  and libertarianism 123
  and neoliberalism 117

Clean Development Mechanism (CDM) 36

climate change 8, 14–56
  causes of 8, 15, 18, 19–22, 253, 259
  and climate change denial 83, 84, 90
  and climate modelling 70
  consequences of 7, 8, 15, 23–9, 98, 112–14, 253, 255, 259
  constraints on effective policy responses to 8, 15, 36–45
  costs of, 112–14
  and the global community 180
  and the IPCC 58, 79, 80, 255
  and the natural world 9, 18, 63, 70, 83, 135, 253
  and the tragedy of the commons 29–30, 35, 139
  see also global warming

climate change denial 59–60, 82–91, 92, 257–8

climate policy, possible future options 8, 15, 46–53
  desirability of policy proposals 46–7
  energy 211, 225–6
  equity 48–9

feasibility of policy proposals 46, 47
market-based policy instruments 99
securitisation 166
sustainable development 50–3
climate sensitivity 23
climatic stability 46–7, 48
Clinton administration (United States) 31, 34, 163, 200
coal 211–20, 229, 230, 239
coastal cities, climate change and 109, 110
Cold War
    and nuclear energy 229
    and security 171
collective action 253
    and the global community 180
    and international climate policy 9–10, 29–30, 134, 135–47, 156, 169
colonialism
    ecocolonialism 49, 51
    and environmental conflict 199
command and control policy measures 116, 121–2, 255
common but differentiated responsibilities 33
conflict
    and climate security 183–4, 200
    environmental conflict 184–6, 198, 199
    and human security 189, 190
    security knowledge and prevention of 198–9
    and the state of nature 192
constraints on effective policy responses 36–45, 253, 254, 259
    effectiveness 36–7
    individual responsibility 42–5
    and international climate policy 134
    international climate policy 146–7
    knowledge constraints 38–9
    political constraints 37–8
    and securitisation 166
    technology 39–42
contraction and convergence scheme 52–3
control experiments, and science 67–8
Cooney, Philip 86
cooperative environmental governance 233
Copenhagen School of Security Studies 171–2, 174–5, 177, 190–1
Costa Rica 27

crop yields, costs of declining 109, 110
Cylone Cidr (2007) 182

Darfur 185
dependent variables, and science 66
deduction 63
deepening axis of security 173–4, 175, 179, 189, 193, 196
deforestation 208
    and carbon sink capacity 21, 69
    and flooding 188
    and livelihood contraction 188
democracy
    deliberative 236–8, 244, 257–8
    and nuclear energy 234–8
democratic deficit 235
denial, see climate change denial
Denmark, carbon taxes 120
dependent variables
    and science 62
desertification
    and livelihood contraction 188
    and resource scarcity 183, 185
Deudney, Daniel 195, 198
developed countries
    emissions reductions by 33, 34
    and responsibility for past industrialisation 33
developing countries
    climate change and unequal localisation of risks 181–2
    electricity production 211, 239
    emissions reductions by 33, 35–6
    and extreme weather events 182–3
    Group of 77 35, 177, 186
    and human security 189–90
    and international climate policy 254–5
    and the Kyoto Protocol 136, 159
development, see sustainability and development
Dimitrov, Radoslav 81
direct causes, of anthropogenic climate change 19
discounting
    future costs of climate change 112, 114–15, 130
    and radioactive waste management 246

discourse
  of climate change 9, 58–60
      denial 59–60, 82–91, 92, 257
      IPCC 71–82, 83, 88, 91, 92, 255
  new policy discourses 256
  of nuclear energy 227–30
  and power 91–3, 254, 255
      and securitisation 176–7, 255
  of sustainability and development 255
disease 109
disinterested subjectivity, and climate
modelling 70
distributed energy 219
Drax power station 211, 212, 213

Earth Summit, *see* United Nations
Conference on Environment and
Development
East Africa, glacial change 16
ecocentrism 40, 234
ecocolonialism 49, 51
ecological economics 99, 127–9, 256
ecological footprints 51–2
ecological modernisation 255–6
  and energy policy 232–4, 250
ecological space 51–2
economic growth
  and carbon-free/low-carbon energy
      sources 208–9
  and ecological economics 127–9
  and fossil fuel consumption 253
  and greenhouse gas emissions 98, 102
  and sustainable development 234
  and technocentrism 40
economics of climate change 9, 98–130,
134, 182, 188, 267
  and the social cost of carbon 98, 100–16
      calculating 108–15
  and state preferences 157, 158
  see also market failure; neoclassical
  economics; neoliberalism
ecosystems 26–7, 50, 101, 224, 225
effectiveness, of policy 36–7
Elbe, Stefan 178, 196
electricity production 209–27
  and carbon emissions 209
  and carbon trading 126
  fossil fuels 210, 211–18

  inequalities in 239
  natural gas 218–20
  wind power 220–4
emissions reductions
  carbon emissions from coal 218–20
  and climate change modelling 70
  and climatic stability 47, 48
  and international climate policy 147–56
  and the Kyoto Protocol 34–6, 136
  policy instruments for 116–27
  political constraints on 37–8
emissions trading 36, 38, 117, 122–7,
see also carbon trading
energy 208–49, 253, 257
  and climate security 183
  and ecological modernisation 232–4, 250
  efficiency 218–20
  and ethics 238–50
  renewable 220–5, 249, 253
  solar energy 220, 222, 224, 254
  and sustainability 227–38
  switch to carbon-free/low-carbon sources
      of 208–9
  see also fossil fuels; nuclear energy
Energy Saving Trust 42–4
energy taxes 117
entropy, and ecological economics 128–9
environmental conflict, and the North/
South dimension 184–6
environmental economics 103–7, 127
environmental refugees 183, 185, 186
epistemic communities 77–82, 90, 92
  and radioactive waste management 248
epistemology 61–2
  equilibrium, and neoclassical economics
  107, 108
equity
  and international climate policy 48–9
  and the Prisoners' Dilemma game 145
  see also intergenerational equity;
  intragenerational equity
ethics 46–53
  and economics 9, 114–15, 130
  and energy 238–50
  and human security 188–91
  and state preferences 157–8
Eurasia, carbon output (2005) 217
Europe, carbon output (2005) 216

European Security Strategy (2003) 184

European Union (EU)
    carbon taxes 117, 120
    and climatic stability 46–7
    and collective action on emissions
    reductions 135–6
    emissions trading system (ETS) 124–7, 161
    fossil fuel subsidies 121
    framing of climate change 30–1
    and international cooperation
        side-payments 153
        threat points 155
    and the IPCC 76
    and the Kyoto Protocol 34–5, 160
    and refugees and migrants 183
    and renewable energy 183
    and security 166
    voluntary agreements on car emissions
    targets 116, 121–2

experts
    and deliberative democracy 236, 237
    and the theory of epistemic
    communities 78

extraordinary measures 177, 190–1, 193,
196, 200

extreme weather events 101, 182

ExxonMobil 58, 84–5, 86, 158
    fallback positions, and international
    cooperation 154–5, 162
    falsification, and hypothesis testing 63–4

feedback effects of climate change 23–6
    and general circulation models 69
    modelling 112
    and uncertainty in climate science 66–7

Finland, carbon taxes 120

first mover problem 34–5

flexibility mechanisms, Kyoto Protocol 35–6

food security 166, 167

food shortages, and flooding 188

footprints, ecological and carbon 51–2

forests
    as carbon sinks 21
    CDM reforestation projects 48–9, 51
    forest fires 25

Forsyth, Tim 91

fossil fuels 208, 253
    and carbon dioxide 20–1
    and CDM forest projects 49

    and domestic energy consumption 44
    and ecocentrism 40
    and electricity production 210, 211–18
    global dependence on 10, 218
    and global dimming 39
    and nuclear energy 229
    subsidies on consumption of 121
    and wind energy 220, 222–3

Foucault, Michel 92

Framework Convention on Climate Change
(FCCC) 31, 33, 75, 81, 136, 155, 160, 161
    and the global community 180
    and island states 186

framing
    climate change 30–1
    security issues 171–2, 175, 177

free riding, and collective action problems
138–9, 146

Friends of the Earth 196, 257

fuel poverty 239

future costs of climate change 112–16

game theory
    and the collective action problem 9–10
    positive-sum games 149–51, 152–3
    power and threat points 153–5
    and the Prisoners' Dilemma 139–42,
    143–5, 148, 149, 150

gas, see natural gas

GCI, see Global Commons Institute

GCMs (general circulation models) 68–70
    and the IPCC 79

Geneva Convention on refugees 183

geological storage, of captured carbon
dioxide 40, 41

Georgescu-Roegen, Nicholas 129

geoscientific time, and radioactive
wastes 244

Germany
    Advisory Council on Global Change 194,
    198, 199
    fossil fuel subsidies 121

Giddens, Anthony 45

GIGO (garbage in–garbage out) 66

glacial change 16–17, 83
    impacts of 109

Glacken, Clarence 208

Global Climate Coalition 84

global commons 29–30

Global Commons Institute (GCI) 52–3

global dimming 39

global warming, *see also* climate change
  anthropogenic nature of 18
  and global dimming 39
  increase in average temperature of the Earth 14
  as market failure 100–8
  modelling the costs of 100–3, 111–15
  speed and scale of temperature rises 194

golden toad 27

Goodwin, Robert 236

Gore, Al 31, 169, 197

green taxes 99, 117, 118–21

greenhouse effect 19, 20

greenhouse gases 19–23, 52–3, 68, 98, 100–4, 105–8, 254
  and carbon footprint 52
  carbon trading 122–7
  individual responsibility for 42–5
  and the Industrial Revolution 208
  and neoliberalism 123
  see also emissions reductions

Greenland, glacial change 16

Greenpeace 38, 179–80, 196

Group of 77 Developing Countries 35, 177, 186

Grudman, Reiner 81

Haas, Peter 78, 80, 90, 92

Hajer, Maarten 91, 232

Hansen, James 87–8

Hardin, Garret 29–30

Harris, P. 192

Hartmann, Betsy 198

Hepburn, C. 115

HFCs (hydrofluorocarbons) 19, 21

Himalayas 17

HIV/AIDS 166, 172–3, 186, 196

Hobbes, Thomas
  and human security 188, 191
  and the state of nature 191–3, 198

Holocene 18

Homer-Dixon, Thomas 184, 198

Houghton, Sir John 76, 169

human security 188–91, 200

Hume, David 115

Hurricane Katrina (2005) 195

hybrid vehicles 121, 122

hypothesis testing 62–4, 67–8

IAEA, *see* International Atomic Energy Agency

IAMs, *see* integrated assessment models (IAMs)

IEA, *see* International Energy Agency

ice ages 18

ice, melting of 14, 15–18, 19, 23, 26, 53, 83, 109
  as a climate change feedback 67
  economic effects of 109, 110

Iceland, and the Kyoto Protocol 136

ICISS, *see* International Commission on Intervention and State Sovereignty

Implementation (of policy) 156, 160–2

income tax, and carbon tax revenues 121

independent variables
  and hypothesis testing 62, 63
  and uncertainty in science 66

India 124, 153, 155, 211, 227
  and the Kyoto Protocol 159

individual rights
  and classical liberalism 123
  and libertarianism 123
  and neoclassical economics 103–4

individuals
  and the agency–structure debate 42–5
  and human security 188–91
  and the state of nature 191–2
  and the tragedy of the commons 29–30, 35, 139

induction 63

Industrial Revolution 208, 211

inequalities
  climate change and the global community 181–3
  and climate security 201
  and the consequences of climate change 23, 28–9

and ecological modernisation 234
and energy policy 209, 227
and international climate policies 8, 22, 32–3, 136–7
of participation 256–8
of power 254–6
unevenness of environmental impact 238–40

instrumental value 41

integrated assessment models (IAMs) 112–13

intergenerational equity 10, 49, 50, 130, 258–9
discounting the future 114–16
and radioactive waste management 244–9, 258

Intergovernmental Panel on Climate Change (IPCC) 71–82, 156
as an epistemic community 77–82
Assessment Reports
First 74
Fourth 23, 58, 59, 72–3, 74, 76, 77, 181–2, 195
Second 74, 83
Third 74
and carbon capture and sequestration 40
editorial and drafting process 77, 86–7
institutional design 74–7
models of 112
and the Nobel Peace Prize 169
plenary negotiations 76
role of 71–4
and scientific uncertainty 72–4, 77
and the United States 84, 92
working groups 72, 73–4

International Atomic Energy Agency (IAEA) 245

International Commission on Intervention and State Sovereignty 190, 191

international climate policy 130, 134–63, 253–4
and carbon trading 126–7
and collective action 9–10, 29–30, 134, 135–47, 156, 169, 253
and epistemic communities 77–82
and equity 48–9
and positive-sum games 149–51
and power relations 8, 32–3, 134, 135, 163
and state preferences 156, 157–60, 163

International Energy Agency (IEA) 245

international security 171, 180

intersubjectivity 78

intragenerational equity 49, 50
and nuclear energy 240–4, 249

intrinsic value 41

IPCC, *see* Intergovernmental Panel on Climate Change

Iraq war
and scarce resources 185
and security knowledge 178

island states, consequences of climate change for 31, 185–6

Japan 190, 227

Jasanoff, Sheila 91

Johnson, Lyndon 172

Jonas, Hans 244

Journal of Libertarian Studies 123

journalism, and climate science 89–90

justice
and ecological modernisation 234
and radioactive waste management 242, 248
and responsibility to the future 247

Kay, John 115, 116

Ki-moon, Ban 182–3, 183–4

King, Sir David 169

knowledge
and epistemology 61–2
scientific knowledge and deliberative democracy 236
and securitisation of climate change 170, 178–9
security knowledge 179, 193, 198–9, 200
and values 8, 41, 62, 134
and energy policy 227
and international climate policy 163
and participation in policy making 257
science and social values 64–6

knowledge constraints (on effective policy) 38–9

Kyoto Protocol 8, 31, 34–6, 81, 137, 145, 160
and Annex 1 (industrialised) states 34, 35, 36, 48, 49, 124, 136, 151, 160, 161
and the Byrd-Hagel resolution 33, 34
and carbon trading 117, 124, 125
and the economics of climate change 99

flexibility mechanisms 35–6, 48–9
and international cooperation 147, 155
and the IPCC 75
and Russia 152–3, 160, 254
and state preferences 159
targets and timetables for emissions reductions 136
and the United States 31, 33, 34, 38, 85, 136, 159, 161, 163, 254

latitudinal migration 27
liberalism, and neoclassical economics 104
libertarianism, and neoliberalism 123
livelihood contraction 188
Livingstone, Ken 122
local communities 179, 186–91, 240, 241
locally unwanted land uses (LULUs) 239–40
Lovelock, James 209–10
low carbon energy options 10, 220–5, 227
Loy, Frank E. 147
LULUs (locally unwanted land uses) 239–40
Luntz Research Companies 85–6

marginal external cost (MEC) 106, 107, 118
and green taxes 118
marginal net private benefit (MNPB) 106, 107, 118
and green taxes 118, 119
marine ecosystems 109, 224
market failure 98, 100–8
and green taxes 118
and neoliberalism 123
market-based policy instruments 117
MEC, see marginal external cost
media
on climate change 25, 192–3
collapse of Antarctic ice shelf 14, 15
and the discourse of denial 89–91
melting ice sheets 14, 15, 18
metaphors, and models of international climate policy 142–5
methane 19, 21
and melting permafrost 25, 26
Middle East
carbon output (2005) 217
conflicts and scarce resources 183, 185

migration
human 27–8
environmental refugees 183
and resource scarcity 184, 185
and security 171
of species 26–7
the military 193, 196–8, 200
mining
and carbon capture and storage (CCS) 218
environmental degradation caused by 213, 214
mitigation policies 31, 33, 34, 38, 257
calculating costs 108, 112
discounting the future 114–15, 130
and international climate policy 149, 162
and the IPCC 79
policy instruments 116–27, 130
and public goods 138
and state preferences 157
and the Stern Review 103
MNPB, see marginal net private benefit
models
climate modelling 65–6, 68–70
economic modelling of global warming 100–3, 111–15, 130
and international climate policy 142–5
the Prisoners' Dilemma 139–42, 143–5, 146, 148, 149, 150, 162
Monbiot, George 88
monetary values (of climate change impacts) 110–11
Montreal Protocol 148, 151
Moravcsik, Andrew 158

national security 171, 180, 192–3, 196–8, 200
natural gas 218–21, 229
nature
and climate change 9, 18, 63, 70, 83, 135, 253
negative externalities
in environmental economics 103, 104, 105–6
and green taxes 118
neoclassical economics 98
and carbon trading 124
and environmental economics 103–7, 127
and green taxes 118–21
and market failure 100–8, 123
and climate change policy 99

neoliberalism 99, 256
    and carbon trading 122–3, 255
    and ecological modernisation 233
    and environmental policies 117–18
    and libertarianism 123
    and NGOs 257
    and the politics of denial 88
Nepal 188
Netherlands 32
New Orleans 182, 195–6
New Zealand, glacial change 17
NGOs (non-governmental organisations) 38
    participation in policy making 257
    and security speech acts 196
nitrogen oxide 211
nitrous oxide 19, 21, 122
Nobel Peace Prize 169
North America
    carbon output (2005) 216
    glacial change 16
North/South dimension, and environmental conflict 184–6, 198, 199
Norway 120
nuclear energy 10, 220, 227–38, 249
    accidents at nuclear power plants 228, 229, 239
    discourses of 228–30
    and ecological modernisation 232–4, 250
    and inequalities of power 255
    and intragenerational equity 240–4
    power and democracy 234–8
    public opinion on 229, 230, 231
    and sustainable development 233
    in the UK 229–30
    world production 228
    see also radioactive waste management
nuclear war 171, 180, 229

Oceania, carbon output (2005) 217
oceans 22, 66
    and carbon dioxide capture and storage 40, 42
Ogata, Sadako 190
oil
    conflicts 183, 185
    and the entropic process 129
    reserves and production 218

opencast mining 213, 214
Organisation for Security and Cooperation in Europe 166
O'Riordan, Tim 39–40
Ostrom, Elinor 143, 146, 147
ozone protection 148, 150

Pacific Ocean islands 254
Pakistan 177
parity, and radioactive waste management 242
participation, inequality of 256–8
Pearce, David 105–6
peer review process (in scientific research) 70, 75, 89
Peres, Shimon 169
peripheral communities 240–4
peripheralisation 240
permafrost 25, 26
Persian Gulf 31
photosynthesis 21, 22
phytoplankton 22
Pigou, Authur 118
Pigovian taxes 118–19
Pittock, Barrie 72
Plato 62, 64
Pleistocene ice age 18
policy instruments 116–27, 130
political constraints
    on policy responses to climate change 37–8
politics
    and climate change denial 60, 82–91
    and energy policy 209
    and environmental policy 9
    and epistemic communities 81
    and the IPCC 75–7
    and the science of climate change 58, 67
pollution 181, 196, 208
    and ecological modernisation 232
    and environmental economics 105
    fossil fuel burning 213–14
    and green taxes 118–21
    and intergenerational equity 244
    and market failure 98
    regulation 122

Popper, Karl 63–4

population displacement 27–8, 183, 184, 185
    and livelihood contraction 188

population growth, and ecological economics 129

positive feedbacks 23–6

positive-sum games 149–51, 152–3

positivism 62, 65, 70

poverty 239

Powell, Colin 178

power 8, 32–3, 134, 135, 163, 201, 254–6, 256,
    and the agency–structure debate 44–5
    and discourse 60, 91–3, 254, 255
        and securitisation 1767, 255
    and energy policy 209, 227, 234–8
        nuclear energy 234–8

precautionary principle 47, 79, 178, 245–6

price mechanisms 98

Prisoners' Dilemma 139–42, 143–5, 146, 148, 149, 150, 162

property rights
    and carbon trading 124
    and libertarianism 123

proportionality, and radioactive waste management 242

public goods 137–9

Rabin, Yitzhak 169

radiative forcing 19, 20, 23, 69

radioactive waste management 229, 230, 248
    deep geological disposal 247–8
    and deliberative democracy 236–7
    and intergenerational equity 244–9, 258
    and intragenerational equity 240–4
    phased geological disposal 248–9

ratification (of international agreements) 156, 160–2, 162–3

Ravetz, Jerome 65

Rawls, John 114, 115

reductionism 69

refugees 183, 185, 186

renewable energy 220–5, 249, 253
    environmental problems of 224–5
    and nuclear energy 230

Renewables Obligation 223

representative democracy 235

resource scarcity
    and climate security 183–6
    and security knowledge 198–9
    and the state of nature 192

responsibility
    and intergenerational equity 244–9
    and participation in policy making 258
    and radioactive waste management 242, 245
    and sustainable energy strategies 238

revenue recycling, and carbon taxes 120–1

Rice, Condoleezza 167

risk society 181

road pricing 122

rock formations, and CCS 40

Rockefeller, Jay 85

Royal Society 85

Russia 77, 152–3, 160, 183, 254

Saudi Arabia 77

Scandinavia
    carbon taxes 120
    glacial change 17

scepticism 83

science and climate change 58–92
    and denial 82–91
    and climate modelling 65–6, 68–70
    and deliberative democracy 236
    and epistemology 61–2
    hypothesis testing 62–4, 67–8
    and the IPCC 71–7
    scientists and securitisation 169–70
    and social values 64–6
    see also Intergovernmental Panel on Climate Change; uncertainty

sea level rises 31, 101, 102, 254
    and Bangladesh 188
    economic effects of 109, 110
    and island states 31, 184–5
    security threats of 192
    and thermal expansion 26

Seager, Joni 197

seasonal disruptions, and climate change 26

securitisation 10, 166–201
    and actors 170, 174–7
    advantages and disadvantages of 193–201

climate change as a security threat 166–7
defining 166
and discourses of power 176–7, 255
and extraordinary measures 177, 190–1,
193, 196, 200
and the global community 179–86
and human security 188–91, 200
and knowledge 170, 178–9
and the military 193, 196–8, 200
and the nuclear industry 233
and state preferences 157, 158
success or failure of 200–1
security knowledge 179, 193, 198–9, 200
Sen, Amartya 189
side payments 151–3, 156, 162
Skodvin, Tora 74–5
small island states 31
Snowe, Olympia 85
social optimum 118, 142
social values, and scientific knowledge 8, 64–6
sociocultural time, and radioactive wastes
244–5
solar activity 18, 63
solar energy 220, 222, 224, 254
solar radiation 19, 20, 23, 24
solar system, predicting planetary
movements and eclipses 67, 68
South America
carbon output (2005) 216
glacial change 16
South Korea 227
sovereign states see state sovereignty
species extinction 27, 109
species migration 26–7
speech acts 170, 171–7, 179, 189–90, 191,
193, 195, 196, 200, 201
state preferences, politics of 156,
157–60, 163
state sovereignty
and human security 191
and international climate policy 147, 155
and the state of nature 192
states
anarchy and the international state
system 146–7
and anthropogenic climate change 22,
28–9

and climate security 179, 191–3, 200
and contraction and convergence 53
dilemmas of collective action 136–7
and ecological modernisation 233
and epistemic communities 81–2
framing climate change policies 30–1
and the Hobbesian state of nature
191–3, 198
and human security 191
and individual security 188
inter-state conflict and scarce resources
184–5
and international climate policies 32–5,
134–5, 153–5
and security speech acts 171
Steiner, Achim 58
Stern Review 9, 99
on calculating the social costs of carbon
108–10, 111
and climate security 168
on discounting the future 115, 116
and game theory 139
on global warming as market failure 98,
100–3
integrated assessment model (IAM)
112–13, 130
strong structuralism, and individual agents
44–5
structuration theory 45
subjectivity, and climate modelling 69–70
Sudan, conflict and environmental
issues in 185
sulphur dioxide emissions 211, 212, 213–14
Susskind, Lawrence 82
sustainability and development 8, 255–6
and climate security 186
discourses of 255
and energy policy 227–38
and international climate policy 134, 137
and neoliberalism 88
sustainable development 50–3, 255–6
and Asia 182
Brundtland Commission and 50,
234, 258
and China 145
and the nuclear industry 233–4
and radioactive waste management 245
strong interpretation of 234, 256
weak interpretation of 234, 256
Sweden 120

taxation
    carbon taxes 38, 117, 119–21, 146
    energy taxes 117
    and free-riding 146
    green taxes 99, 117, 118–21
    and libertarianism 123
technocentrism 40
technology
    and carbon trading 124, 125–6
    and distributed energy 219
    and effective policy responses 39–42
    and the military 197
    and neoclassical economics 128
    and pollution-free production 105
    and nuclear energy 227–8
    renewable energy 220–5
technology-based standards 116
tectonic plate movements 18
terrorism
    and climate security 167, 170, 171, 195–6
    and migration 183
    and nuclear energy 229
    and speech acts 172
thermal expansion 26
thermodynamics, and ecological economics
128–9
threat points, and international cooperation
154–5
tidal energy 222, 223, 224
time
    causes and effects of carbon
    emissions 106
    and climate security 193, 194–6
    of environmental degradation 208
    impacts of climate change 253
    and international climate policy 134, 137,
    144, 149
    and Pigovian taxes 119
    sustainability and development 51, 238
    tipping point 26
    see also intergenerational equity
Tol, R.S.J. 114
Toles, Tom (cartoonist) 194–5
Townsend, P. 192
tragedy of the commons 29–30, 35, 139
transcience 66
transnational corporations 84–5
Tuvalu 27

uncertainty
    and climate security 169
    defining 66–8
    economic 169
    and intergenerational equity 244, 258–9
    and the precautionary principle 47
    and responsibility for the future 246
    and scientific knowledge 38–9, 59–60,
    66–70, 72–4, 77, 85–6
    and security knowledge 179
underlying causes, of anthropogenic climate
change 19–21
Union of Concerned Scientists and the
Government Accountability Project 87
United Kingdom
    carbon dioxide emissions, by sector 210
    and carbon taxes 120
    Committee on Radioactive Waste
    Management (CoRWM) 236, 237
    electricity production 211–27
    emissions trading system (ETS) 126
    energy consumption 210
    energy tax 117
    Green Party 53
    Labour government 37–8, 50–1
    London congestion charge 122
    Nuclear Decommissioning Authority
    (NDA) 233
    nuclear energy 229–30
    Public and Stakeholder Engagement (PSE)
    236–7
    radioactive waste inventory 243
    Renewables Obligation 223
    Sustainable Development
    Commission 232
    wind farms 222, 223–4
United Nations
    Commission on Human Security 190
    Conference on Environment and
    Development (UNCED) 31
    Development Programme (UNDP) 188–9
        Human Development Report (1994)
        189–90
    Economic and Social Council 177
    Environment Programme (UNEP) 58, 185
    Framework Convention on Climate
    Change (FCCC), see Framework
    Convention on Climate Change
    and the IPCC 71
    Security Council 166, 168–9, 172, 177, 178
        debate on climate change (2007) 180,
        182–4, 186

United States 31, 34, 83–8, 136, 163, 200
  Byrd-Hagel resolution 33, 34, 85, 159
  and carbon trading 124
  glacial change 16
  Hurricane Katrina 182, 195–6
  and international climate policy 32, 38,
    84–5, 150–1, 155, 158–60, 161, 178
      the Prisoners' Dilemma game
        140–2, 144
  and the IPCC 77, 82
  and the Kyoto Protocol 31, 33, 34, 38, 85,
    136, 159, 161, 163, 254
  and neoliberalism 88
  and state sovereignty 147
  vehicle fuel efficiency legislation 121, 122
  see also Bush administration (United States)
urgency
  and extraordinary measures 193
  framing climate change in terms of 30–1
  and the imperative of action 194–6
  and security knowledge 179

values 227, 163, 257
  and knowledge 8, 41, 62
    science and social values 64–6
Vari, Anna 242
Vaughan, David 14
Victor, David 157
volcanic eruptions 18, 63
voluntary agreements 116, 117, 121–2
vulnerability, and radioactive waste
management 242

Waever, Ole 171
Walt, Stephen 171
wars
  and climate security 195, 200
  and human security 189, 191
  and the military 196, 198
  and speech acts 172, 173
  and the state of nature 192
Wasdell, David 76–7
Washington Post 194–5
water supplies 101, 102, 239
Watson, Dr Bob 84, 92
wave power 222, 223, 224
Weinberg, Alvin 66
well-being, and radioactive waste
management 242
Williams, Michael 176
wind power 220–4, 239
  offshore wind farms 223, 224
  public opinion on 224
World Commission on Environment and
Development (Brundtland commission) 50,
234, 245, 258
world government, absence of 146–7
World Meterological Organisation 71
World Wide Fund for Nature (WWF) 257

Yohe, G.W. 114